Introduction to Differential Equations

Mark H. Holmes

ISBN 13: 978-1-97507-720-4

4750 Venture Drive, Suite 400
Ann Arbor, MI 48108
800-562-2147
www.xanedu.com

Contents

Preface

This textbook is written for an introductory, or beginning, course in differential equations. It is more concise than most textbooks at this level. The reason is that most books are encyclopedic, and this enables them to also be used in more advanced courses. The approach taken here is to concentrate on the intended audience, and leave the additional material to textbooks written explicitly for the more advanced, or specialized, courses (and there are some very good ones available). It should also be pointed out that the greater length means that they are more expensive.

One of the principal objectives of the text is fairly simple, and it is, given a differential equation, find the solution. Most of the text is dedicated to doing exactly this. The reason there is more than one chapter is that the way you solve the equation depends on what type of equation it is. A second important objective is to be able to determine the basic geometrical properties of the solution, and to be able to do this from the differential equation. This is important because real-world problems often involve equations that are difficult to solve, or you can solve them but the formula for the solution is complicated. In such cases, to be able to infer the basic properties of the solution directly from the differential equation is invaluable. If you want an example of what this means, read Section 2.4.

There are students, even very good ones, who do not read a lot of what is written in a mathematics textbook. If you are one of them, here are some tips. First, any text that is in **bold font**, make sure you read what it says. As a second tip, the table below is a listing of the 10 most often used words or phrases in the text related to differential equations. Given that there are only about 220 pages of text, these words are used a lot. Make sure, when the word or phrase is first used, that you know what it means.

The prerequisites for this text vary with the chapter. The basic requirement is calculus, and it is essential that this includes integration rules such as integration by parts and partial fractions. The material requiring the calculus of vector-valued functions is in Chapters 4 and 5, and at the end of Chapter 6. These chapters also require an understanding of a few of the elementary properties of matrices, and a short summary

Word or Expression	Used
solution(s)	805
differential equation(s)	232
linear/nonlinear	223
steady state	197
stable/unstable/stability	180
eigenvalue(s)	161
general solution	155
initial value problem/IVP	105
initial condition(s)	104
homogeneous/inhomogeneous	96

Table 1. *Number of times the word, or phrase, is used in this textbook.*

of what you need to know is given in Appendix A. It is not necessary to have taken a course in matrix algebra. However, there is a fundamental connection between differential equations and linear algebra, and this connection is used throughout this textbook. The material is written so it is self-contained, so a previous course in linear algebra is not necessary. You will see comments, such as "if you recall from linear algebra," which are used to indicate where the connections are, but the material required for differential equations is then written out explicitly. Occasionally there are facts, or results, from linear algebra that are needed and they are stated without proof. This is also done with other topics, and in such cases references are often given where you can find out more about the subject.

A computer, or computer software, are not required anywhere in this text. There are, however, a small number of exercises that require you to evaluate a mathematical expression using a calculator.

There is a web-page for the text, and it is reachable via the author's web-page. It includes plots needed for some of the exercises, videos for Chapter 7, and, assuming there are any, a listing of the typos.

I would like to thank Peter Kramer for numerous, very useful, suggestions on how to improve the text. Also, as usual, I would like to thank those who developed and have maintained TeXShop, a free and very good TeX previewer.

Mark H. Holmes
Department of Mathematical Sciences
Rensselaer Polytechnic Institute
May, 2020

Chapter 1

Introduction

We begin with a question: why are most students who are majoring in engineering or science required to take an entire course dedicated to something called differential equations?

We'll start to answer this by giving a couple of examples where they arise, and this will also provide an opportunity to introduce some of the terminology used in the subject.

Example 1: Rate Laws

These describe the fluctuations, or changes, in something. The something in this case could be the concentration of a chemical, a population of animals, or perhaps the temperature of an object. As a simple example, a radioactive isotope is unstable, and will decay by emitting a particle, transforming into another isotope. The assumption usually used to model such situations is that the rate of decrease in the amount of radioactive isotope is proportional to the amount currently present. To translate this into mathematical terms, let $N(t)$ designate the amount of the radioactive material present at time t. In this case we obtain the rate equation

$$\frac{dN}{dt} = -kN, \quad \text{for } 0 < t, \tag{1.1}$$

where k is a positive constant. This is a differential equation for N. Usually one knows the amount N_0 of the isotope at the beginning, which gives us the requirement that

$$N(0) = N_0. \tag{1.2}$$

Introduction to Differential Equations, M. H. Holmes, 2020

This is known as an **initial condition**. Together, (1.1) and (1.2) form what is called an **initial value problem (IVP)**. ■

Example 2: Mechanics

One of the biggest generators of differential equations is Newton's second law, which states that $F = ma$. Any situation, electrical, mechanical or otherwise, involving non-static forces will almost inevitability result in having to solve a differential equation. To illustrate, consider the simple case of dropping an object off a building. If $x(t)$ is the distance of the object from the ground, then its velocity is $v = x'(t)$, and its acceleration is $a = x''(t)$. If the forces on the object are gravity $F_g = -mg$, and air resistance $F_r = -cv$, then $F = F_g + F_r$. Together, these expressions result in the following differential equation for $x(t)$:

$$m\frac{d^2x}{dt^2} = -mg - c\frac{dx}{dt}.\quad ■ \tag{1.3}$$

The differential equations in (1.1) and (1.3) have a few things in common, such as there is one independent variable, t, and one dependent variable, N and x. There are also differences, and an example is that (1.3) involves the second derivative and (1.1) only involves the first derivative. It is important to be able to recognize these differences as they are often used in this textbook to determine how to solve the problem.

1.1 ▪ Terminology for Differential Equations

Problems involving differential equations can involve a single equation, or several equations. They can also have one independent variable, or several. There are other differences, and to help illustrate some of the possibilities we will use the following examples.

Example 1: $\dfrac{d^2y}{dt^2} - 2\dfrac{dy}{dt} + 4ty = 0$ Example 2: $\dfrac{\partial u}{\partial t} - 2\dfrac{\partial u}{\partial x} = u^3$

Example 3: $\dfrac{du}{dt} = u + v + 1$

$\dfrac{dv}{dt} = -u + v$

Dependent variable(s): This is the variable(s) being solved for.

Example 1: y Example 2: u Example 3: u and v

Independent variable(s): These are usually time (t) and/or space (x).

Example 1: t Example 2: x and t Example 3: t

Order: The order of the highest derivative in the equation (or equations).

Example 1: second-order   Example 2: first-order
Example 3: first-order

Linear or Nonlinear: A differential equation is linear if it is a linear expression of the dependent variable and its derivatives, otherwise it is nonlinear.

Example 1: linear   Example 2: nonlinear (because of the u^3)
Example 3: linear

ODE or PDE: If there is one independent variable, then it is an ordinary differential equation (ODE). If there is more than one independent variable, then it is a partial differential equation (PDE).

Example 1: ODE   Example 2: PDE   Example 3: ODEs

Homogeneous or Inhomogeneous: A linear differential equation is homogeneous if the identically zero function is a solution. Otherwise, it is inhomogeneous.

Example 1: homogeneous since $y \equiv 0$ is a solution

Example 2: inapplicable since the equation is not linear

Example 3: inhomogeneous since $u \equiv 0$ and $v \equiv 0$ is not a solution

1.2 ▪ Solutions and Non-Solutions of Differential Equations

One of the central questions of this textbook is how to find the solution of a differential equation. The examples below are about the reverse situation, where a function is given and the question is whether it is a solution of a particular differential equation.

Example 1: Show that $y = te^{-2t}$ is a solution of $y' = -2y + e^{-2t}$.

Answer: Since

$$y' = e^{-2t} - 2te^{-2t} = (1 - 2t)e^{-2t},$$
$$-2y + e^{-2t} = -2te^{-2t} + e^{-2t} = (1 - 2t)e^{-2t},$$

it follows that $y' = -2y + e^{-2t}$ (i.e., y is a solution). ■

Example 2: For what value(s) of r and c, if any, is $y = ce^{rt}$ a solution of the IVP: $y' + y = 0$, where $y(0) = 3$?

Answer: Since $y' = rce^{rt}$, then from the differential equation we require that $rce^{rt} + ce^{rt} = 0$. This can be written as $(r+1)ce^{rt} = 0$. Given that e^{rt} is never zero, we conclude that either $c = 0$ or else $r = -1$. From the initial condition $y(0) = 3$, we need $c = 3$, and so this means that $r = -1$. ■

Example 3: For what value(s) of r, if any, is $y = e^{rt}$ a solution of the equation $y'' - y' - 6y = 0$?

Answer: Since $y' = re^{rt}$, and $y'' = r^2 e^{rt}$, then from the differential equation we require that $(r^2 - r - 6)e^{rt} = 0$. Given that e^{rt} is never zero, we conclude that $r^2 - r - 6 = 0$. Solving this, we get that $r = 3$ and $r = -2$ are the only values for which $y = e^{rt}$ is a solution. ■

Example 4: For what value(s) of r and c, if any, is $y = e^{rt}$ a solution of $y' = 2y^3$?

Answer: Since $y' = re^{rt}$, then from the differential equation we require that $re^{rt} = 2e^{3rt}$. Given that e^{rt} is never zero, we need $r = 2e^{2rt}$. The left hand side is constant. The only way to have the right hand side a constant is to take $r = 0$. In this case, the differential equation becomes $0 = 2$. This is not possible, and so the answer is that no values result in a solution. ■

Exercises

1. Show that the given function $y(t)$ is a solution of the given differential equation.

    a) $y = e^{2t} - 1$, $y' = 2y + 2$ e) $y = e^t + 1$, $y'' + 2y' - 3y = -3$

    b) $y = te^{-t}$, $y' + y = e^{-t}$ f) $y = \frac{1}{1+t}$, $y' + y^2 = 0$

    c) $y = \cos(3t)$, $y'' = -9y$ g) $y = \tan\left(\frac{1}{3}t + 1\right)$, $3y' = 1 + y^2$

    d) $y = e^{3t}$, $y'' + y' - 12y = 0$ h) $y = \ln(1 + t^2)$, $y' = 2te^{-y}$

2. For what value(s) of r, if any, is $y = e^{rt}$ a solution of the differential equation?

    a) $y' = -2y$ f) $y'' - 4y' + 4y = 0$

    b) $3y' = y$ g) $y'' + y' + y = e^{-3t}$

    c) $y' = y + 1$ h) $y'' - 3y' + y = 1$

    d) $y'' + 4y' = 0$ i) $y' = -2y^3$

    e) $2y'' + 5y' - 3y = 0$ j) $y' = y^2$

3. For what value of r and c is $y = ce^{rt}$ a solution of the IVP?

a) $y' = -2y$, $y(0) = 1$

b) $y' + y = 0$, $y(0) = -1$

c) $3y' - y = 0$, $y(0) = 3$

d) $y' - y = 0$, $y(0) = -1$

e) $5y' = -2y$, $y(0) = -7$

f) $y' + 4y = 0$, $y(0) = 3$

4. The following are *linear* and *homogeneous* first-order differential equations. The given function $y_1(t)$ is a solution, and you are to show that $y = cy_1$ is a solution for any value of the constant c.

a) $y' = 2y$, $y_1 = e^{2t}$

b) $y' + y = 0$, $y_1 = e^{-t}$

c) $y' - 4y = 0$, $y_1 = e^{4t}$

d) $3y' = y$, $y_1 = e^{t/3}$

5. The following are *linear* and *homogeneous* second-order differential equations. The given functions $y_1(t)$ and $y_2(t)$ are solutions, and you are to show that $y = c_1 y_1 + c_2 y_2$ is a solution for any value of the constants c_1 and c_2.

a) $y'' - 3y' + 2y = 0$,
   $y_1 = e^{2t}$, $y_2 = e^t$

b) $y'' - y' - 2y = 0$,
   $y_1 = e^{2t}$, $y_2 = e^{-t}$

c) $y'' + y' = 0$,
   $y_1 = e^{-t}$, $y_2 = 1$

d) $y'' + 2y' + 5y = 0$,
   $y_1 = e^{-t}\cos(2t)$
   $y_2 = e^{-t}\sin(2t)$

Important Conclusion: Problems 4 and 5 are demonstrations of the fact that if $y_1(t)$ and $y_2(t)$ are solutions of a *linear* and *homogeneous* differential equation, then $c_1 y_1(t) + c_2 y_2(t)$ is a solution of the equation for any value of c_1 and c_2. This is known as the **principle of superposition**, and it holds for all linear homogeneous differential equations (ODEs or PDEs). Moreover, as demonstrated in the following exercise, this does not (usually) hold for a nonlinear differential equation.

6. Both $y_1(t)$ and $y_2(t)$ are solutions of the given *nonlinear* differential equation. Show that (i) $y = c_1 y_1(t)$ is not a solution unless $c_1 = 1$, and (ii) $y = c_1 y_1 + c_2 y_2$ is not a solution if c_1 and c_2 are both nonzero.

a) $y' = t/(1+y)$,
   $y_1 = -1 + t$, $y_2 = -1 - t$

b) $y' = \sqrt{1+y}$,
   $y_1 = \frac{1}{4}t^2 + t$, $y_2 = \frac{1}{4}t^2 + 2t + 3$

7. Fill out the table on the next page. Assume that any constants in the equation(s) are nonzero. Also, in the last column, the answer Inapplicable (IA) is possible. Reference for Schrödinger's equation image: Eigler [2020].

Equation(s)	dep var(s)	indep var(s)	order	linear (L) or nonlinear (NL)	ODE or PDE	homog (H) or inhomog (IH)
Radioactive decay $$\frac{dy}{dt} = -ry$$						
Mass-Spring-Dashpot system $$m\frac{d^2y}{dt^2} + c\frac{dy}{dt} + ky = \sin t$$						
Pendulum equation $$\frac{d^2\theta}{dt^2} = -\frac{g}{\ell}\sin\theta$$						
Schrödinger's equation $$i\hbar\frac{\partial u}{\partial t} = -\frac{\hbar^2}{2m}\frac{\partial^2 u}{\partial x^2} + Vu$$						
Beam equation $$\frac{\partial^4 w}{\partial x^4} + \frac{\partial^2 w}{\partial t^2} = P$$						
Michaelis-Menten equations $$\frac{dS}{dt} = -k_1 ES + k_{-1}(E_0 - E)$$ $$\frac{dE}{dt} = -k_1 ES + k_3(E_0 - E)$$						

Chapter 2

First-Order Equations

This chapter concerns solving differential equations of the form

$$\frac{dy}{dt} = f(t, y).$$

There are no known analytical methods that can solve the general version of this problem. Consequently, assumptions have to be made on the function $f(t, y)$ to be able to derive a solution. The two more useful assumptions are that the function is separable or it is linear, and both are considered in this chapter. The fact is, however, that for many real world problems it is not possible to solve the differential equation by hand. Consequently, the ability to determine the properties of the solution, without actually solving the problem, becomes essential. What this entails is introduced in Section 2.4.

2.1 ▪ Separable Equations

To introduce this method we begin by considering the differential equation

$$\frac{dy}{dt} = 3y^2. \tag{2.1}$$

We are going to treat the derivative as if it were a fraction, and rewrite the above equation as

$$\frac{dy}{y^2} = 3dt. \tag{2.2}$$

So, the variables have been separated in the sense that all of the y terms are on the left hand side, and the t terms are on the right. We now

Introduction to Differential Equations, M. H. Holmes, 2020

integrate both sides, which gives

$$\int \frac{dy}{y^2} = \int 3dt.$$

Carrying out the integrations, and including the usual integration constant, we have

$$-\frac{1}{y} = 3t + c. \tag{2.3}$$

Solving this for y, we obtain the solution

$$y = -\frac{1}{3t + c}. \tag{2.4}$$

The last step is to check on whether the separation of variables step might involve dividing by zero. This happens for (2.2) when $y = 0$. Moreover, the constant function $y = 0$ is a solution of (2.1), and it is not included in (2.4). Consequently, another solution of the differential equation is

$$y = 0. \tag{2.5}$$

The method used to solve (2.1) is rather simple, but it contains the questionable step of splitting the derivative to obtain (2.2). To explain why this is possible, note that (2.1) can be written as $y^{-2}\frac{dy}{dt} = 3$. Using the chain rule, this can be written as $-\frac{d}{dt}(y^{-1}) = 3$. Integrating this equation yields (2.3). So, the splitting the derivative step is effectively a compact version of using the chain rule.

2.1.1 ▪ General Version

To explain how the method can be used for other problems, suppose the differential equation to solve is

$$\frac{dy}{dt} = f(t, y). \tag{2.6}$$

The method requires that it is possible to find a factorization of the form $f(t, y) = F(t)G(y)$. This means that it is possible to write the differential equation as

$$\frac{dy}{dt} = F(t)G(y). \tag{2.7}$$

Separating variables gives

$$\frac{dy}{G(y)} = F(t)dt,$$

and integrating we get

$$\int \frac{dy}{G(y)} = \int F(t)dt. \tag{2.8}$$

In theory, you carry out the above integrations, and then solve for y. How difficult this might be depends on how complicated the y integral is, and the examples that follow illustrate some of the complications that can arise. It is also important to note that the above method requires that $G(y) \neq 0$. Consequently, in addition to the solutions that come from (2.8), you must include as solutions any constant that satisfies $G(y) = 0$.

Example 1: Find all solutions of $4y' = -y^3$.

Answer: Since $f(t, y) = -\frac{1}{4}y^3$, we can take $F(t) = \frac{1}{4}$ and $G(y) = -y^3$. So, (2.8) becomes

$$-\int \frac{dy}{y^3} = \int \frac{1}{4}dt.$$

Integrating gives us

$$\frac{1}{2y^2} = \frac{1}{4}t + c,$$

which is rewritten as

$$y^2 = \frac{2}{t + 4c}.$$

From this we obtain the two solutions

$$y = \pm\sqrt{\frac{2}{t + 4c}}. \tag{2.9}$$

To check on the $G(y) = 0$ solutions, solving $G(y) = 0$ gives $y = 0$. This constant function is not included in the above expressions for y, so it is a third solution of the equation. ∎

Example 2: Find the solution of the IVP: $4y' = -y^3$, where $y(0) = -3$.

Answer: The three solutions of the differential equation were derived in the previous example. Because the initial condition requires the solution to be negative, the solution we need is

$$y = -\sqrt{\frac{2}{t + 4c}}.$$

Setting $y = -3$ and $t = 0$ in this equation gives $3 = 1/\sqrt{2c}$, which means that $c = 1/18$. Therefore, the solution is

$$y = -\sqrt{\frac{18}{9t + 2}}. \quad ∎$$

Example 3: Is $y' + y = t$ a separable equation?

Answer: No. For this equation, $f(t, y) = t - y$, and it is not possible to factor this as $f(t, y) = F(t)G(y)$. How to solve this equation is explained in the next section. ■

Example 4: Solve $\dfrac{dw}{dx} = \dfrac{x}{1 + w}$, where $w(0) = -2$.

Answer: In this problem the independent variable is x and the dependent variable is w. Separating variables, so $(1 + w)dw = x dx$, and then integrating gives

$$\int (1 + w)dw = \int x dx.$$

Carrying out the integrations we get that

$$w + \frac{1}{2}w^2 = \frac{1}{2}x^2 + c.$$

To satisfy the initial condition, substitute $w = -2$ and $x = 0$ into the above equation, from which we get that $c = 0$. This leaves $w + \frac{1}{2}w^2 = \frac{1}{2}x^2$, or equivalently, $w^2 + 2w - x^2 = 0$. This is a quadratic equation in w, and solving it we get the two solutions

$$w = -1 \pm \sqrt{1 + x^2}.$$

The initial condition is needed to determine which sign to use, and since $w(0) = -2$ then we need the minus sign. Therefore, the solution of the IVP is $w = -1 - \sqrt{1 + x^2}$. ■

Example 5: Solve $y' = -\dfrac{y}{1 + y}$, where $y(0) = 1$.

Answer: Separating variables yields

$$\frac{1 + y}{y}dy = -dt.$$

Since $(1 + y)/y = 1/y + 1$, and $y(0) > 0$, then integrating we get that

$$y + \ln y = -t + c.$$

It is not possible to solve this for y as in the previous examples, without resorting to more advanced mathematical methods. For this reason, this is an example of what is called an *implicit solution*, and they are very common when solving nonlinear differential equations. Even so, it is still possible to find c from the initial condition. Substituting $y = 1$ and $t = 0$ into the above equation we get that $c = 1$. Therefore, the solution of the IVP is defined implicitly through the equation

$$y + \ln y = -t + 1. \quad \blacksquare \tag{2.10}$$

A few comments need to be made about separation of variables before ending this section.

Integration Constant: The integration constant plays an essential role in the solution of a differential equation. It is useful to be aware that there are different ways you can write it. As an example, instead of (2.9), you can write the solution as

$$y = \pm \sqrt{\frac{2}{t + \bar{c}}},$$

where $\bar{c} = 4c$. Similarly, if the solution is found to be

$$y = \frac{3t - 2c + 4}{t + 2c - 4},$$

you can write it as

$$y = \frac{3t - \bar{c}}{t + \bar{c}}, \tag{2.11}$$

where $\bar{c} = 2c - 4$. For both of these examples, the solution contains one undetermined constant, just as in the original version of each solution. It should also be mentioned that this simplification is often used when giving the answers to the exercises. Moreover, instead of (2.11), the answer will likely be written as

$$y = \frac{3t - c}{t + c}.$$

Linear or Nonlinear: The method works on linear and nonlinear first-order differential equations. However, it does not work on every linear or nonlinear equation.

Non-uniqueness of Factorization: The factorization $f(t, y) = F(t)G(y)$ is not unique. For example, for $f(t, y) = y + ty$ you can take $F(t) = 1 + t$ and $G(y) = y$. You can also take $F(t) = \frac{1}{2}(1 + t)$ and $G(y) = 2y$. It makes no difference which one you use, it is just required that $f(t, y) = F(t)G(y)$. Any such factorization will lead, eventually, to the same, or an equivalent, solution of the differential equation.

Existence and Uniqueness: When solving an IVP there is always the question of whether there is a solution (existence), and whether there is more than one solution (uniqueness). It is possible to find problems that have no solution (see Exercise 6(b)), have a solution only for $0 \le t < T$ (see Exercise 6(c)), or have multiple solutions (see Exercise 6(d)). It is important to be aware of this, but the theory underlying existence and uniqueness is beyond the purview of this text. It is, however, a topic covered in most upper division courses on ODEs.

Exercises

1. Find all of the solutions of the given differential equation.

   a) $y' = -3y^4$

   b) $y' = y^3 e^{-t}$

   c) $y' + y^2 \sin t = 0$

   d) $2y' = t/(y - 3)$

   e) $y' = -(2 + t)e^y$

   f) $(1 + t)y' = -e^{3y}$

   g) $y' = -e^{2t + 4y}$

   h) $y' = -2^y$

   i) $y' + (1 + 3y)^3 = 0$

   j) $y' = y^2 + 4y + 4$

   k) $2y' = y^2 - 6y + 9$

   l) $3y' = y^2 + 1$

   m) $y' - te^y = te^{-y}$

   n) $y' - e^{-y} = 1$

   o) $y' = t(y + 1/y)$

2. Find the solution of the IVP.

   a) $y' = -y^3$, $y(0) = 5$

   b) $y' = -2y^3$, $y(0) = 0$

   c) $(1 + t)y' = 3 + y$, $y(0) = 4$

   d) $(4 + e^t)y' + e^t y^2 = 0$, $y(0) = 1$

   e) $y' = te^{-y}$, $y(0) = -1$

   f) $y' = \dfrac{1}{2 + y}$, $y(0) = 0$

   g) $y' = 1 + \cos(y)$, $y(0) = \pi/2$

   h) $y' = y^2 - 5y$, $y(0) = 1$

   i) $y' + e^{-2y} = 1$, $y(0) = 1$

   j) $y' = 1/(e^{-y} + e^y)$, $y(0) = 0$

   k) $y' = \sqrt{1 - y^2}$, $y(0) = 0$
      Hint: $y' \ge 0$

3. Find the solution of the IVP. In these problems, the independent variable is not t and the dependent variable is not y.

   a) $\dfrac{dq}{dr} = -7q^3$, $q(0) = -1$

   b) $\dfrac{dp}{dr} = -4p^3$, $p(0) = 0$

   c) $3\dfrac{dh}{d\tau} = 2 + h$, $h(0) = 2$

   d) $\dfrac{dh}{dx} = h^2 - 3h$, $h(0) = 2$

   e) $(1 + e^{-r})\dfrac{dz}{dr} + z^2 = 0$, $z(0) = 6$

   f) $4\dfrac{dw}{d\tau} = \tau^3 e^{-2w}$, $w(0) = 0$

   g) $(\theta + 1)^3 \dfrac{dr}{d\theta} = r^2$, $r(0) = 2$

   h) $\dfrac{dr}{d\theta} = \dfrac{2\theta}{1 + r}$, $r(0) = 0$

4. Find the solution of the IVP in implicit form.

a) $y' = 1 + \dfrac{1}{y}$, $\quad y(0) = 1$ $\qquad$ c) $y' = \dfrac{1+y}{2+y}$, $\quad y(0) = 5$

b) $y' = \dfrac{3}{1+y^4}$, $\quad y(0) = -1$ $\qquad$ d) $y' = \dfrac{e^y}{1+e^y}$, $\quad y(0) = 2$

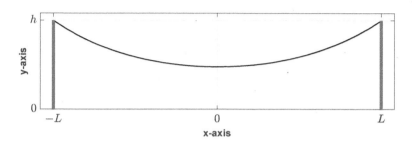

Figure 2.1. *Cable hanging between two poles, as described in Exercise 5.*

5. A cable is hung between two poles as illustrated in Figure 2.1. The poles are located at $x = -L$ and $x = L$, and each has height h. The curve $y(x)$ determined by the cable minimizes the cable's potential energy. From this, one obtains the equation

$$a\frac{d^2 y}{dx^2} = \sqrt{1 + \left(\frac{dy}{dx}\right)^2}, \quad \text{for } -L < x < L,$$

where a is a positive constant. Because of the symmetry in the problem, $y'(0) = 0$.

a) Letting $w(x) = y'(x)$, rewrite the differential equation as a first-order equation involving w and w'. Also, what is $w(0)$?

b) Solve the problem in part (a) for w.

c) Integrate $y'(x) = w(x)$, and use the condition $y(L) = h$, to determine $y(x)$. The solution you are finding is an example of what is called a catenary.

6. The following illustrate some of the complications that can arise when solving nonlinear differential equations.

a) The question is whether the implicit solution (2.10) actually has a solution. To show this, rewrite (2.10) as $\ln y = -y - t + 1$. Setting $g(y) = \ln y$, and $h(y) = -y - t + 1$, let $t = 0$ and then sketch $g(y)$ and $h(y)$ on the same axes for $0 < y < \infty$. Explain why this shows that there is exactly one solution of (2.10). Do the same thing for $t = 1$ and $t = 2$. Use this sketching procedure to determine what value y approaches as $t \to \infty$.

b) Consider the IVP: $ty' = y + 1$, where $y(0) = 1$. Try solving this and show that there is no solution.

c) Solve $y' = \frac{1}{2}y^3$, where $y(0) = 1$. Explain why there is no solution for $t \geq 1$.

d) Show that there are an infinite number of solutions of $ty' = y + 1$, where $y(0) = -1$.

2.2 ▪ Integrating Factor

The equation to be solved is

$$y' + p(t)y = g(t). \tag{2.12}$$

What is important here is that this equation is linear, as well as first-order.

The solution will be derived using two formulas from calculus. The first is the product rule, which states that

$$\frac{d}{dt}(\mu y) = \mu(t)y'(t) + \mu'(t)y(t). \tag{2.13}$$

The second is the Fundamental Theorem of Calculus, which states that if

$$\frac{d}{dt}(\mu y) = q(t),$$

then

$$\mu y = \int_0^t q(s)ds + c. \tag{2.14}$$

The first step is the observation that the left hand side of (2.12) resembles the right hand side of (2.13). To make it so they are exactly the same we need to multiply the differential equation by $\mu(t)$, which gives us

$$\mu y' + \mu py = \mu g. \tag{2.15}$$

What we need, to get this to work, is that μ must be such that

$$\mu' = p\mu. \tag{2.16}$$

It will make the formula for the solution a bit simpler if we require

$$\mu(0) = 1. \tag{2.17}$$

The differential equation (2.16) is separable, and one finds that the solution that satisfies (2.17) is

$$\mu(t) = e^{\int_0^t p(r)dr}. \tag{2.18}$$

With this choice for μ, the differential equation for y in (2.15) can be written as

$$\frac{d}{dt}(\mu y) = \mu g. \tag{2.19}$$

From (2.14) we get that

$$\mu y = \int_0^t \mu(s)g(s)ds + c,$$

where c is the usual integration constant. The solution of (2.12) is therefore

$$y(t) = \frac{1}{\mu(t)}\left[\int_0^t \mu(s)g(s)ds + c\right]. \tag{2.20}$$

The function $\mu(t)$, which is given in (2.18), is said to be an **integrating factor** for the original differential equation.

There are two important special cases to mention. First, suppose that the problem has an initial condition, say $y(0) = y_0$. Since $\mu(0) = 1$, then from (2.20) the solution of the resulting IVP is

$$y(t) = \frac{1}{\mu(t)}\left[\int_0^t \mu(s)g(s)ds + y_0\right]. \tag{2.21}$$

The second special case arises for the homogeneous equation $y' + p(t)y = 0$. Setting $g = 0$ in (2.20), gives us the solution

$$y(t) = ce^{-\int_0^t p(r)dr}. \tag{2.22}$$

If $y(0) = y_0$, then the resulting solution is

$$y(t) = y_0 e^{-\int_0^t p(r)dr}. \tag{2.23}$$

Example 1: Solve $y' + 3y = e^{2t}$.

Answer: Since $p = 3$, then

$$\int_0^t p(r)dr = \int_0^t 3dr = 3t.$$

From (2.18), the integrating factor is $\mu = e^{3t}$. So, since $g(t) = e^{2t}$, then from (2.20),

$$y(t) = e^{-3t}\left[\int_0^t e^{3s}e^{2s}ds + c\right] = e^{-3t}\left[\int_0^t e^{5s}ds + c\right].$$

Carrying out the integration,

$$y(t) = e^{-3t}\left[\frac{1}{5}e^{5s}\Big|_{s=0}^{t} + c\right] = e^{-3t}\left[\frac{1}{5}e^{5t} - \frac{1}{5} + c\right]$$

$$= \frac{1}{5}e^{2t} + \bar{c}e^{-3t},$$

where $\bar{c} = c - 1/5$ is an arbitrary constant.   ■

Example 2: Solve $2y' - ty = 6$, where $y(0) = 5$.

Answer: Since $p = -t/2$, then from (2.18), $\mu = e^{-t^2/4}$. Given that $g = 3$, then from (2.21) we have

$$y(t) = e^{t^2/4}\left[\int_0^t 3e^{-s^2/4}ds + 5\right].$$

The integral in the above expression can not be written in terms of elementary functions, and so that is the final answer.   ■

Example 3: Solve $\dfrac{dh}{dz} - 4h = 2z$, where $h(0) = -1$.

Answer: In this problem the independent variable is z and the dependent variable is h. The formula for the solution can still be used, we just need to make the appropriate substitutions. Since $p = -4$, then

$$\int_0^z p(r)dr = \int_0^z -4dr = -4z.$$

From (2.18), the integrating factor is $\mu = e^{-4z}$. So, since $g(z) = 2z$, then from (2.21),

$$h(z) = e^{4z}\left[\int_0^z 2se^{-4s}ds - 1\right]$$

$$= -\frac{1}{8}(4z + 1) - \frac{7}{8}e^{4z}.   ■$$

2.2.1 ▪ General and Particular Solutions

We have shown that the solution of the linear differential equation

$$y' + p(t)y = g(t), \tag{2.24}$$

is

$$y(t) = \frac{1}{\mu(t)}\left[\int_0^t \mu(s)g(s)ds + c\right]. \tag{2.25}$$

Any, and all, solutions of (2.24) are included in this formula, and for this reason (2.25) is said to be the **general solution**.

A useful observation about (2.25) is that it can be written as

$$y(t) = y_p(t) + y_h(t), \tag{2.26}$$

where

$$y_p(t) = \frac{1}{\mu(t)} \int_0^t \mu(s)g(s)ds, \tag{2.27}$$

and

$$y_h(t) = \frac{c}{\mu(t)} = ce^{-\int_0^t p(r)dr}. \tag{2.28}$$

The formulas for y_p and y_h are not important here. What is important is that y_p is a solution of the differential equation (2.24). It does not contain the arbitrary constant, and for this reason it is said to be a **particular solution**. In contrast, the function $y_h(t)$, which contains an arbitrary constant, is a solution of the differential equation

$$y' + p(t)y = 0. \tag{2.29}$$

This is the homogeneous equation coming from (2.24). Consequently, $y_h(t)$ is said to be the **general solution of the associated homogeneous equation**.

Example 4: In Example 1 we found that the general solution is

$$y(t) = \frac{1}{5}e^{2t} + \bar{c}e^{-3t},$$

where $\bar{c}$ is an arbitrary constant. In this case, a particular solution is $y_p = \frac{1}{5}e^{2t}$, and the general solution of the associated homogeneous equation is $y_h = \bar{c}e^{-3t}$. ∎

The observation in the previous paragraph that the general solution can be written as the sum of a particular solution and the general solution of the associated homogeneous equation holds for all linear differential equations (not just those that are first-order). Because we are able to derive a formula for the solution, which is given in (2.25), this observation is not really needed to solve first-order linear differential equations. However, for second-order equations, which will be studied in the next chapter, this observation serves a fundamental role in finding the solution.

2.2.2 ▪ Interesting But Tangentially Useful Topics

The following topics are worth knowing about. However, you can skip this material, if you wish, as it is not required to solve any of the problems in this chapter.

Method of Undetermined Coefficients

Most first-order linear differential equations that arise in applications have constant coefficients, which means that they can be written as

$$y' + ay = g(t), \qquad (2.30)$$

where a is a constant. This can be solved using an integrating factor, but there is often an easier way to find the solution. This involves making an educated guess for the particular solution. The guess depends on the specific form of the function $g(t)$, and it is the basis of what is called the method of undetermined coefficients. This is explained in Section 3.7 for second-order equations, but it works on first-order equations as well. The reason it is easier is that it avoids having to integrate anything, and you therefore do not need to remember integration rules to find the solution. In fact, for a problem such as the one in Example 1, you can solve it in your head and simply write the answer down. On the other hand, the method will not work for Example 2, and it will not work for Example 1 if $g(t) = e^{2t}$ is replaced, say, with $g(t) = \sqrt{t}$. If you want to pursue this idea a bit more, after reading Section 3.7, you should look at Exercise 4 on page 59.

Connections with Linear Algebra

For those who have taken a course in linear algebra, there is a connection between that subject and linear differential equations that is worth knowing about. To explain, a central problem in linear algebra is to solve $\mathbf{Ax} = \mathbf{b}$, where $\mathbf{A}$ is a $m \times n$ matrix. It's possible to prove that if there is a solution of this equation, then it has the form $\mathbf{x} = \mathbf{x}_p + \mathbf{x}_h$, where $\mathbf{x}_p$ is a particular solution and $\mathbf{x}_h$ is the general solution of the associated homogeneous equation $\mathbf{Ax} = \mathbf{0}$. This is basically the same statement we made for the solution of the linear differential equation (2.24). The key property these equations have in common is that they are both linear. A consequence of this is that the principle of superposition can be used (see page 5) when solving the associated homogeneous equation. We will make use of this fact in every chapter of this textbook, except for Chapter 5. This illustrates the beauty, and profundity, of mathematical abstraction. Namely, it is possible to make rather significant conclusions about the solution of an equation, irrespective of whether it is algebraic or differential, simply from the basic properties these equations have in common.

Exercises

1. Find the general solution of the given differential equation.

a) $y' + 3y = 0$

b) $y' - 2y = t$

c) $4y' - y = 6 + 2t$

d) $y' = -y + 2e^t - 1$

e) $(3t + 2)y' + 3y = \sin(4t) + 5$

f) $(2 + t)y' + y = 1$

g) $y' - 3y = 1 + \sqrt{t}$

h) $2y' + y = \frac{t}{1+t}$

2. Find the solution of the IVP.

a) $y' - y = 4$, $y(0) = -1$

b) $y' + 4y = 3t$, $y(0) = 0$

c) $5y' + y = 0$, $y(0) = 2$

d) $2y' = y + e^{-t} - 2$, $y(0) = 1$

e) $(5 + t)y' + y = -1$, $y(0) = 2$

f) $3y' + ty = -2$, $y(0) = 0$

3. Find the solution of the IVP. In these problems, the independent variable is not t and the dependent variable is not y.

a) $\frac{dq}{dz} + 2q = 4$, $q(0) = -1$

b) $\frac{dp}{dx} + 4p = -x$, $p(0) = 0$

c) $2\frac{dw}{d\tau} - w = e^{2\tau}$, $w(0) = 0$

d) $\frac{dz}{d\tau} = 4z + 1 + \tau$, $z(0) = 0$

e) $(x + 7)\frac{dh}{dx} + h = -1$, $h(0) = 2$

f) $(5z + 1)\frac{dh}{dz} + 5h = 3$, $h(0) = -1$

4. Find a particular solution, and the general solution to the associated homogeneous equation, of the following differential equations.

a) $y' - 2y = 6$

b) $y' + y = 3e^{-t}$

c) $7y' - y = e^{2t} + 3$

d) $y' + 2ty = 1$

5. A Maxwell viscoelastic material is one for which the stress $T(t)$ and the strain-rate $r(t)$ satisfy

$$T + \tau \frac{dT}{dt} = \kappa r,$$

where τ and κ are positive constants. By solving this equation for T, and assuming $T_0 = T(0)$, show that

$$T = T_0 e^{-t/\tau} + \frac{\kappa}{\tau} \int_0^t e^{(s-t)/\tau} r(s) ds.$$

6. The Bernoulli equation is $w' = p(t)w + q(t)w^n$, which is nonlinear if $n \neq 0, 1$. What is significant is that it can be solved by making the substitution $w = y^{1/(1-n)}$, which results in a linear equation for $y(t)$. This was discovered by Leibniz, although it is not clear he was aware of the solution (2.20) for a linear equation [Parker, 2013].

a) If $w' = w - 5w^3$, where $w(0) = 1$, what IVP does y satisfy?

b) Solve the IVP for y, and then transform back to determine the function w.

c) One of Bernoulli's brothers solved the Bernoulli equation by assuming that $w(t) = u(t)v(t)$, where u satisfies $u' = pu$, for $u(0) = 1$. Use this method to solve $w' = w - 5w^3$, where $w(0) = 1$. This approach is the precursor to what is now known as the method of variation of parameters.

2.3 ▪ Modeling

The principal objective of the examples to follow is to show how a differential equation is the mathematical consequence of the assumptions about a physical system.

2.3.1 ▪ Mixing

Typical mixing problems involve a continuously stirred tank, as illustrated in Figure 2.2. As an example, suppose that water, containing salt, is flowing into a well-stirred tank. At the same time, the mixture in the tank is flowing out. The goal is to determine how much salt is in the tank as a function of t.

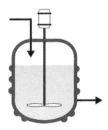

Figure 2.2. *Schematic of a continuous stirred tank.*

The quantities of interest in this problem are:

$Q(t)$: This is the amount of salt in the tank at time t. If the volume of water in the tank is V, and c is the concentration of salt in the water, then $Q = cV$.

R_{in}: This is the rate that salt is flowing into the tank. If the incoming volumetric flow rate is F_{in}, and c_{in} is the concentration of salt in the incoming water, then $R_{in} = c_{in}F_{in}$.

R_{out}: This is the rate that salt is flowing out of the tank. If the outgoing volumetric flow rate is F_{out}, then $R_{out} = cF_{out}$.

If the initial amount of salt in the tank is Q_0, then the resulting IVP for Q is:

$$\frac{dQ}{dt} = R_{in} - R_{out},$$
$$Q(0) = Q_0.$$

Example 1

Suppose that salt water, containing 1/2 lbs of salt per gal, is poured into a tank at 2 gal/min. Also, the water flows out of the tank at the same rate. If the tank starts out with 100 gal of water, with 10 lbs of salt per gal, find a formula for the total amount of salt in the tank.

Setup

inflow: Since $F_{in} = 2$, and $c_{in} = 1/2$, then $R_{in} = 1$.

outflow: Since the mixture flows out at 2 gal/min, then the volume of water in the tank stays at 100 gal. Also, since $F_{out} = 2$ and $c = Q/100$, then $R_{out} = \frac{1}{50}Q$.

$t = 0$: Given that at the start there are 10 lbs of salt per gal, $Q(0) = 1000$.

The resulting IVP for Q is:

$$\frac{dQ}{dt} = 1 - \frac{1}{50}Q, \tag{2.31}$$
$$Q(0) = 1000. \tag{2.32}$$

Note that because of the way the variables have been defined, Q is measured in pounds and t is measured in minutes.

Solution

Using separation of variables, or the integrating factor solution (2.21), one finds that $Q(t) = 50 + 950e^{-t/50}$.

Question: What is the eventual concentration of salt in the tank?

Answer using solution: Since $\lim_{t\to\infty} Q(t) = 50$, then the eventual concentration is $50/V = \frac{1}{2}$ lbs/gal.

Answer using physical reasoning: The concentration in the tank will eventually be the same as the concentration for the incoming flow, and so the answer is $\frac{1}{2}$ lbs/gal.

Answer using math reasoning: It is possible to determine the eventual concentration directly from the differential equation, without knowing the solution. How this is done is explained in Section 2.4 (also, see Exercise 5 in that section). ∎

Example 2

Salt water, containing 3 lbs of salt per gal, flows into a 50 gal drum at 2 gal/sec. If the drum initially contains 10 gal of pure water, find a formula for Q as a function of t.

Comments about this problem: There is no outflow, so the volume of water will increase. However, it's a 50 gal drum, so eventually it will fill and start running over. When this occurs there is outflow, at a rate equal to the incoming rate. To account for this, the problem needs to be split into two phases, one where the volume is increasing, and the second when it is a constant.

Solution

Phase 1: In this case, $R_{in} = 6$, $R_{out} = 0$, and $Q(0) = 0$. The resulting IVP is

$$\frac{dQ}{dt} = 6$$
$$Q(0) = 0$$

The solution is $Q(t) = 6t$. Also, the volume of water in the tank is $V = 10 + 2t$. So, this solution for Q holds for $V \leq 50$, which means that $t \leq 20$.

Phase 2: As before, $R_{in} = 6$. For the outflow, the rate is 2 gal/sec and the concentration in the outflow is $Q/50$. This means that $R_{out} = Q/25$. Now, this phase starts at $t = 20$, and the amount of salt in the tank at the start is 120 (this comes from the solution for Phase 1). This means that the problem to solve is

$$\frac{dQ}{dt} = 6 - \frac{1}{25}Q, \quad \text{for } 20 < t,$$
$$Q(20) = 120.$$

What is different about this problem is the time interval, which is not the usual $0 \leq t$. However, this does not interfere with our solution methods, and the solution can be found using an integrating factor or separation of variables. One finds that the general solution of the differential equation is

$$Q(t) = 150 + Ae^{-t/25}.$$

From the requirement that $Q(20) = 120$ it follows that $A = -30e^{4/5}$.

The Solution: Combining the Phase 1 and Phase 2 solutions, we have that

$$Q(t) = \begin{cases} 6t & \text{if } 0 \leq t \leq 20, \\ 150 - 30e^{(20-t)/25} & \text{if } 20 < t. \end{cases} \blacksquare$$

2.3.2 ▪ Newton's Second Law

Suppose an object with mass m is moving along the x-axis. Letting $x(t)$ be its position, then its velocity is $v = \frac{dx}{dt}$, and its acceleration is $a = \frac{d^2x}{dt^2} = \frac{dv}{dt}$. If the object is acted on by a force F, then from Newton's second law, which states that $F = ma$, we have that

$$m\frac{dv}{dt} = F. \tag{2.33}$$

What sort of differential equation this might be depends on how F depends on v. Once (2.33) is solved for v, then the position is determined by integrating the equation

$$\frac{dx}{dt} = v. \tag{2.34}$$

Typically, the initial velocity $v(0)$ and initial position $x(0)$ are given, and these are used to determine the integration constants obtained when solving the problem.

Vertical Motion

The object is assumed to be moving vertically, either up or down. In this case, $x(t)$ is the distance of the object from the ground. It is also assumed that it is acted on by gravity, F_g, and a drag force, F_r. Consequently, the total force is $F = F_g + F_r$. As for what these forces are:

Gravitational force: Assuming the gravitational field is uniform, then $F_g = -mg$, where g is the gravitational acceleration constant. The minus sign is because the force is in the downward direction.

Drag force: As long as the object is not moving very fast, the drag is proportional to the velocity (see Exercise 10). In this case, $F_r = -cv$, where c is a positive constant (the minus sign is because the force is in the opposite direction to the direction of motion).

Units and Values: In the exercises, the value to use for g is usually stated. If it is not given, then you should leave g unevaluated. Whatever value is used, it is only approximate. If a more physically realistic value is needed, then you should probably use the Somigliana equation. Finally, weight is a force, so for an object that weighs w lbs, its mass can be determined from the equation $w = mg$.

Example: Suppose a ball with a mass of $2\,\text{kg}$ is dropped, from rest, from a height of $1000\,\text{m}$. Assume that the forces acting on the object are gravity, and a drag force due to air resistance, with $c = \frac{1}{2}\,\text{kg/s}$. Assume that $g = 10\,\text{m/s}^2$.

Question 1: What is the resulting IVP for v, and what problem must be solved to find x?

Answer: Since $F = F_g + F_r = -mg - cv$, where $m = 2$ and $c = 1/2$, then from (2.33) the differential equation is

$$\frac{dv}{dt} = -10 - \frac{1}{4}v. \tag{2.35}$$

Since the object is dropped from rest, then the initial condition is $v(0) = 0$. Once v is known, then x is found by integrating (2.34), and using the fact that $x(0) = 1000$. Also, note that v is measured in meters per second, t is measured in seconds, and x in meters.

Question 2: What is the solution of the IVP, and the resulting solution for x?

Answer: Using the integrating factor solution (2.21), it is found that the general solution is $v = -40 + ce^{-t/4}$. Applying the initial condition we get that

$$v = 40(-1 + e^{-t/4}). \tag{2.36}$$

Integrating $x' = 40(-1 + e^{-t/4})$, yields $x = 40(-t - 4e^{-t/4}) + c$. Since $x(0) = 1000$, then $c = 1160$. So, $x = 40(-t - 4e^{-t/4}) + 1160$.

Question 3: What is the terminal velocity v_T of the object?

Answer: The terminal velocity is defined as

$$v_T = \lim_{t \to \infty} v(t).$$

Consequently, from (2.36), we get that $v_T = -40\,\text{m/s}$. It is also possible to determine v_T without solving the IVP, and how this is done is explained in Section 2.4.

Question 4: When does the object hit the ground?

Answer: It hits the ground when $x = 0$, which means that it is the value of t that satisfies $t + 4e^{-t/4} = 29$. This can be solved using a computer, but it is possible to obtain an approximate value fairly easily. Assuming it takes several seconds to hit the ground, then the $4e^{-t/4}$ term should be relatively small. For example, at $t = 10$, $4e^{-t/4} \approx 0.3$, and at $t = 20$, $4e^{-t/4} \approx 0.03$. Consequently, as an approximation, we can replace the equation $t + 4e^{-t/4} = 29$ with $t = 29$. In comparison, the numerically computed value is about $28.997\,\text{s}$. ∎

2.3.3 ▪ Logistic Growth or Decay

An assumption often made for the growth of the population of a species is that the population grows at a rate proportional to the current population.

If $P(t)$ is the population at time t, then this assumption results in the equation $P' = kP$. The solution is $P(t) = P(0)e^{kt}$, which means that there is exponential growth in the population. This is not sustainable in the real world, and it is more realistic to assume that the rate of growth slows down as the population increases. In fact, if the population is very large, the population should decrease instead of increase. A simple model for this is to assume that $k = r(1 - \frac{P}{N})$, where r and N are positive constants. The resulting differential equation is

$$P' = r\left(1 - \frac{P}{N}\right)P, \tag{2.37}$$

which is known as the *logistic equation*. This nonlinear equation can be solved using separation of variables, and partial fractions. Doing this, in the case of when $0 < P < N$,

$$\frac{N dP}{(N - P)P} = r dt \tag{2.38}$$

$\Rightarrow$

$$\int \left(\frac{1}{P} + \frac{1}{N - P}\right) dP = rt + c$$

$\Rightarrow$

$$\ln \frac{P}{N - P} = rt + c$$

$\Rightarrow$

$$\frac{P}{N - P} = e^{rt + c}.$$

From this, we get
$$P = (N - P)\bar{c}e^{rt}, \tag{2.39}$$

where $\bar{c} = e^c$ is a positive constant. Doing the same thing for the case of when $N < P$, one again gets (2.39) except that $\bar{c}$ is a negative constant. Moreover, for the divide by zero case of when $P = 0$, you get (2.39) but $\bar{c} = 0$. In other words, except for when $P = N$, (2.39) holds with the understanding that $\bar{c}$ is an arbitrary constant. Solving (2.39) for P yields

$$P = \frac{N\bar{c}e^{rt}}{1 + \bar{c}e^{rt}}, \tag{2.40}$$

where $\bar{c}$ is an arbitrary constant. If $P(0) = P_0$, and if $P_0 \neq N$, then one finds that $\bar{c} = P_0/(N - P_0)$. When $P(0) = N$, this is a divide by zero situation in (2.38), and the resulting solution is just the constant $P(t) = N$.

The solution we have derived in (2.40) is known as the *logistic function* or the *logistic curve*. When plotted for $-\infty < t < \infty$ it has a S, or

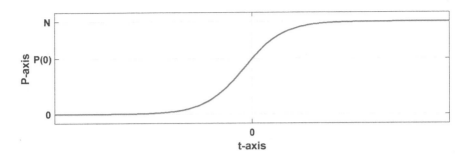

Figure 2.3. *The logistic function (2.40), for $-\infty < t < \infty$, in the case of when $P(0) < N$.*

sigmoidal, shape as shown in Figure 2.3. It is one of those functions that appears in so many applications that it deserves its own graph in this textbook (hence Figure 2.3). ■

2.3.4 ▪ Newton's Law of Cooling

The assumption is that the rate of change of the temperature of an object is proportional to the difference between its temperature and the ambient temperature (i.e., the temperature of its surroundings). This is often referred to as Newton's law of cooling, but it also applies to heating an object.

To write down the mathematical form of this statement, we introduce the following:

$T(t)$: This is the temperature of the object at time t.

T_a: This is the ambient temperature.

k: This is the proportionality coefficient.

If the initial temperature of the object is T_0, then the resulting IVP for T is:

$$\frac{dT}{dt} = -k(T - T_a), \tag{2.41}$$

$$T(0) = T_0. \tag{2.42}$$

This problem can be solved using the integrating factor solution (2.21), or by using separation of variables. It is found that $T = T_a + (T_0 - T_a)e^{-kt}$.

Example 1: Cooling a Cup of Coffee

According to the National Coffee Association, the ideal temperature for brewing coffee is $200°$ F, and to get the most flavor out of it, you should drink it when the coffee is between 120 and $140°$ F.

Question 1: If the room temperature is 70° F, what is the solution of the resulting IVP for T?

> *Answer:* Since $T_0 = 200$ and $T_a = 70$, then
>
> $$T = 70 + 130e^{-kt}. \tag{2.43}$$

Question 2: If the temperature is 180° F after 2 minutes, determine k.

> *Answer:* From (2.43), $180 = 70 + 130e^{-2k}$. From this one finds that $k = \frac{1}{2}\ln(13/11)\,\frac{1}{\min}$.

Question 3: When should you start drinking the coffee (according to the National Coffee Association)?

> *Answer:* The time when $T = 140$ occurs when $140 = 70 + 130e^{-kt}$, from which one finds that
>
> $$t = 2\frac{\ln(13/7)}{\ln(13/11)} \text{ min.} \tag{2.44}$$

Question 4: What is the computed value for the answer for Question 3?

> *Answer:* It is $t \approx 7.4$ minutes. ∎

Example 2: Nonlinear Cooling

Experimentally it has been observed that for certain fluids the k in (2.41) is not constant. To account for this, according to what is known as the Dulong-Petit law of cooling, the k in (2.41) is replaced with $k(T - T_a)^{1/4}$. The resulting differential equation is

$$\frac{dT}{dt} = -k(T - T_a)^{5/4}.$$

This requires cooling, and so it requires $T \geq T_a$.

Question: As in Example 1, suppose that the room temperature is 70° F and $T(0) = 200°$ F. What is the solution of the resulting IVP?

> *Answer:* Separating variables,
>
> $$-\frac{dT}{(T - 70)^{5/4}} = kdt$$
>
> $$\Rightarrow \quad \frac{4}{(T - 70)^{1/4}} = kt + c$$
>
> $$\Rightarrow \quad (T - 70)^{1/4} = \frac{4}{kt + c}.$$

Solving this for T, we get that

$$T = 70 + \left(\frac{4}{kt + c}\right)^4.$$

Since $T(0) = 200$, then the above equation gives us that $130 = (4/c)^4$. Solving this we obtain $c = 4/130^{1/4}$. ∎

Reality Check: The models that are considered here are used to illustrate how, and where, differential equations arise. As with all models, simplifying assumptions are made to obtain the resulting mathematical problem. Many of these assumptions are not considered or accounted for in our examples, and the same is true for the exercises. As a case in point, Newton's Law of Cooling is usually limited to cases of when $|T - T_a|$ is not very large, and its applicability depends on whether the heat flow is due to conduction, convection, or radiation. Said another way, if you want to impress your family at Thanksgiving by using the solution of the cooking a turkey exercise (see below), just make sure to check on the turkey temperature regularly to make sure your predictions are correct.

Exercises

In answering the following questions, do not numerically evaluate numbers such as $\sqrt{2}$, $\pi/3$, e^2, $\ln(4/3)$, etc. The exception to this is when the question explicitly asks you to *compute* the answer.

1. The IVP for radioactive decay was derived in Example 1, on page 1.

   a) What is the solution of the IVP for a radioactive material?

   b) If 12 mg of a radioactive material decays to 9 mg in one day, find k.

   c) The half-life of a radioactive material is the time required for it to reach one-half of the original amount. What is the half-life of the material in part (b)?

2. Radiocarbon dating uses the decay of carbon-14 to estimate how long ago something died. The assumption is that the amount of carbon-14 satisfies the radioactive decay problem derived in Example 1, on page 1.

   a) What is the solution of the IVP for a radioactive material?

   b) The half-life of a radioactive material is the time required for it to reach one-half of the original amount. The half-life of carbon-14 is 5,730 years. Use this to determine k.

   c) The amount of carbon-14 is the same in all living organisms. When an organism dies the amount starts to undergo radioactive decay.

So, for radioactive dating you know N_0, as well as the current value of N. Explain how knowing N_0, N, and k can be used to determine t (which is the time that has passed since the organism died).

d) Measurements in 1991 determined that the amount of carbon-14 in the Temple Scroll, which is one of the Dead Sea scrolls found at Qumran, to be 186.18. The amount in living organisms is 238. Determine (i.e., compute) what two years the scroll could have been written in. Note that in the BC/AD system there is no year zero, so it goes from 1 BC to 1 AD.

Comments: In this problem, the amount of carbon-14 refers to the amount relative to carbon-12. Also, the organism is the parchment from the scroll, and the testing is described in Bonani et al. [1992].

Mixing

3. A tank contains 100 L of salt water with a concentration of 2 g/L. To flush the salt out, pure water is poured in at 4 L/min, and the mixture in the tank flows out at the same rate.

   a) What is the resulting IVP for the total amount $Q(t)$ of salt in the tank?

   b) Solve the IVP determined in part (a).

   c) How long does it take until the amount of salt in the tank is 1% of its original amount?

4. A tank contains 20 L of fresh water. Suppose water, containing $\frac{1}{4}$ g/L of salt, starts to flow into the tank at 2 L/min, and the well-stirred mixture flows out at the same rate.

   a) What is the resulting IVP for the amount $Q(t)$ of salt in the tank?

   b) Solve the IVP determined in part (a).

   c) How much salt is in the tank after one hour?

5. Ten years ago, a factory started operation in a pristine valley. The valley's volume is $10^6 \, \mathrm{m}^3$. Each year the factory releases $10^5 \, \mathrm{m}^3$ of exhaust through its smoke stacks, and this exhaust contains 1000 kg of pollutants. Assume that the well-mixed polluted air leaves the valley at $10^5 \, \mathrm{m}^3/\mathrm{yr}$.

   a) What is the IVP for the amount of pollutant in the valley?

   b) How much pollutant is in the valley now?

6. A small lake contains 60,000 gal of pure water. There is an inlet stream of pure water into the lake, as well as an outlet stream, both flowing at a rate of 100 gal/min. Suppose someone starts pouring water into the lake at the rate of 10 gal/min that contains 5 lbs/gal of a chemical, and they do this for 8 hours. While this happens the inlet stream of pure water is unchanged, and the outflow rate from the lake remains at 100 gal/min.

a) What is the formula for the volume of the lake while the person is pouring?

b) What IVP must be solved to determine the amount of the chemical in the lake?

c) How much of the chemical is in the lake when the person stops pouring?

d) Once the person stops pouring, what IVP must be solved to determine how much of the chemical is in the lake?

Newton's Second Law

7. A mass of 10 kg is shot upward from the surface of the Earth with a velocity of 100 m/s. In addition to gravity, assume that there is a drag force $F_r = -cv$, where $c = 5$ kg/s. Assume that $g = 10$ m/s^2.

   a) Write down the IVP for v, and then find its solution.

   b) Find x.

   c) How high does the object get?

8. A skydiver weighing 176 lbs drops from a plane that is at an altitude of 5000 ft. Assume that $g = 32$ ft/s^2.

   a) Before the parachute opens, the forces on the skydiver are gravity and a drag force $F_r = -cv$. Assuming $v(0) = 0$, write down the IVP for v, and then find the solution.

   b) It is claimed that the terminal velocity of a person falling is -120 mph. Use this to determine c.

   c) If the parachute is opened after 10 s of free fall, what is the speed of the skydiver when it opens?

   d) Find the distance the skydiver falls before the parachute opens.

   e) When the parachute is open, the drag force increases by a factor of 8 from the free fall drag force. What is the resulting terminal velocity of the skydiver?

9. A spherical object sinking to the bottom of a lake is acted on by three forces: a drag force $F_r = -cv$, a buoyant force F_b, and gravity F_g. According to Archimedes' principle, the buoyant force is equal to the weight of the water that is displaced by the sphere.

   a) What is the formula for F_b in terms of the sphere's radius a, the water density ρ, and g?

   b) The differential equation for the velocity of the sphere has the form $mv' = A - cv$. What is A?

   c) Assuming the sphere is released from rest, solve the resulting IVP for v.

   d) Find a formula for the terminal velocity in terms of c, a, ρ, and g. What condition must be satisfied if the sphere is sinking?

e) Assume the object is released a distance L from the bottom of the lake. Also assume that it takes a while for it to hit the bottom. Use an approximation similar to the one used in Question 4 on page 24 to derive an approximate formula for the time it takes it to hit the bottom.

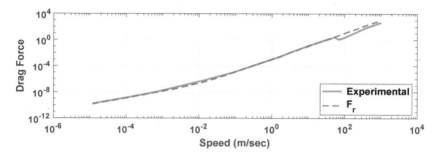

Figure 2.4. *Drag force on a smooth sphere as a function of the speed [Roos and Willmarth, 1971, NASA, 2020]. The function F_r is used in Exercise 10.*

10. A spherical object falling in the atmosphere is acted on by gravity, F_g, and a drag force F_r. It is assumed that $F_r = -cv(1 - \beta v)$, where v is the velocity. Both c and β are positive constants.

a) Assuming the sphere is dropped from rest, what is the resulting IVP for v?

b) Solve the IVP for v.

c) Find a formula for the terminal velocity in terms of m, c, β, and g.

d) The constants in F_r are $c = 6\pi R\mu$ and $\beta = R\rho/(9\pi\mu)$, where R is the radius of the sphere, ρ is the air density, and μ is the air viscosity. For a baseball falling in the atmosphere, $R = 0.037$, $\mu = 1.8 \times 10^{-5}$, and $\rho = 1.2$ (using kg, m, s units). Also, $m = 0.14$ and assume that $g = 9.8$. Compute the terminal velocity. How does this compare to what is the speed of a typical fastball in professional baseball? Comment: The drag force used in this problem is close to what is observed experimentally. To demonstrate this, the experimentally determined values of the drag, and the values determined using F_r, are shown in Figure 2.4 as a function of the speed $|v|$. This data also shows that the assumption $F_r = -cv$ is only valid if the speed is no more than about 10^{-2} m/s.

Logistic Growth or Decay

11. It is often found that a population will grow exponentially if the population is very small, and it will decrease exponentially if the population is very large. A model for this is due to Beverton and Holt, and the

equation to solve is

$$P' = r\frac{1 - \frac{P}{N}}{1 + \frac{P}{N}}P,$$

where r and N are positive constants.

a) Assuming that $P(0) = \frac{1}{2}N$, solve the resulting IVP for P.

b) What is the limiting population $P(\infty) = \lim_{t \to \infty} P(t)$?

12. The population of fish in a large lake can be modeled using the logistic equation. If, in addition, the fish are caught at a constant rate h, the equation for the population becomes

$$P' = r\left(1 - \frac{P}{N}\right)P - h,$$

where r and N are positive constants. In this problem take $r = 4$, $h = 750$, and $N = 1000$. Also, $P(0) = 1000$.

a) Solve the IVP for P.

b) What is the limiting population? In other words, what is $P(\infty) = \lim_{t \to \infty} P(t)$?

Cooling or Heating

13. Suppose coffee has a temperature of $200°$ F when freshly poured, and the room temperature is $72°$ F. In this exercise use Newton's law of cooling.

a) What IVP does the temperature of the coffee satisfy?

b) What is the solution of the IVP?

c) If the coffee cools to $136°$ F in five minutes, what is k?

d) When does the coffee reach a temperature of $150°$ F?

14. Redo the previous exercise but use the Dulong-Petit law of cooling.

15. To cook a turkey you are to put it into a $350°$F oven, and cook it until it reaches $165°$F. In answering the following questions, assume Newton's law of cooling is used.

a) Suppose the turkey starts out at room temperature, which is $70°$F. What IVP does the temperature satisfy?

b) Suppose that after two hours in the oven, the temperature of the turkey is $140°$F. How much longer before it is done?

c) Suppose the turkey is taken from the refrigerator, which is set to $40°$F, and put directly into the oven. How much longer does it take to cook than when the turkey starts out at room temperature? The value for k is the same as in part (b).

16. A homicide victim was discovered at 1 p.m. in a room that is kept at $70°$F. When discovered, the temperature of the body was $90°$F, and one hour later it had dropped to $85°$F.

a) Assuming Newton's Law of Cooling, and normal body temperature is 98.6°F, how long had the person been dead when the body was discovered?

b) Compute the time of death. Round your answer so it just gives the hour and minute (e.g., 7:13 a.m. or 5:32 p.m.).

17. Suppose that in Newton's Law of Cooling that k is found to depend on temperature. A common assumption is that $k = k_0 + k_1(T - T_a)$, where k_0 and k_1 are positive constants.

a) What is the resulting differential equation for T?

b) To find T it makes things easier to introduce the variable $S(t) = T(t) - T_a$. Rewrite the differential equation in part (a) in terms of S. Also, if $T(0) = T_0$, what is $S(0)$?

c) Solve the resulting IVP in part (b) for S, and then use this to show that
$$T = T_a + \frac{k_0 c e^{-k_0 t}}{1 - k_1 c e^{-k_0 t}},$$
where $c = S_0/(k_0 + k_1 S_0)$ and $S_0 = T_0 - T_a$.

d) Using (2.43), it was found you have to wait about 7.4 minutes to drink the coffee. Taking $k_0 = \frac{1}{2}\ln(13/11)$ and $k_1 = 0.01$, compute how long you need to wait using the solution for T from part (c).

2.4 ▪ Steady States and Stability

All of the applications considered in the previous section have one thing in common: the solution eventually approaches a constant value, or steady state. This is not unusual, as this is what often happens. What is of interest here is whether it is possible to determine the eventual steady state without actually having to solve the problem.

To illustrate, as explained in the previous section, the population $P(t)$ of a species is determined by solving

$$P' = f(P), \tag{2.45}$$

where, for this example, we will take

$$f(P) = 2(3 - P)P. \tag{2.46}$$

The solution of this equation is given in (2.40), and it is plotted in Figure 2.5 for the case of when $P(0) = 0.1$, and when $P(0) = 4.5$. It shows that for both initial values, the population approaches, asymptotically, $P = 3$. In both cases the approach is monotonic, either increasing or decreasing.

What is important for this discussion is that it is possible to determine the general behavior of the solution seen in Figure 2.5 without solving the problem. This requires the following three observations:

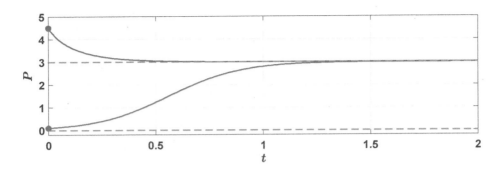

Figure 2.5. *Solution of (2.45) and (2.46) in the case of when $P(0) = 0.1$, and when $P(0) = 4.5$. The dashed red lines are the steady state values.*

Steady States: If the solution does asymptotically approach a constant value $\overline{P}$, then $P = \overline{P}$ must be a solution of the differential equation. This means that it is required that $f(\overline{P}) = 0$. From this and (2.46) we get the two values $\overline{P} = 0$ and $\overline{P} = 3$. These are called **steady states** for this equation.

Unstable: Even though the initial value $P(0) = 0.1$ is close to the steady state $\overline{P} = 0$, the solution moves away from $\overline{P} = 0$. This happens because of $f(P)$. To explain, the function $f(P)$ is plotted in Figure 2.6. It shows that $f(P) > 0$ for $0 < P < 3$. So, in this interval $P'(t) > 0$, and this means that P is increasing. Similarly, since $f(P) < 0$ for $3 < P$, then P is decreasing in this interval. The arrows in Figure 2.6 indicate the corresponding movement of P. The conclusion we derive from the arrows is that if $P(0)$ is anywhere in $0 < P < 3$, then the solution will move away from the steady state $\overline{P} = 0$. Because of this, the steady state is said to be **unstable**.

Stable: The second conclusion we make from the arrows in Figure 2.6 is that if $P(0)$ is anywhere in $0 < P < 3$, then the solution increases

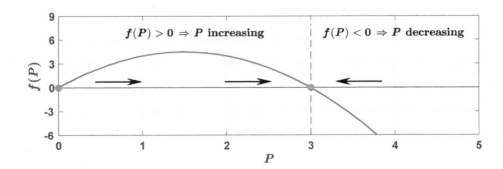

Figure 2.6. *The function $f(P)$ in (2.46). The two steady states are shown by the reds dots. The arrows indicate the direction P moves in the respective interval.*

towards the steady state $\overline{P} = 3$. Moreover, if $P(0)$ is anywhere in $3 < P$, then the solution decreases towards the steady state $\overline{P} = 3$. A consequence of this is that, no matter what initial condition we pick near $P = 3$,

$$\lim_{t \to \infty} P(t) = 3.$$

For this reason, $\overline{P} = 3$ is said to be an **asymptotically stable** steady state.

The key to what guarantees that the steady state $P = 3$ is asymptotically stable is that $f(P)$ is positive to the left of $P = 3$, and negative to the right of it. In other words, $f(P)$ is a deceasing function at $P = 3$. Consequently, if $f'(3) < 0$ then $P = 3$ is asymptotically stable. A similar test can be made for an unstable steady state.

2.4.1 ▪ General Version

The reasoning used in the above example is easily extended to more general differential equations. To do this, assume that the equation is

$$y' = f(y), \tag{2.47}$$

where $f'(y)$ is a continuous function of y. Because $f(y)$ is assumed to not depend explicitly on t, the equation is said to be *autonomous*. So, $y' = 1 + y^3$ is autonomous, but $y' = t + y^3$ is not.

Steady State. *$y = Y$ is a steady state for (2.47) if it is constant and $f(Y) = 0$.*

Stability Theorem. *A steady state $y = Y$ is asymptotically stable if $f'(Y) < 0$ and it is unstable if $f'(Y) > 0$.*

The idea underlying asymptotic stability is that if $y(0)$ is any point close to Y, then

$$\lim_{t \to \infty} y(t) = Y. \tag{2.48}$$

To explain this more mathematically, a steady state is either stable or unstable. It is stable if you can control how far the solution gets from Y by picking $y(0)$ close to Y. Specifically, given any $\varepsilon > 0$, you can find a $\delta > 0$ so that $|y(t) - Y| < \varepsilon$ if $|y(0) - Y| < \delta$. If this is not possible then Y is *unstable*. So, the steady state $P = 0$ in Figure 2.6 is unstable as it is not possible to find $P(0)$'s near $P = 0$ that will result in the solution staying near $P = 0$.

In addition, a stable steady state is either asymptotically stable, which means that the limit (2.48) holds, or it is said to be *neutrally stable*. The latter occur, for example, for the steady states of $y' = 0$. Neutrally stable steady states are not considered in this chapter but will be in Chapters 4 and 5.

The case of when $y(0) = Y$ merits a comment. No matter if the steady state is stable or unstable, if $y(0) = Y$, then $y(t) = Y$ is a solution of the resulting IVP. Consequently, what is of interest is what the solution does if you start close, but not exactly at, a steady state.

Example 1: Find the steady states, and determine their stability, for

$$y' = y^2 - y - 6.$$

Answer: The steady states are found by solving $y^2 - y - 6 = 0$, and from this we get $Y = 3$ and $Y = -2$. To determine their stability, since $f(y) = y^2 - y - 6$, then $f'(y) = 2y - 1$. Since $f'(3) = 5 > 0$, then $Y = 3$ is unstable, and since $f'(-2) = -5 < 0$, then $Y = -2$ is asymptotically stable. ∎

2.4.2 ▪ Sketching the Solution

As demonstrated in the above example, the stability theorem makes it is relatively simple to determine if a steady state is stable or unstable. It is also relatively easy to sketch the solution, and the following example illustrates how this is done. Moreover, as you will see, this is done using nothing more than the sketch of the function $f(y)$.

Example 2: Sketch the solution of $y' = f(y)$, where $f(y)$ is given in Figure 2.7.

Answer: To do this it is necessary to know $y(0)$. Before picking this value, we first see what can be determined about the solution.

Steady States: The steady states are the points where $f(y) = 0$. From Figure 2.7, this happens when $y = -2$, $y = 1$, and $y = 3$. These are identified using red dots in the figure. From the graph it is evident that $f'(-2) < 0$ and $f'(3) < 0$, and this means that $y = -2$ and $y = 3$ are asymptotically stable. Similarly, since $f'(1) > 0$, then $y = 1$ is unstable.

Increasing or Decreasing: If $f(y) > 0$, then the solution is increasing, and if $f(y) < 0$, then the solution is deceasing. The respective y intervals where this happens are shown in Figure 2.7 using arrows.

We will now use the above conclusions to sketch the solution.

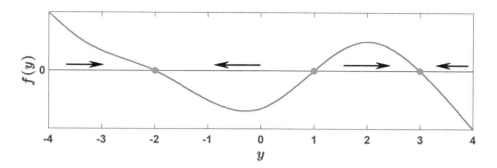

Figure 2.7. *The sketch of the function $f(y)$ for Example 2.*

$y(0) = 1.3$: This point is located between two steady states, specifically,
  $1 < y(0) < 3$. According to Figure 2.7, $y(t)$ increases monotonically
  in this interval, and asymptotically approaches $y = 3$. A curve with
  these properties is shown in Figure 2.8.

$y(0) = 0.8$: In this case, the point is located between two steady states,
  namely, $-2 < y(0) < 1$. From Figure 2.7, $y(t)$ decreases monotonically in this interval, and asymptotically approaches $y = -2$. A
  curve with these properties is shown in Figure 2.8.

$y(0) = -4$: For this initial condition, according to the information in Figure 2.7, $y(t)$ increases monotonically, and asymptotically approaches
  $y = -2$. A curve with these properties is shown in Figure 2.8. ■

The sketching procedure outlined above leaves some things undeter-

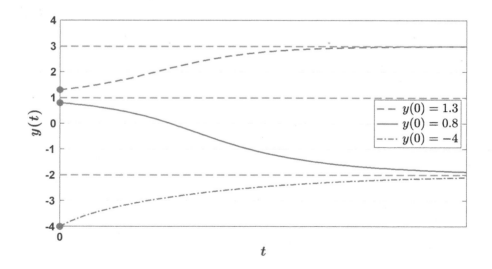

Figure 2.8. *Solution curves obtained using the information in Figure 2.7.
The dashed red lines are the steady state values.*

mined. For example, nothing was said about how steep the curves are, or whether they are concave up or down. It is possible to determine this using Figure 2.7, but this level of analysis is not considered in this text.

2.4.3 ▪ Parting Comments

A few closing comments about the material in this section are in order.

1. What is defined as a steady state here is sometimes called a critical point, or an equilibrium point. Referring to them as a steady state is consistent with what is used for time independent solutions of partial differential equations.

2. The stability theorem does not cover the case of when $f'(Y) = 0$. However, the graphical method, as in Figure 2.6, can still be used.

3. When a solution moves away from an unstable steady state, it does not necessarily approach the closest stable steady state. An example of this is shown in Figure 2.8. Although $Y = 3$ is closer to the initial point $y(0) = 0.8$, $f(y)$ is negative for $-2 < y < 1$, and this means the solution must decrease.

Exercises

1. For each equation, verify that $Y = 0$ is a steady state. Determine if it is unstable or asymptotically stable.

   a) $y' = \sin(1 - e^y)$ c) $y' = -e^y \sin(y)$

   b) $y' = y^5 - 3y^2 + y$ d) $y' = (1 + y^9)\ln(1 + y)$

2. For each differential equation, find the steady states and determine if they are asymptotically stable or unstable.

   a) $y' = y^2 + y - 2$ c) $y' = 4y - y^3$ e) $y' = y^4 - 3y^2 - 4$

   b) $y' = y^3 - y$ d) $y' = e^{-y} - 2$ f) $y' = e^{2y} - 4e^y + 3$

3. Sketch the solution curve for each of the given initial conditions.

   a) $y' = y^2 + y - 2$
   $y(0) = -3; y(0) = 0$

   b) $y' = y^3 - y$
   $y(0) = 3/4; y(0) = -1/4$

   c) $y' = 4y - y^3$
   $y(0) = 1/2; y(0) = 3$

   d) $y' = e^{-y} - 2$
   $y(0) = 1; y(0) = 2$

   e) $y' = y^4 - 3y^2 - 4$
   $y(0) = 1; y(0) = -3$

   f) $y' = e^{2y} - 4e^y + 3$
   $y(0) = -1; y(0) = \ln 2$

4. Sketch the solution of (2.47) based on the information provided. Assume that $f(y)$ is zero only at $y = -2$ and $y = 3$.

a) $f(2) = -4$,   b) $f'(-2) = 1$,   c) $f'(3) = 2$,
    $y(0) = 1$ $y(0) = 0$ $y(0) = -1$

5. For the mixing problem given in (2.31), (2.32), sketch the solution without using the formula for the solution. Make sure to explain how you do this.

6. For the population problem in Exercise 11, on page 31, sketch the solution without using the formula for the solution. Use this to answer part (b) of that exercise.

7. For the drag on a sphere, as described in Exercise 10 on page 31, determine the terminal velocity without solving the IVP. In other words, answer part (c) using only part (a) of that exercise.

8. This problem concerns solving $y' = -\sqrt{1+y}$, where $y(0) = 0$.

a) Using separation of variables, what is the solution? It helps to note, from the differential equation, that $y'(0) = -1$.

b) Using the method outlined in Example 2, sketch the solution.

c) Sketch the solution you found in part (a). Assuming your sketch in part (b) is correct, is there anything wrong with your solution in part (a)? If so, how should it be modified? Does your sketch from part (b) need to be modified as well?

9. The population of fish in a lake can be modeled using the logistic equation. However, assuming that the fish are caught at a constant rate h, the equation for the population becomes

$$P' = r\left(1 - \frac{P}{N}\right)P - h,$$

where r and N are positive constants.

a) Assuming that the loss due to fishing is small enough that $0 < h < rN/4$, find the two steady states for the equation. Label these values as P_1 and P_2, where $P_1 < P_2$.

b) Determine whether P_1 and P_2 are unstable or asymptotically stable.

c) Letting $f(P)$ be the right hand side of the differential equation, sketch $f(P)$ for $0 \le P < \infty$. With this, answer the question in Exercise 12(b) on page 32.

d) Assuming that $P_1 < P(0) < P_2$, sketch the solution. Do the same for the case of when $P_2 < P(0)$.

e) Sketch the solution if $0 < P(0) < P_1$. In doing this remember that $P(t)$ can not be negative. Note that you will find that there is a time t_e where extinction occurs, and the differential equation does not apply to the fish population for $t_e < t$.

10. The solution of a differential equation is shown in Figure 2.9. Explain
    why it can not be the plot of the solution of the following differential
    equations. You only need to provide one reason (even though there
    might be several).

    a) $y' = 1 + y^2$ c) $y' = (y - 4)(y - 3)(y - 1)$

    b) $y' = y - 4$ d) $y' = (y - 2)(4 - y)$

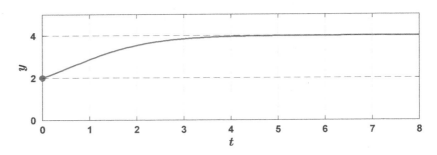

Figure 2.9. *Plot used in Exercise 10. The starting point is* $y(0) = 2$.

11. The following refer to the solution of (2.47), where $f(y)$ is continuous.
    Sketch a function $f(y)$ so the stated conditions hold. Make sure to pro-
    vide a short explanation of why your function satisfies the conditions
    stated. If it is not possible to find such a function, explain why.

    a) The solution is strictly monotone increasing for $y < 0$, is strictly
       monotone decreasing for $y > 0$, and there are no steady states.
    b) The only asymptotically stable steady state is $Y = 0$, and the only
       unstable steady states are $Y = -1$ and $Y = 1$.
    c) The only asymptotically stable steady state is $Y = 0$, and the only
       unstable steady states are $Y = 1$ and $Y = 2$.

12. This problem concerns what is known as one-sided stability, or semi-
    stability. The differential equation considered is

    $$y' = 2(3 - y)^2.$$

    a) Show that there is one steady state Y, and $f'(Y) = 0$.
    b) Sketch $f(y)$ for $-\infty < y < \infty$. Use this to explain why, except
       when $y = Y$, y is an increasing function of t.
    c) Using the same reasoning as for the population example, explain
       why, if $y(0) < Y$, then $\lim_{t \to \infty} y(t) = Y$. However, if $y(0) > Y$,
       then $\lim_{t \to \infty} y(t) = \infty$.
    d) Use the results from part (c) to explain why this is an example of
       one-sided stability.

Chapter 3

Second-Order Linear Equations

The general version of the differential equations considered in this chapter can be written as

$$\frac{d^2y}{dt^2} + p(t)\frac{dy}{dt} + q(t)y = f(t), \qquad (3.1)$$

where $p(t)$, $q(t)$, and $f(t)$ are given. One of the reasons this equation gets its own chapter is Newton's second law, which, if you recall, is $F = ma$. To explain, if $y(t)$ is the displacement, then the acceleration is $a = y''$, and this gives us the differential equation $my'' = F$. In this chapter we are considering problems when F is a linear function of velocity y' and displacement y. Later, in Chapter 5, we will consider equations where the dependence is nonlinear. It is because of the connections with the second law that $f(t)$ in (3.1) is often referred to as the **forcing function**.

In the previous chapter, for first-order linear differential equations, we very elegantly derived a formula for the general solution. This will not happen for second-order equations. *All* of the methods derived in this chapter are, in fact, just good, or educated, guesses on what the answer is. There are non-guessing methods, and one example involves using a Taylor series expansion of the solution. An illustration of how this is done can be found in Exercise 8 on page 51.

To use a guessing approach, it becomes essential to know the mathematical requirements for what can be called a general solution. This is where we begin.

Introduction to Differential Equations, M. H. Holmes, 2020

3.1 ▪ Initial Value Problem

A typical initial value problem (IVP) consists of solving (3.1), for $t > 0$, with the initial conditions

$$y(0) = y_0, \quad \text{and} \quad y'(0) = y_0', \tag{3.2}$$

where y_0 and y_0' are given numbers. Given that our solution methods involve guessing, it is important that we know when to stop guessing and conclude we have found the solution. This is why the next result is useful.

Existence and Uniqueness Theorem. *If $p(t)$, $q(t)$, and $f(t)$ are continuous for $t \geq 0$, then there is exactly one smooth function $y(t)$ that satisfies (3.1) and (3.2).*

In stating that $y(t)$ is a smooth function, it is meant that $y''(t)$ is defined and continuous for $t \geq 0$. Those interested in the proof of this theorem, or the theoretical foundations of the subject, should consult Coddington and Carlson [1997].

So, according to the above theorem, if we find a smooth function that satisfies the differential equation and initial conditions, then that is the solution, and the only solution, of the IVP.

3.2 ▪ General Solution of a Homogeneous Equation

The **associated homogeneous equation** for (3.1) is

$$\frac{d^2y}{dt^2} + p(t)\frac{dy}{dt} + q(t)y = 0. \tag{3.3}$$

We need to spend some time discussing what it means to be the general solution of this equation. So, consider Exercise 5(a), in Section 1.2. Assuming you did this exercise, you found that given solutions $y_1 = e^{2t}$ and $y_2 = e^t$ of $y'' - 3y' + 2y = 0$, then

$$y(t) = c_1 y_1(t) + c_2 y_2(t) \tag{3.4}$$

is a solution for any value of c_1 and c_2. What is important here is that this is a **general solution** of the differential equation. As in the last chapter, this means that any, and all, solutions of the differential equation are included in this formula.

This gives rise to the question: what is required so a solution like the one in (3.4) can be claimed to be a general solution? The key to answering this is the uniqueness guaranteed by the above theorem. The specifics of the analysis are not needed here. What is needed is the conclusion, which is stated next.

General Solution. *The function $y = c_1 y_1(t) + c_2 y_2(t)$, where c_1 and c_2 are arbitrary constants, is a general solution of (3.3) if the following are true:*

1. *y_1 and y_2 are solutions of (3.3), and*

2. *y_1 and y_2 are linearly independent.*

Stating that y_1 and y_2 are **linearly independent** means that the only constants c_1 and c_2 that satisfy

$$c_1 y_1(t) + c_2 y_2(t) = 0, \quad \forall\, t \geq 0, \tag{3.5}$$

are $c_1 = 0$ and $c_2 = 0$. This is, effectively, the same definition of linear independence used in linear algebra. The difference is that we have functions rather than vectors. If it is possible to find either $c_1 \neq 0$ or $c_2 \neq 0$ so (3.5) holds, then y_1 and y_2 are said to be **linearly dependent**. Finally, in (3.5), the symbol $\forall$ is a mathematical shorthand for "for all" or "for every."

Given two solutions y_1 and y_2 of (3.3), the easiest way to determine if they are independent is to use what is called the Wronskian. To explain, the **Wronskian** of y_1 and y_2 is defined as

$$W(y_1, y_2) \equiv \det \begin{pmatrix} y_1 & y_2 \\ y_1' & y_2' \end{pmatrix}. \tag{3.6}$$

For those unfamiliar with determinants, this can be written as

$$W(y_1, y_2) \equiv y_1 y_2' - y_2 y_1'. \tag{3.7}$$

The usefulness of this function is due, in part, to the next result.

Independence Test. *If y_1 and y_2 are solutions of (3.3), then y_1 and y_2 are independent if, and only if, $W(y_1, y_2)$ is nonzero.*

To explain how the Wronskian comes into this problem, (3.5) must hold on the interval $0 \leq t < \infty$. So, (3.5) can be differentiated, which gives us the equation $c_1 y_1' + c_2 y_2' = 0$. This, along with (3.5), provides two equations for c_1 and c_2. It is not hard to show that if $W(y_1, y_2) \neq 0$, then the only solution to these two equations is $c_1 = c_2 = 0$. Consequently, y_1 and y_2 are independent. The rest of the proof, along with some additional information, can be found in Exercises 5 and 6.

Example: Show that $y = c_1 e^{-3t} + c_2 e^t$ is a general solution of $y'' + 2y' - 3y = 0$.

Answer: In this case, $y_1(t) = e^{-3t}$ and $y_2(t) = e^t$. It is not hard to show that they are solutions of the differential equation (see Section 1.2). To check on independence, from (3.7), $W = e^{-3t} e^t - (-3) e^{-3t} e^t = 4e^{-2t}$. This is not zero, and so the functions are independent. Therefore, y is a general solution. ∎

In the remainder of the chapter, except in Section 3.11 and in some of the exercises for Section 3.9, we will only consider differential equations of the form

$$\frac{d^2y}{dt^2} + b\frac{dy}{dt} + cy = f(t), \tag{3.8}$$

where b and c are given constants. The reasons are that these are easier to solve, and, more importantly, they are also the most common second-order differential equations that arise in applications.

Exercises

1. Assuming $b \neq 0$, show that $y_1 = 1$ and $y_2 = e^{-bt}$ are independent solutions of $y'' + by' = 0$.
2. Assuming $\omega \neq 0$, show that $y_1 = \cos(\omega t)$ and $y_2 = \sin(\omega t)$ are independent solutions of $y'' + \omega^2 y = 0$.
3. Assuming $\omega \neq 0$, show that $y = c_1 e^{\omega t} + c_2 e^{-\omega t}$ is a general solution of $y'' - \omega^2 y = 0$.
4. Show $y = c_1 e^{-\alpha t} + c_2 t e^{-\alpha t}$ is a general solution of $y'' + 2\alpha y' + \alpha^2 y = 0$.
5. If y_1 and y_2 are solutions of (3.3), show that $\frac{d}{dt}W + p(t)W = 0$. Use this to derive Abel's formula, which is that

$$W(y_1, y_2) = ce^{-\int_0^t p(r)dr},$$

where c is a constant.
6. Let $y_1 = (t-1)^2$ and $y_2 = -(t-1)|t-1|$.

   a) On the same axes, sketch y_1 and y_2 for $0 \leq t < \infty$.

   b) Use (3.5) to show that y_1 and y_2 are linearly independent for $0 \leq t < \infty$. Hint: Consider $t = 0$ and $t = 2$.

   c) Show that $W(y_1, y_2) = 0$. Explain why this, together with the result in part (b), does not contradict the Independence Test.

3.3 ▪ Solving a Homogeneous Equation

The solution of the homogeneous equation

$$\frac{d^2y}{dt^2} + b\frac{dy}{dt} + cy = 0 \tag{3.9}$$

can be found by assuming that $y = e^{rt}$. With this, $y' = re^{rt}$, and $y'' = r^2 e^{rt}$, and so (3.9) becomes $(r^2 + br + c)e^{rt} = 0$. Since e^{rt} is never zero, we conclude that

$$r^2 + br + c = 0. \tag{3.10}$$

This is called the **characteristic equation** for (3.9). It is easily solved using the quadratic formula, which gives us that

$$r = \frac{1}{2}\left(-b \pm \sqrt{b^2 - 4c}\right). \tag{3.11}$$

There are three possibilities here:

1. there are two real-valued r's: this happens when $b^2 - 4c > 0$,

2. there is one r: this happens when $b^2 - 4c = 0$, and

3. there are two complex-valued r's: this happens when $b^2 - 4c < 0$.

The case of when the roots are complex-valued requires a short introduction to complex variables, and so it is done last.

3.3.1 ▪ Two Real Roots

When there are two real-valued roots, say, r_1 and r_2, then the two corresponding solutions of (3.9) are $y_1 = e^{r_1 t}$ and $y_2 = e^{r_2 t}$. It is left as an exercise to show they are independent. Therefore, the resulting general solution of (3.9) is

$$y = c_1 e^{r_1 t} + c_2 e^{r_2 t}.$$

3.3.2 ▪ One Real Root and Reduction of Order

When there is only one root, the second solution can be found using what is called the *reduction of order method*. To explain, if you know a solution $y_1(t)$, it is possible to find a second solution by assuming that $y_2(t) = w(t)y_1(t)$. In our case, we know that $y_1(t) = e^{rt}$, where $r = -b/2$, is a solution. So, to find a second solution it is assumed that $y(t) = w(t)e^{rt}$. Substituting this into (3.9), and simplifying, yields the differential equation

$$w'' + (2r + b)w' + r^2 + br + c = 0.$$

Since $r = -b/2$, and $4c = b^2$, then the above differential equation reduces to just $w'' = 0$. Integrating this once gives $w' = d_1$ and then integrating again yields $w = d_1 t + d_2$, where d_1 and d_2 are arbitrary constants. With this our second solution is $y = (d_1 t + d_2)e^{rt}$. A solution that is independent of $y_1 = e^{rt}$ is obtained by taking $d_1 = 1$ and $d_2 = 0$, which means that $y_2 = te^{rt}$. Therefore, the resulting general solution of (3.9) is

$$y = c_1 e^{rt} + c_2 t e^{rt}.$$

3.4 ▪ Complex Roots

An example of a differential equation that generates complex-valued roots
is

$$y'' + 4y' + 13y = 0. \tag{3.12}$$

Assuming $y = e^{rt}$, we obtain the characteristic equation $r^2 + 4r + 13 = 0$.
The two solutions of this are $r_1 = -2 + 3i$ and $r_2 = -2 - 3i$. Proceeding
as in the case of two real-valued roots, the conclusion is that the resulting
general solution of (3.12) is

$$\begin{aligned}
y &= c_1 e^{r_1 t} + c_2 e^{r_2 t} \\
&= c_1 e^{(-2+3i)t} + c_2 e^{(-2-3i)t}.
\end{aligned} \tag{3.13}$$

Because complex numbers are used in the exponents, if this expression is
used as the general solution, then c_1 and c_2 must be allowed to also be
complex-valued.

Although solutions as in (3.13) are used, particularly in physics, there
are other ways to write the solution that do not involve complex numbers.
Even if (3.13) is used, there is still the question of how to evaluate an
expression such as e^{3i}. For this reason, a short introduction to complex
variables is needed.

3.4.1 ▪ Euler's Formula and its Consequences

The key for working with complex exponents is the following formula.

Euler's Formula. *If θ is real-valued then*

$$e^{i\theta} = \cos\theta + i\sin\theta. \tag{3.14}$$

It is not possible to overemphasize the importance of this formula. It is
one of those fundamental mathematical facts that you must memorize.
For those who might wonder how this formula is obtained, it comes from
writing down the Maclaurin series of $e^{i\theta}$, $\cos\theta$, and $\sin\theta$, and then showing
that they satisfy (3.14).

As it must, (3.14) is consistent with the usual rules involving arith-
metic, algebra, and calculus. The examples below provide illustrations of
this fact.

Example 1: Since, by definition, $i = \sqrt{-1}$, then $i^2 = -1$, $i^3 = -i$, and
$i^4 = 1$. Also,

$$\begin{aligned}
(a + ib)^2 &= (a + ib)(a + ib) \\
&= a^2 - b^2 + 2iab.
\end{aligned}$$

It is useful to be able to identify the real and imaginary part of a complex number. So, if $r = a + ib$, and a and b are real, then

$$\text{Re}(r) = a, \quad \text{and} \quad \text{Im}(r) = b.$$

As an example, $\text{Re}(5 - 16i) = 5$, and $\text{Im}(5 - 16i) = -16$. Finally, two complex numbers are equal only when their respective real and imaginary parts are equal. So, for example, to state that $e^{i\theta} = \frac{1}{2}\sqrt{2}(1 - i)$ requires that, using Euler's formula, $\cos\theta = \frac{1}{2}\sqrt{2}$ and $\sin\theta = -\frac{1}{2}\sqrt{2}$. ∎

Example 2: $e^{i\pi} = \cos\pi + i\sin\pi = -1$.

This shows that the exponential function can be negative. Moreover, since $e^{i\pi} = -1$ then, presumably, $\ln(-1) = i\pi$ (i.e., you can take the logarithm of a negative number). This is true, but there are complications related to the periodicity of the trigonometric functions, and to learn more about this you should take a course in complex variables. ∎

Example 3: $e^{i\pi/2} = \cos\pi/2 + i\sin\pi/2 = i$. ∎

Example 4: Assuming θ and φ are real-valued, then

$$
\begin{aligned}
e^{i\theta}e^{i\varphi} &= (\cos\theta + i\sin\theta)(\cos\varphi + i\sin\varphi) \\
&= \cos\theta\cos\varphi - \sin\theta\sin\varphi + i(\cos\theta\sin\varphi + \sin\theta\cos\varphi) \\
&= \cos(\theta + \varphi) + i\sin(\theta + \varphi) \\
&= e^{i(\theta+\varphi)}. \quad ∎
\end{aligned}
$$

Example 5: Assuming r is real-valued, then

$$
\begin{aligned}
\frac{d}{dt}e^{irt} &= \frac{d}{dt}(\cos rt + i\sin rt) \\
&= -r\sin rt + ir\cos rt \\
&= ir(\cos rt + i\sin rt) \\
&= ire^{irt}. \quad ∎
\end{aligned}
$$

The next step is to extend Euler's formula to a general complex number. With this in mind, let $z = x + iy$, where x and y are real-valued. Using the usual law of exponents,

$$
\begin{aligned}
e^z = e^{x+iy} &= e^x e^{iy} \\
&= e^x\big(\cos y + i\sin y\big).
\end{aligned}
\tag{3.15}
$$

The above expression is what we need for solving differential equations.

3.4.2 ▪ Second Representation

We return to the general solution given in (3.13). With (3.15), we get the following

$$
\begin{aligned}
y &= c_1 e^{(-2+3i)t} + c_2 e^{(-2-3i)t} \\
&= c_1 e^{-2t} \big(\cos 3t + i \sin 3t \big) + c_2 e^{-2t} \big(\cos 3t - i \sin 3t \big) \\
&= (c_1 + c_2) e^{-2t} \cos 3t + i(c_1 - c_2) e^{-2t} \sin 3t.
\end{aligned}
$$

We have therefore shown that the general solution can be written as

$$
y(t) = d_1 e^{-2t} \cos 3t + d_2 e^{-2t} \sin 3t. \tag{3.16}
$$

It is not difficult to check that the functions $\bar{y}_1 = e^{-2t} \cos 3t$ and $\bar{y}_2 = e^{-2t} \sin 3t$ are solutions of (3.12), and they have a nonzero Wronskian. Moreover, since $\bar{y}_1$ and $\bar{y}_2$ do not involve complex numbers, then d_1 and d_2 in the above formula are arbitrary real-valued constants.

3.4.3 ▪ Third Representation

There is a third way to write the general solution that can be useful when studying vibration, or oscillation, problems. This comes from making the observation that given the values of d_1 and d_2 in (3.16), we can write them as a point in the plane (d_1, d_2). Using polar coordinates, it is possible to find R and φ so that $d_1 = R \cos \varphi$ and $d_2 = R \sin \varphi$. In this case,

$$
\begin{aligned}
y &= d_1 e^{-2t} \cos 3t + d_2 e^{-2t} \sin 3t \\
&= R e^{-2t} \big(\cos \varphi \cos 3t + \sin \varphi \sin 3t \big) \\
&= R e^{-2t} \cos(3t - \varphi).
\end{aligned} \tag{3.17}
$$

This last expression is the formula we are looking for. In this representation of the general solution, R and φ are arbitrary constants that satisfy $0 \le R$, and $0 \le \varphi < 2\pi$. The advantage of this form of the general solution is that it is much easier to sketch the solution, and to determine its basic properties. Its downside is that it can be a bit harder to find R and φ from the initial conditions than the other two representations.

3.5 ▪ Summary for Solving a Homogeneous Equation

To solve

$$
y'' + by' + cy = 0, \tag{3.18}
$$

where b and c are constants, assume $y = e^{rt}$. This leads to solving the characteristic equation $r^2 + br + c = 0$, and from this the resulting general solution is given below.

Two Real Roots: $r = r_1, r_2$ (with $r_1 \neq r_2$).

$$y = c_1 e^{r_1 t} + c_2 e^{r_2 t} \tag{3.19}$$

One Real Root: $r = \lambda$.

$$y = c_1 e^{\lambda t} + c_2 t e^{\lambda t} \tag{3.20}$$

Complex Roots: $r = \lambda \pm i\mu$ (with $\mu \neq 0$). Any of the following can be used:

$$y = c_1 e^{(\lambda + i\mu)t} + c_2 e^{(\lambda - i\mu)t}, \text{ where } c_1, c_2 \text{ are complex-valued} \tag{3.21}$$

$$y = d_1 e^{\lambda t} \cos(\mu t) + d_2 e^{\lambda t} \sin(\mu t), \text{ where } d_1, d_2 \text{ are real-valued} \tag{3.22}$$

$$y = R e^{\lambda t} \cos(\mu t - \varphi), \text{ where } R \geq 0, \text{ and } 0 \leq \varphi < 2\pi \tag{3.23}$$

In what follows, (3.22) is used. The exception is in Section 3.10, where (3.23) is preferred because it is easier to sketch.

Example 1: Find a general solution of $y'' + 2y' - 3y = 0$.

Answer: The assumption that $y = e^{rt}$ leads to the characteristic equation $r^2 + 2r - 3 = 0$. The solutions of this are $r = -3$ and $r = 1$. Therefore, a general solution is $y = c_1 e^{-3t} + c_2 e^t$. ∎

Example 2: Find the solution of the IVP: $y'' + 2y' = 0$ where $y(0) = 3$ and $y'(0) = -4$.

Answer: The assumption that $y = e^{rt}$ leads to the characteristic equation $r^2 + 2r = 0$. The solutions of this are $r = -2$ and $r = 0$. Therefore, a general solution is $y = c_1 e^{-2t} + c_2$. To satisfy $y(0) = 3$ we need $c_1 + c_2 = 3$, and for $y'(0) = -4$ we need $-2c_1 = -4$. This gives us that $c_1 = 2$, and $c_2 = 1$. Therefore, the solution is $y = 2e^{-2t} + 1$. ∎

Example 3: Find the solution of the IVP: $y'' - 2y' + 26y = 0$ where $y(0) = 1$ and $y'(0) = -4$.

Answer: The characteristic equation is $r^2 - 2r + 26 = 0$, and the solutions of this are $r = 1 + 5i$ and $r = 1 - 5i$. Using (3.22), since $\lambda = 1$ and $\mu = 5$, the general solution has the form

$$y = d_1 e^t \cos(5t) + d_2 e^t \sin(5t).$$

To satisfy the initial conditions we need to find y', which for our solution is

$$y' = (d_1 + 5d_2)e^t \cos(5t) + (-5d_1 + d_2)e^t \sin(5t).$$

So, to satisfy $y(0) = 1$ we need $d_1 = 1$, and for $y'(0) = -4$ we need $d_1 + 5d_2 = -4$. This means that $d_2 = -1$, and therefore the solution of the IVP is $y = e^t \cos(5t) - e^t \sin(5t)$. ∎

Example 4: Find the solution of the IVP: $y'' - 9y = 0$ where $y(0) = -2$ and $y(t)$ is bounded for $0 \le t < \infty$.

Answer: The assumption that $y = e^{rt}$ leads to the quadratic equation $r^2 = 9$. The solutions of this are $r = -3$ and $r = 3$. Therefore, a general solution is $y = c_1 e^{-3t} + c_2 e^{3t}$. To satisfy $y(0) = 1$ we need $c_1 + c_2 = -2$. As for boundedness, e^{-3t} is a bounded function $0 \le t < \infty$ but e^{3t} is not. This means we must take $c_2 = 0$. The resulting solution is $y = -2e^{-3t}$. ∎

As you might have noticed, in the above examples the formula for the roots in (3.11) was not used. The reason is that it is much easier to remember the way the characteristic equation is derived (by assuming $y = e^{rt}$, etc) than by trying to remember the exact formula for the roots.

Exercises

1. Assuming that $z_1 = 1 + i$, and $z_2 = e^{2 + i\frac{\pi}{6}}$, find $\text{Re}(z)$ and $\text{Im}(z)$:

a) $z = z_1 - 8$ c) $z = z_2$ e) $z = z_1 z_2$

b) $z = 2iz_1$ d) $z = z_1 + 4z_2$ f) $z = (z_2)^6$

2. Assuming θ and φ are real-valued, show that the following hold:

a) $\dfrac{1}{i} = -i$ f) $e^{i(\theta + 2\pi)} = e^{i\theta}$

b) $\dfrac{1}{a + ib} = \dfrac{a - ib}{a^2 + b^2}$ g) $e^{i(\theta - \varphi)} = \dfrac{e^{i\theta}}{e^{i\varphi}}$

c) $e^{i\theta} \ne 0, \forall \theta$ h) $\int e^{i\theta} d\theta = -ie^{i\theta} + c$

d) $e^{-i\theta} = \dfrac{1}{e^{i\theta}}$ i) $\cos \theta = \frac{1}{2}\left(e^{i\theta} + e^{-i\theta}\right)$

e) $(e^{i\theta})^2 = e^{2i\theta}$ j) $\sin \theta = \frac{1}{2i}\left(e^{i\theta} - e^{-i\theta}\right)$

3. Find the general solution of the given differential equation.

a) $y'' + y' - 2y = 0$ f) $y'' - 6y' + 9y = 0$

b) $2y'' + 3y' - 2y = 0$ g) $4y'' + 4y' + y = 0$

c) $y'' + 3y' = 0$ h) $4y'' + y = 0$

d) $4y'' - y = 0$ i) $y'' - 2y' + 2y = 0$

e) $y'' = 0$ j) $y'' + 2y' + 5y = 0$

4. Find the solution of the IVP.

   a) $y'' - y' - 2y = 0$, $y(0) = 0$, $y'(0) = -1$

   b) $2y'' + 3y' - 2y = 0$, $y(0) = -1$, $y'(0) = 0$

   c) $y'' + 3y' = 0$, $y(0) = -1$, $y'(0) = -1$

   d) $5y'' - y' = 0$, $y(0) = -1$, $y'(0) = -1$

   e) $3y'' - y = 0$, $y(0) = 3$, $y(t)$ is bounded for $0 \le t < \infty$

   f) $y'' - \frac{3}{2}y' - y = 0$, $y(0) = 5$, $y(t)$ is bounded for $0 \le t < \infty$

   g) $y'' + 2y' + y = 0$, $y(0) = -1$, $y'(0) = 0$

   h) $y'' + 9y = 0$, $y(0) = -1$, $y'(0) = -1$

   i) $y'' + 2y' + 5y = 0$, $y(0) = -1$, $y'(0) = -1$

   j) $y'' - y' + \frac{13}{36}y = 0$, $y(0) = 2$, $y'(0) = 1$

5. The roots of the characteristic equation are given. You are to find the original differential equation (of the form given in (3.18)). If only one value is given, that is the only root.

a) $r = -1, 1$	d) $r = 0, 2$	g) $r = 2 \pm 5i$
b) $r = 3, 5$	e) $r = 1$	h) $r = \pm 2i$
c) $r = \pm 2$	f) $r = 0$	

6. Use the method of reduction of order to find a second solution $y_2(t)$, and then show it is linearly independent of the given solution $y_1(t)$.

   a) $(t + 1)^2 y'' - 4(t + 1)y' + 6y = 0$, $y_1(t) = (t + 1)^2$

   b) $(t + 3)y'' - y' + 4(t + 3)^3 y = 0$, $y_1(t) = \sin(t^2 + 6t)$

   c) $(t + 1)y'' - (t + 2)y' + y = 0$, $y_1(t) = e^t$

7. Answer the following questions by either providing one example showing it is true, or explaining why it is not possible.

   a) Is it possible to find values for b and c so that the solution of (3.18) is such that $\lim_{t \to \infty} y = 0$, no matter what the initial conditions?

   b) Is it possible to find values for b and c so that the solution of (3.18) is a bounded function of t, no matter what the initial conditions?

   c) Is it possible to find values for b and c so that the solution of (3.18) is a periodic function of t, no matter what the initial conditions?

8. Suppose $y(t)$ satisfies the IVP: $y'' - 2y' + 2y = 0$, where $y(0) = -1$ and $y'(0) = 0$.

   a) Without solving the IVP, determine $y''(0)$.

   b) Without solving the IVP, determine $y'''(0)$, $y''''(0)$, and $y'''''(0)$.

   c) Explain how it is possible to determine the Maclaurin series expansion of $y(t)$ directly from the differential equation and initial conditions.

3.6 ▪ Solution of an Inhomogeneous Equation

We now turn to the problem of solving the inhomogeneous second-order differential equation

$$\frac{d^2y}{dt^2} + b\frac{dy}{dt} + cy = f(t). \tag{3.24}$$

As with the homogeneous equation, the first task is to explain what form a general solution will have.

Equation (3.24) shares a property with all linear inhomogeneous differential equations. Namely, the general solution can be written as

$$y(t) = y_p(t) + y_h(t), \tag{3.25}$$

where y_p is a **particular solution** of the differential equation, and $y_h(t)$ is the **general solution of the associated homogeneous equation**. That the solution can be written in this way was discussed for linear first-order equations in Section 2.2.1. As you recall, we had solved the problem and then made the observation that the solution can be written as in (3.25). For the second-order problems we are now considering, the situation is reversed, and we will use (3.25) to construct the general solution.

The associated homogeneous equation for (3.24) is just

$$\frac{d^2y}{dt^2} + b\frac{dy}{dt} + cy = 0. \tag{3.26}$$

How to find the general solution of this has been discussed in some detail, and formulas for the solution are given in Section 3.5.

So, what remains is to determine how to find a particular solution of (3.24). As you should recall, a particular solution is *any* function that satisfies the differential equation. Since any function will do, we are not really picky on how this function is determined. In fact, our go-to method is nothing more than guessing what a particular solution might be. For those who prefer a more systematic approach, an alternative method is derived in Section 3.9. The guessing method, what is called the method of undetermined coefficients, is considered first.

3.6.1 ▪ Non-Uniqueness of a Particular Solution

A particular solution is only required to be a solution of the differential equation. It is possible, for any given differential equation, to have two rather different looking functions both be particular solutions. As an example, both $y = 1 - t$ and $y = 1 - t + 3e^t - 5e^{-2t}$ are particular solutions of $y'' + y' - 2y = 4t$. To explain what's going on here, the general solution of the differential equation is

$$y = 1 - t + c_1e^t + c_2e^{-2t},$$

where c_1 and c_2 are arbitrary constants. A particular solution of this equation is a solution with particular choices for c_1 and c_2. For the two particular solutions given earlier, the first has $c_1 = c_2 = 0$ and the second has $c_1 = 3$ and $c_2 = -5$.

For the most part, when trying to find a particular solution we will be looking for the case of when $c_1 = c_2 = 0$.

3.7 ▪ The Method of Undetermined Coefficients

The objective is to be able to find a solution, any solution, that satisfies

$$\frac{d^2y}{dt^2} + b\frac{dy}{dt} + cy = f(t). \tag{3.27}$$

Depending on $f(t)$, it is often possible to simply guess a solution. To illustrate, suppose the equation to solve is

$$y'' + y' + 2y = 5e^{3t}. \tag{3.28}$$

This equation is asking for a function y, which if you differentiate it as indicated, and add the results together you get $5e^{3t}$. A function that will generate e^{3t} in this way is e^{3t}. In other words, it is reasonable to expect that a particular solution will have the form $y = Ae^{3t}$. Since $y' = 3Ae^{3t}$ and $y'' = 9Ae^{3t}$, then from the differential equation we require that $14Ae^{3t} = 5e^{3t}$. This will hold by taking $A = 5/14$, and therefore a particular solution is $y_p = \frac{5}{14}e^{3t}$.

Example 1: Find a particular solution of

$$y'' - 2y' + y = 2\cos 4t. \tag{3.29}$$

Answer: The functions which will, if you differentiate them once or twice, generate $\cos(4t)$ are $\cos(4t)$ and $\sin(4t)$. So, the assumption is that a particular solution can be found of the form

$$y = A\cos 4t + B\sin 4t. \tag{3.30}$$

Since $y' = -4A\sin 4t + 4B\cos 4t$, and $y'' = -16A\cos 4t - 16B\sin 4t$, then (3.29) requires that

$$(-15A - 8B)\cos 4t + (-15B + 8A)\sin 4t = 2\cos 4t. \tag{3.31}$$

Equating the coefficients of the $\cos 4t$ terms, and the coefficients of the $\sin 4t$ terms, we get that $-15A - 8B = 2$ and $-15B + 8A = 0$. Solving these two equations gives us that $A = -30/289$, and $B = -16/289$. Therefore, a particular solution of (3.29) is

$$y_p = -\frac{30}{289}\cos 4t - \frac{16}{289}\sin 4t. \ \blacksquare \tag{3.32}$$

The key observation coming from the last example is that if you be-lieve a function needs to be included in the guess for y_p, then all of its derivatives must be included. So, looking at (3.29) you would expect that $\cos(4t)$ needs to be part of the guess, which means you must also in-clude $\sin(4t)$. You do not need to include $4\sin(4t)$, or $-4\sin(4t)$, because $\sin(4t)$ is multiplied by an arbitrary constant in the guess (3.30), and this can account for any constant factors that might be generated by taking a derivative.

There are two situations when this guessing approach runs into trou-ble. One is easily fixable and this is demonstrated in the next example. The other situation is not fixable, and the cause of the difficulty is illus-trated in Example 7 below.

Example 2: Find a particular solution of

$$y'' + 4y = 3\cos 2t.$$

Answer: Given what happened in the last example, you would ex-pect that to find a particular solution you would assume that

$$y = A\cos 2t + B\sin 2t.$$

However, both $\cos 2t$ and $\sin 2t$ are solutions of the associated ho-mogeneous equation. Because of this, the guess would give us that $y'' + 4y = 0$, no matter what the values are for A and B. The fix is to take the guess, and for the terms that are solutions of the associ-ated homogeneous equation, multiply them by t. So, the modified guess for this example would be

$$y = t(A\cos 2t + B\sin 2t).$$

To check that this works, since

$$y' = A\cos 2t + B\sin 2t + t(-2A\sin 2t + 2B\cos 2t),$$

and

$$y'' = 2(-2A\sin 2t + 2B\cos 2t) + t(-4A\cos 2t - 4B\sin 2t),$$

then from the differential equation we get

$$2(-2A\sin 2t + 2B\cos 2t) = 3\cos 2t.$$

Equating the coefficients of the $\cos 2t$ and $\sin 2t$ terms we get that $-4A = 0$ and $4B = 3$. Therefore, $A = 0$, $B = \frac{3}{4}$, and a particular solution is $y_p = \frac{3}{4}t\sin 2t.$ ■

When using the method of undetermined coefficients, the step that requires the most thought is getting the guess correct. After that, it is relatively straightforward to find the coefficients. Consequently, in the examples below, only the appropriate guess is determined. In these examples, $y_h(t)$ is the general solution of the associated homogeneous equation, and $f(t)$ is the forcing function.

Example 3: What guess should be made for $y'' - y' - 6y = t^3 + 2$?

Answer: Since $f(t) = t^3 + 2$, then $f' = 3t^2$, $f'' = 6t$, and $f''' = 6$. So, a complete guess is $y = At^3 + Bt^2 + Ct + D$. It remains to make sure that none of the functions in this guess is a solution of the associated homogeneous equation. Since $y_h = c_1 e^{3t} + c_2 e^{-2t}$, and the guess does not include e^{3t} or e^{-2t}, then our guess is, indeed, complete. ■

Example 4: What guess should be made for $y'' - y' - 6y = te^{-5t}$?

Answer: The initial guess is $y = Ate^{-5t}$. However, $y' = A(e^{-5t} - 5te^{-5t})$, and this includes a new function e^{-5t}. This must be included in the guess, and so a complete guess is $y = Ate^{-5t} + Be^{-5t}$. Finally, since $y_h = c_1 e^{3t} + c_2 e^{-2t}$, and the guess does not include e^{3t} or e^{-2t}, then our guess is, indeed, complete. ■

Example 5: What guess should be made for $y'' - y' - 6y = 4t^2 + 1 - \sin(\pi t)$?

The guess for $f(t) = 4t^2 + 1$ is $y = A_0 t^2 + A_1 t + A_2$, and the guess for $f(t) = \sin(\pi t)$ is $y = B_0 \sin \pi t + B_1 \cos \pi t$. So, for the equation as given, a guess is

$$y = A_0 t^2 + A_1 t + A_2 + B_0 \sin \pi t + B_1 \cos \pi t.$$

Finally, since $y_h = c_1 e^{3t} + c_2 e^{-2t}$, and the guess does not include e^{3t} or e^{-2t}, then our guess is, indeed, complete. ■

Example 6: What guess should be made for $y'' + 4y' + 4y = 5e^{-2t}$?

Answer: The initial guess is $y = Ae^{-2t}$. However, for this equation, $y_h = c_1 e^{-2t} + c_2 te^{-2t}$ and one of these functions appears in the guess. The first modification $y = Ate^{-2t}$ also appears in y_h, and this means we need to multiply by t again. Therefore, the complete guess is $y = At^2 e^{-2t}$. ■

Example 7: What guess should you make if $f(t) = \ln(1 + t)$?

Answer: The initial guess is $y = A\ln(1 + t)$. Its derivatives are $y' = A/(1 + y)$, $y'' = -A/(1 + y)^2$, $y''' = 2A/(1 + t)^3$, etc. Unlike the other examples, the list of different derivative functions does not

if $f(t)$ contains	then $y_p(t)$ contains all of the following
e^{at}	e^{at}
$\cos(\omega t)$ or $\sin(\omega t)$	$\cos(\omega t)$, $\sin(\omega t)$
t^n	t^n, t^{n-1}, $\cdots$, 1
$t^n e^{at}$	$t^n e^{at}$, $t^{n-1}e^{at}$, $\cdots$, e^{at}
$e^{at}\cos(\omega t)$ or $e^{at}\sin(\omega t)$	$e^{at}\cos(\omega t)$, $e^{at}\sin(\omega t)$

Table 3.1. *Guesses when using the method of undetermined coefficients. Note that the exponent n must be a non-negative integer. Also, adjustments are needed if $y_p(t)$ contains a solution of the associated homogeneous equation (see Examples 2 and 6, and Example 3 in Section 3.8).*

stop. In such cases, the method of undetermined coefficients should not be used. So, the answer to the question is, there is no guess and the method described in Section 3.9 should be used. ■

3.7.1 ▪ Finding the Coefficients

In Example 1, we ended up with the equation

$$(-15A - 8B)\cos 4t + (-15B + 8A)\sin 4t = 2\cos 4t, \ \forall t \geq 0. \qquad (3.33)$$

To find A and B we equated the coefficients of the $\cos 4t$ and $\sin 4t$ terms in this equation. This can be done because these functions are linearly independent, and this is explained below. This approach does *not* require that you prove the functions are independent. Rather, if you think they might be, and you then determine values for A and B so (3.33) is satisfied based on this assumption, then you have found a particular solution.

The explanation of why linear independence can be used to determine A and B starts with rewriting (3.33) as

$$c_1 \cos 4t + c_2 \sin 4t = 0, \ \forall t \geq 0,$$

where $c_1 = -15A - 8B - 2$ and $c_2 = -15B + 8A$. According to the definition of linear independence, as given in (3.5), if $\cos 4t$ and $\sin 4t$ are independent then it must be that $c_1 = 0$ and $c_2 = 0$. In other words, $-15A - 8B = 2$ and $-15B + 8A = 0$.

3.7.2 ▪ Odds and Ends

Most textbooks on differential equations have tables for various guesses that you should make for the method of undetermined coefficients. The fact is that they are mostly unreadable. It is much easier to just remember the rules used in formulate the guess, and the earlier examples should be reviewed for the particulars.

However, some do find a table useful, and one is provided in Table 3.1. A few comments need to be made about what is listed. First, if $f(t)$ contains t^n, as well as t^{n-1}, or t^{n-2}, or t^{n-2}, etc, then the guess for t^n is all that you need (see Example 4 above). Second, when solving (3.9), if one the functions in the left column is a solution of the associated homogeneous differential equation the guess must be modified. The needed modification was explained earlier (see Examples 2 and 6).

3.8 ▪ Solving an Inhomogeneous Equation

As stated earlier, the general solution of

$$\frac{d^2y}{dt^2} + b\frac{dy}{dt} + cy = f(t), \tag{3.34}$$

can be written as

$$y(t) = y_p(t) + y_h(t), \tag{3.35}$$

where y_p is a particular solution, and y_h is the general solution of the associated homogeneous equation. We now know how to find y_p and y_h, and so we consider a few examples.

Example 1: Find a general solution of $y'' - 3y' + 2y = 5t^2 - 3$.

Step 1: Find y_h. The associated homogeneous equation is $y'' - 3y' + 2y = 0$. Assuming $y = e^{rt}$, one gets the characteristic equation $r^2 - 3r + 2 = 0$. The roots are $r = 1$ and $r = 2$, and so $y_h = c_1e^t + c_2e^{2t}$.

Step 2: Find y_p. The guess is $y = At^2 + Bt + C$, which means that $y' = 2At + B$ and $y'' = 2A$. Inserting these into the differential equation we get that

$$2At^2 + (-6A + 2B)t + 2A - 3B + 2C = 5t^2 - 3.$$

The coefficients of the respective t^n terms on the left and right hand sides must be equal. This means that:

$$\begin{array}{ll} t^2: & 2A = 5 \\ t^1: & -6A + 2B = 0 \\ t^0: & 2A - 3B + 2C = -3 \end{array}.$$

Solving, we get that $A = 5/2$, $B = 15/2$, and $C = 29/4$.

Step 3: The general solution is

$$y = \frac{5}{2}t^2 + \frac{15}{2}t + \frac{29}{4} + c_1e^t + c_2e^{2t}. \quad ∎$$

Example 2: Find the solution of the IVP: $y'' - 4y' + 5y = 10 - e^{3t}$ where $y(0) = 3/2$ and $y'(0) = 0$.

Step 1: Find y_h. The associated homogeneous equation is $y'' - 4y' + 5y = 0$. Assuming $y = e^{rt}$, one gets the characteristic equation $r^2 - 4r + 5 = 0$. The roots are $r = 2 \pm i$, and so $y_h = c_1 e^{2t} \cos t + c_2 e^{2t} \sin t$.

Step 2: Find y_p. The guess is $y = A + Be^{3t}$, which means that $y' = 3Be^{3t}$ and $y'' = 9Be^{3t}$. Inserting these into the differential equation we get that

$$2Be^{3t} + 5A = 10 - e^{3t}.$$

Equating the coefficients of the respective functions, $2B = -1$ and $5A = 10$. Solving, we get that $A = 2$ and $B = -1/2$.

Step 3: The general solution is $y = 2 - \frac{1}{2}e^{3t} + c_1 e^{2t} \cos t + c_2 e^{2t} \sin t$.

Step 4: To satisfy $y(0) = 3/2$ we need $3/2 + c_1 = 3/2$, so $c_1 = 0$. For $y'(0) = 0$ we need $-3/2 + c_2 = 0$, giving $c_2 = 3/2$. The conclusion is that the solution of the IVP is

$$y = 2 - \frac{1}{2}e^{3t} + \frac{3}{2}e^{2t} \sin t. \quad \blacksquare$$

Example 3: Find a general solution of $y'' - 2y' = -3t^2$.

Step 1: Find y_h. The associated homogeneous equation is $y'' - 2y' = 0$. Assuming $y = e^{rt}$, one gets the characteristic equation $r^2 - 2r = 0$. The roots are $r = 0$ and $r = 2$, and so $y_h = c_1 + c_2 e^{2t}$.

Step 2: Find y_p. The initial guess is $y = At^2 + Bt + C$. However, one of the terms in this guess is a solution of the homogeneous equation, and so the guess must be modified to $y = t(At^2 + Bt + C)$. Inserting this into the differential equation we get that

$$6At + 2B - 2(3At^2 + 2Bt + C) = -3t^2.$$

Equating the coefficients of the respective powers of t, we get that $-6A = -3$, $6A - 4B = 0$, and $2B - 2C = 0$. Solving yields $A = 1/2$, $B = 3/4$, and $C = 3/4$.

Step 3: The general solution is therefore

$$y = \frac{1}{4}t(2t^2 + 3t + 3) + c_1 + c_2 e^{2t}. \quad \blacksquare$$

Exercises

1. Find the general solution of the given differential equation.

a) $y'' - y' - 6y = 6e^t$

b) $y'' + 3y' + 2y = \sin \pi t$

c) $y'' + 4y' - 5y = 2t^2$

d) $5y'' - y' = e^{-t} + 3\cos 2t$

e) $3y'' - 5y' - 2y = t^3 - 2t$

f) $8y'' - 2y' - y = 4 + 5\sin 2t$

g) $y'' + 4y = te^t$

h) $y'' - 5y' - 6y = 10t\sin(3t)$

i) $y'' - 2y' + 5y = 5t^2 + 4$

j) $y'' + 2y' + 10y = 3e^t + 1$

k) $y'' - 3y' = t^3 - 6$

l) $3y'' + y' - 2y = 3e^{-2t} - e^t$

m) $y'' - 8y' + 17y = e^{4t}\sin t$

n) $y'' - 5y' - 6y = -3\sin(t+7)$

o) $y'' + 3y' + 2y = \sin^2 t$

p) $4y'' + y' = \sin(t)\cos(t)$

2. Find the solution of the given IVP.

a) $y'' + y' - 2y = 3t$, $y(0) = 0$, $y'(0) = 0$

b) $y'' + 4y = t^2$, $y(0) = 1$, $y'(0) = 0$

c) $y'' - y' = \sin t$, $y(0) = 1$, $y'(0) = -1$

d) $y'' + 3y' = 2t$, $y(0) = 1$, $y'(0) = 0$

e) $y'' + 4y' + 4y = -3e^{2t}$, $y(0) = 1$, $y'(0) = 0$

f) $4y'' - y = e^{-t/2} + 1$, $y(0) = 0$, $y'(0) = 0$

g) $y'' + 9y = -2\sin(3t)$, $y(0) = 0$, $y'(0) = 0$

h) $y'' + 2y' + 5y = e^{-t}$, $y(0) = -1$, $y'(0) = 0$

i) $y'' - y' + \frac{1}{2}y = 25\cos 3t$, $y(0) = -1$, $y'(0) = 0$

3. For the following, determine a complete guess that can be used to find a particular solution (you do not need to find the coefficients).

a) $y'' + y' - 2y = t^5 - t^2$

b) $y'' + 4y = t\cos t$

c) $y'' + 4y = t + \sin 2t$

d) $y'' - y' = 1 + \sin t$

e) $y'' + 3y' = 1 + e^{-3t}$

f) $y'' + y' + 2y = t^3 e^{-2t}$

g) $y'' - y' + 6y = e^{-t}\cos 3t$

h) $4y'' - y = -2(t-1)^7$

i) $y'' - 2y' + 2y = e^{t-5}\cos t$

j) $y'' + 4y = \cos(2t + 3)$

k) $y'' + 25y = -3\sin(5t + 7)$

l) $y'' + y' + y = \int_0^1 \sqrt{s}\cos(2t - s)ds$

4. The idea underlying undetermined coefficients has nothing to do with the differential equation being second-order. What is required is a linear differential equation with constant coefficients. As an example, for the first-order equation $y' + y = e^{2t}$ you assume a particular solution of the form $y = Ae^{2t}$. The associated homogeneous equation is $y' + y = 0$, which means that $y_h = c_1 e^{-t}$. Finding the solution in this way is easier than using an integrating factor (which is the way it is done in Example 1 of Section 2.2). Find the general solution of the following first-order equations using the method of undetermined coefficients.

a) $y' - 6y = 2e^t$

b) $3y' + 2y = \sin \pi t$

c) $y' + 3y = 2t$

d) $5y' - y = e^{-t} + 3t$

e) $y' - 4y = t \sin 2t$

f) $y' - 6y = te^{-t} + 2$

g) $3y' + 2y = e^{-t} \cos(t)$

h) $y' - 2y = \cos(2t + 5)$

3.9 ▪ Variation of Parameters

When the method of undetermined coefficients works, it is relatively easy to use it to find a particular solution. However, as illustrated in Example 7 of Section 3.7, it does not always work. In such cases, the method of variation of parameters can be used. Interestingly, this method is also based on a guess. Namely, to find a particular solution of

$$\frac{d^2y}{dt^2} + b\frac{dy}{dt} + cy = f(t), \tag{3.36}$$

it is assumed that

$$y = u_1(t)y_1(t) + u_2(t)y_2(t), \tag{3.37}$$

where y_1 and y_2 are independent solutions of the associated homogeneous equation. As you should notice, the guess (3.37) resembles the general solution of the associated homogeneous equation. However, instead of arbitrary constants, there are now unknown functions u_1 and u_2. Our job is to find these functions. Although it might not appear to be significant right now, we are looking for a single function, y_p, yet our guess contains two unknown functions. This means that we have the option to pick one of these two functions anyway we wish. We will use this option to advantage to find y_p.

Our task is simple in that (3.37) must be a solution of (3.36). So, in preparation for substituting (3.37) into (3.36) note that

$$y' = u_1'y_1 + u_1y_1' + u_2'y_2 + u_2y_2'.$$

We now use the option of picking u_1 or u_2 anyway we want. The specific choice is that

$$u_1'y_1 + u_2'y_2 = 0. \tag{3.38}$$

So $y' = u_1y_1' + u_2y_2'$, and $y'' = u_1y_1'' + u_1'y_1' + u_2y_2'' + u_2'y_2'$. Substituting these into (3.36), we get that

$$u_1'y_1' + u_2'y_2' + u_1(y_1'' + by_1' + cy_1) + u_2(y_2'' + by_2' + cy_2) = f. \tag{3.39}$$

Using the fact that y_1 and y_2 are solutions of the associated homogeneous equation, then the above equation reduces to

$$u_1'y_1' + u_2'y_2' = f. \tag{3.40}$$

Therefore, to find u_1 and u_2, we must solve (3.38) and (3.40). This is fairly easy. First, from (3.38), $u_2' = -u_1' y_1 / y_2$. Inserting this into (3.40) we get that

$$(y_2 y_1' - y_1 y_2') u_1' = y_2 f.$$

This can be written as

$$-W(y_1, y_2) u_1' = y_2 f,$$

where $W(y_1, y_2)$ is the Wronskian as defined in (3.6). Solving this gives us that

$$u_1(t) = -\int_0^t \frac{y_2(s) f(s)}{W(y_1(s), y_2(s))} ds. \tag{3.41}$$

Inserting into (3.38), and integrating, we obtain

$$u_2(t) = \int_0^t \frac{y_1(s) f(s)}{W(y_1(s), y_2(s))} ds. \tag{3.42}$$

Therefore, the particular solution we have found is

$$y_p(t) = -y_1(t) \int_0^t \frac{y_2(s) f(s)}{W(y_1(s), y_2(s))} ds + y_2(t) \int_0^t \frac{y_1(s) f(s)}{W(y_1(s), y_2(s))} ds. \tag{3.43}$$

Example 1: Find a particular solution of $y'' - 3y' + 2y = t$ using variation of parameters.

Step 1: Find y_1 and y_2. The associated homogeneous equation is $y'' - 3y' + 2y = 0$. Assuming $y = e^{rt}$, one gets the characteristic equation $r^2 - 3r + 2 = 0$. The roots are $r = 1$ and $r = 2$, and so $y_1 = e^t$ and $y_2 = e^{2t}$.

Step 2: Find u_1. Since $W = y_1 y_2' - y_2 y_1' = e^{3t}$, and $f = t$, then from (3.41),

$$u_1(t) = -\int_0^t \frac{e^{2s} s}{e^{3s}} ds = -\int_0^t s e^{-s} ds.$$

Using integration by parts yields $u_1 = (1 + t) e^{-t} - 1$.

Step 3: Find u_2. From (3.42), and using integration by parts,

$$u_2(t) = \int_0^t \frac{e^s s}{e^{3s}} ds = \int_0^t s e^{-2s} ds = \frac{1}{4} \left[1 - (2t + 1) e^{-2t} \right].$$

Step 4: Collecting our results,

$$y_p = \left[(1 + t) e^{-t} - 1 \right] e^t + \frac{1}{4} \left[1 - (2t + 1) e^{-2t} \right] e^{2t}$$

$$= \frac{1}{2} t + \frac{3}{4} - e^t + \frac{1}{4} e^{2t}. \quad \blacksquare$$

3.9.1 ▪ The Solution of an IVP

It is not hard to show that $y_p(t)$, given in (3.43), satisfies $y_p(0) = 0$ and $y_p'(0) = 0$. Therefore, the solution of the IVP

$$\frac{d^2 y}{dt^2} + b\frac{dy}{dt} + cy = f(t),$$

where $y(0) = y_0$ and $y'(0) = y_0'$, is

$$y(t) = c_1 y_1(t) + c_2 y_2(t) + y_p(t), \tag{3.44}$$

where c_1 and c_2 are found by solving

$$c_1 y_1(0) + c_2 y_2(0) = y_0, \tag{3.45}$$
$$c_1 y_1'(0) + c_2 y_2'(0) = y_0'. \tag{3.46}$$

It needs to be remembered that $y_p(t)$ appearing in (3.44) is the particular solution given in (3.43).

Example 2: Find the solution of the IVP: $y'' + 4y = \sqrt{t}$, where $y(0) = 1$, and $y'(0) = 0$.

Step 1: Find y_1 and y_2. The associated homogeneous equation is $y'' + 4y = 0$. Assuming $y = e^{rt}$, one gets the characteristic equation $r^2 = -4$. The roots are $r = \pm 2i$, and so $y_1 = \cos 2t$ and $y_2 = \sin 2t$.

Step 2: Find u_1. Since $W = y_1 y_2' - y_2 y_1' = 2$, and $f = \sqrt{t}$, then from (3.41),

$$u_1(t) = -\int_0^t \frac{1}{2}\sqrt{s}\sin(2s)ds.$$

The answer is left as a definite integral because it is not possible to express it in terms of elementary functions.

Step 3: Find u_2. From (3.42),

$$u_2(t) = \int_0^t \frac{1}{2}\sqrt{s}\cos(2s)ds.$$

Step 4: Solve (3.45) and (3.46). One finds that $c_1 = 1$ and $c_2 = 0$.
Step 5: Therefore, from (3.43) and (3.44), the solution is

$$y = \cos(2t) + \frac{1}{2}\int_0^t \sqrt{s}\left[\sin(2t)\cos(2s) - \cos(2t)\sin(2s)\right]ds$$

$$= \cos(2t) + \frac{1}{2}\int_0^t \sqrt{s}\sin\left(2(t-s)\right)ds. \quad \blacksquare$$

A couple of comments need to be made about (3.44). First, it is the solution of the IVP, irrespective of what continuous function $f(t)$ is used. It can also be adapted so it is the solution for more general problems (see Exercise 3). A drawback is that it can require more work to find the solution. As a case in point, it is much easier to do Example 1 using undetermined coefficients. However, for Example 2, undetermined coefficients does not work, and this means that (3.44) is the method of choice. The recommendation is to first consider whether undetermined coefficients can be used, as it is usually fairly simple to carry out. It also has the advantage that it is easier to remember than the variation of parameters formula.

Exercises

1. Using variation of parameters, find a particular solution of the given differential equation.

   a) $2y'' + 3y' - 2y = 25e^{-2t}$ d) $y'' + 3y' = t^{3/2} + 1$

   b) $y'' - 2y' + 2y = 6$ e) $5y'' - y' = \frac{2}{1+t}$

   c) $y'' + y' - 2y = 3\ln(1+t)$ f) $4y'' - y = \sin(1+t^2)$

2. Find the solution of the IVP where the differential equation comes from the previous problem, and the initial conditions are $y(0) = 1$ and $y'(0) = 0$.

3. The formula for a particular solution given in (3.43) applies to the more general problem of solving $y'' + p(t)y' + q(t)y = f(t)$. In this case, y_1 and y_2 are independent solutions of the associated homogeneous equation $y'' + p(t)y' + q(t)y = 0$. In the following, show that y_1 and y_2 satisfy the associated homogeneous equation, and then determine a particular solution of the inhomogeneous equation.

   a) $t^2 y'' - t(t+2)y' + (t+2)y = 2t^3$; $y_1(t) = t$, $y_2(t) = te^t$

   b) $ty'' - (t+1)y' + y = t^2 e^{2t}$; $y_1(t) = 1+t$, $y_2(t) = e^t$

   c) $t^2 y'' - 3ty' + 4y = t^{5/2}$; $y_1(t) = t^2$, $y_2(t) = t^2 \ln t$

4. The *Bessel equation* of order p is $t^2 y'' + ty' + (t^2 - p^2)y = 0$. In this problem assume that $p = \frac{1}{2}$.

   a) Show that $y_1 = \sin t / \sqrt{t}$ and $y_2 = \cos t / \sqrt{t}$ are linearly independent solutions for $0 < t < \infty$.

   b) Use the result from part (a), and the preamble in Exercise 3, to find a particular solution of $t^2 y'' + ty' + (t^2 - 1/4)y = t^{3/2} \cos t$.

3.10 ▪ Linear Oscillator

The problem considered involves a mass, spring, and dashpot as illustrated in Figure 3.1. The differential equation in this case has the form

$$mu'' + cu' + ku = f(t), \qquad (3.47)$$

where $f(t)$ is an external forcing function. In this equation, $u(t)$ is the displacement of the mass from its rest position, with positive in the upward direction. The physical interpretation of the terms in this differential equation, and the basic properties of the solution are described in the following pages.

Figure 3.1. *Mass-spring-dashpot system.*

3.10.1 ▪ The Spring Constant

To begin, a spring of length ℓ is suspended as illustrated in Figure 3.2. After this, an object with mass m is attached, which stretches the spring a distance L. The forces on the object in this case are gravity, F_g, and the restoring force from the spring, F_s. The gravitational force is just $F_g = -mg$, where g is the gravitational acceleration constant. The spring force is determined using **Hooke's law**, which states that the restoring force is proportional to how much the spring is stretched. To translate this into a mathematical formula, according to Hooke's law, $F_s = kL$, where k is the proportionally constant, and it is referred to as the **spring constant**. The whole system is at rest, and so, from Newton's second law, we have that $F_s + F_g = 0$. From this we obtain

$$k = \frac{mg}{L}. \qquad (3.48)$$

3.10.2 ▪ Simple Harmonic Motion

Now, with the mass attached, we set it in motion. For example, as illustrated in Figure 3.2, the mass is pushed up and then released. The equation governing the motion is, again, determined from Newton's second law. As before, the gravitational force is $F_g = -mg$. From Hooke's law, the restoring force due to the spring is $F_s = k(L - u)$, where $u(t)$ is the displacement of the mass from its rest position. Since $F = ma$, and the force in this problem is $F = F_g + F_s$, we get the following differential

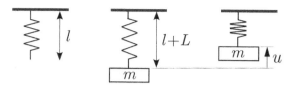

Figure 3.2. *Left: The original spring. Middle: The situation after the mass is attached, and at rest. Right: Displacement $u(t)$ of the mass from its rest position.*

equation

$$mu'' + ku = 0. \tag{3.49}$$

To find the general solution of (3.49), from the assumption that $u = e^{rt}$ the characteristic equation is found to be $mr^2 + k = 0$. This produces the roots $r = \pm\omega_0 i$, where

$$\omega_0 = \sqrt{\frac{k}{m}}. \tag{3.50}$$

From (3.23), the general solution can be written as

$$u = R\cos(\omega_0 t - \varphi), \tag{3.51}$$

where $R \geq 0$, and $0 \leq \varphi < 2\pi$. This periodic function corresponds to what is called **simple harmonic motion**. In this context, the coefficient R is the **amplitude**, ω_0 is the **natural frequency**, and the **period** is $T = 2\pi/\omega_0$. The argument $\theta = \omega_0 t - \varphi$ of the cosine is called the phase, and $-\varphi$ is the phase shift, or the phase constant.

In terms of initial conditions, it is usual to specify the initial displacement and the initial velocity. Together, these correspond to

$$u(0) = u_0, \quad \text{and} \quad u'(0) = u_0', \tag{3.52}$$

where u_0 and u_0' are given. To satisfy these, from (3.51), we get that

$$R\cos(\varphi) = u_0, \tag{3.53}$$

$$R\sin(\varphi) = \frac{u_0'}{\omega_0}. \tag{3.54}$$

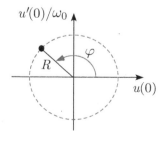

Figure 3.3. *The initial conditions as expressed in (3.53) and (3.54), located using the black dot, and the value of R and φ.*

Finding R: Using the identity $\cos^2(\varphi) + \sin^2(\varphi) = 1$, it follows that

$$R = \sqrt{u_0^2 + \left(\frac{u_0'}{\omega_0}\right)^2}. \tag{3.55}$$

Finding φ: The value for φ depends on whether u_0 and u_0' are positive or negative, as illustrated in Figure 3.3. To compute φ, assuming that $u_0 \neq 0$, the ratio of (3.54) with (3.53) yields

$$\tan(\varphi) = \frac{u_0'}{\omega_0 u_0}.$$

The principal value of the arctan function is denoted as Arctan, and it satisfies $-\frac{\pi}{2} < \text{Arctan}(z) < \frac{\pi}{2}$. This is the value most calculators, or programs like MATLAB, give when evaluating $\arctan(z)$. So, setting $z = u_0'/(\omega_0 u_0)$,

$$\varphi = \begin{cases} \text{Arctan}(z) & \text{if} \quad u_0 > 0 \text{ and } u_0' \geq 0, \\ \text{Arctan}(z) + \pi & \text{if} \quad u_0 < 0, \\ \text{Arctan}(z) + 2\pi & \text{if} \quad u_0 > 0 \text{ and } u_0' < 0. \end{cases} \tag{3.56}$$

If $u_0 = 0$, then $\varphi = \pi/2$ if $u_0' > 0$, and $\varphi = 3\pi/2$ if $u_0' < 0$.

Example 1: Suppose the mass is set in motion by pulling it down $2\,\text{cm}$ and then releasing it with an upward velocity of $1\,\text{cm/s}$. Also, assume that $k = 1\,\text{kg/s}^2$ and $m = 9\,\text{kg}$.

Question 1: Find the resulting simple harmonic motion, and then sketch the solution.
  Answer: The initial conditions are $u(0) = -2$, and $u'(0) = 1$. Also, from (3.50), $\omega_0 = 1/3$, and this means, using (3.51), that the general solution is $u = R\cos(t/3 - \varphi)$. From (3.55), the amplitude is $R = \sqrt{13}$. As for φ, from (3.56), $\varphi = \text{Arctan}(-3/2) + \pi$. The resulting solution is shown in Figure 3.4. Note that the period $T = 2\pi/\omega_0 = 6\pi$.

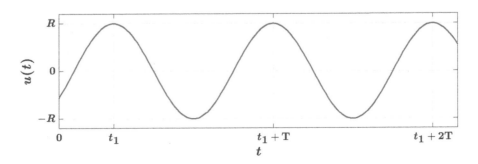

Figure 3.4. *Simple harmonic motion solution for Example 1.*

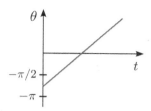

Figure 3.5. *Phase function θ for Example 1.*

Question 2: When is the first time that $u(t) = R$?

    Answer: The solution can be written as $u = R\cos\theta$, where the phase is $\theta = t/3 - \varphi$. This linear function of t is shown in Figure 3.5, and it includes the fact that $\pi/2 < \varphi < \pi$. Now, $\cos\theta = 1$ when $\theta = 0, \pm 2\pi, \pm 4\pi, \cdots$. According to Figure 3.5, the first possible value is $\theta = 0$ and this occurs when $t = 3\varphi$. This is labeled as t_1 in Figure 3.5. ∎

3.10.3 ▪ Damping

We will now include a damping mechanism. It is assumed that the damping force is proportional to the velocity. For the mass-spring system the resistance is usually illustrated as a dashpot, as shown in Figure 3.1. Irrespective of exactly what mechanism is involved, the result is that the damping force is $F_d = -cv$, where $v = u'$ is the velocity, and c is the **damping constant** and it is non-negative. From the equation $F = ma$, and the fact that $F = F_s + F_g + F_d$, the resulting differential equation is

$$mu'' + cu' + ku = 0. \tag{3.57}$$

Finding the general solution is straightforward. Assuming $u = e^{rt}$, then the resulting characteristic equation is $mr^2 + cr + k = 0$. The roots are

$$r = \frac{1}{2m}\left(-c \pm \sqrt{c^2 - 4mk}\right). \tag{3.58}$$

Just as in Section 3.5, there are three cases to consider. The only difference now is that certain terminology is introduced to identity the cases.

Over-damped: This means that the damping constant is large enough that $c^2 > 4mk$. In this case both roots are real-valued, and the resulting general solution is

$$u = c_1 e^{r_1 t} + c_2 e^{r_2 t}, \tag{3.59}$$

where $r_1 = \frac{1}{2m}\left(-c + \sqrt{c^2 - 4mk}\right)$ and $r_2 = \frac{1}{2m}\left(-c - \sqrt{c^2 - 4mk}\right)$. It is worth noting that not only are the roots real, they are both negative. Therefore, no matter what the initial conditions,

$$\lim_{t \to \infty} u = 0. \tag{3.60}$$

Critically damped: This means that the damping constant has just that right value that $c^2 = 4mk$. So, there is one root, and the resulting general solution is

$$u = (c_1 + c_2 t)e^{rt}, \qquad (3.61)$$

where $r = -c/(2m)$. So, as for the previous case, no matter what the initial conditions, (3.60) holds.

Under-damped: This means that the damping constant is small enough that $c^2 < 4mk$. The roots are complex-valued, and the resulting general solution is

$$u = Re^{\lambda t} \cos(\mu t - \varphi), \qquad (3.62)$$

where $\lambda = -c/(2m)$, and $\mu = \sqrt{4mk - c^2}/(2m)$. The solution is not periodic, but it is oscillatory with an amplitude $Re^{\lambda t}$ that decays to zero (assuming, of course, that $c > 0$). Consequently, no matter what the initial conditions, (3.60) holds.

One conclusion coming from the above discussion is that because of damping, no matter what the initial conditions, the solution decays exponentially to zero. The role of damping, and how it affects the solution, is explored in the next examples.

Example 2: For a mass-spring-dashpot system, suppose that $m = 2$, $k = 1$, and $c = 1$. Also, assume that the initial conditions are $u(0) = 1$, and $u'(0) = 2$.

Question 1: What is the solution?
  Answer: From (3.58), the roots are $r = (-1 \pm i\sqrt{7})/4$. So, this is a case of under-damping, with $\lambda = -1/4$ and $\mu = \sqrt{7}/4$. From (3.62), the general solution is

$$u = Re^{-t/4} \cos\left(\frac{1}{4}\sqrt{7}t - \varphi\right). \qquad (3.63)$$

To satisfy the initial conditions, we need $R\cos\varphi = 1$, and $R\sin\varphi = 9/\sqrt{7}$. From this we get that $R = 2\sqrt{22/7}$, and $\varphi = \arctan(9/\sqrt{7})$.

Question 2: Sketch the solution.
  Answer: From (3.63), we know that the solution oscillates between $Re^{-t/4}$ and $Re^{-t/4}$. These are the red dashed curves in Figure 3.6 (the under-damped plot). Since $u'(0) > 0$, then the solution starts out at $u(0) = 1$, and moves upward. From that point on it simply bounces back and forth between the red dashed curves.

Question 3: When is the first time that $u(t) = 0$?
  Answer: Writing the solution as $u = Re^{-t/4}\cos\theta$, the phase function is $\theta = \frac{1}{4}\sqrt{7}t - \varphi$. Sketching this as in Figure 3.5, but now with

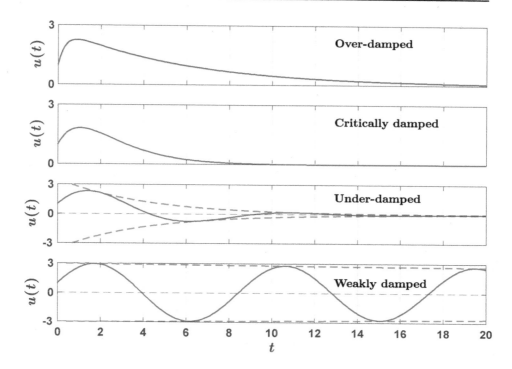

Figure 3.6. *Response of a damped mass-spring system, depending on the strength of damping that is present. The dashed red curves in the two lower graphs are the functions $\pm Re^{\lambda t}$, where $\lambda = -c/(2m)$.*

$0 < \varphi < \pi/2$, it is seen that the first time $\cos\theta = 0$ is when $\theta = \pi/2$. Consequently, $t = 2[\pi + 2\arctan(\sqrt{7})]/\sqrt{7}$. ■

Example 3: For a given mass-spring-dashpot system, how does the solution change as the damping coefficient changes?

Answer: Taking $m = 2$, $k = 1$, then, from (3.58), $r = \left(-c \pm \sqrt{c^2 - 8}\right)/4$. Using the initial conditions $u(0) = 1$, and $u'(0) = 2$, the resulting solution is shown in Figure 3.6, for different values for the damping constant. The values used give rise to: over-damping ($c = 6$), critically damped ($c = \sqrt{2}$), under-damped ($c = 1$), and weakly damped ($c = 1/40$). To say it is **weakly damped** means that it is under-damped, and c is so small that the solution resembles the periodic solution of an undamped oscillator, at least at the beginning. Eventually, the damping does reduce the amplitude enough to be noticeable.

For over-damping, and critical damping, except near the beginning, the solution simply decays monotonically to zero. In comparison, for both under-damped cases the solution oscillates as it decays to zero. In both cases the solution bounces back and forth between the two dashed red curves, which are just the functions $Re^{\lambda t}$ and $-Re^{\lambda t}$. ■

3.10.4 ▪ Resonance

We now consider what happens when a simple harmonic oscillator is forced periodically. The specific equation to solve is

$$mu'' + ku = F\cos\omega t, \tag{3.64}$$

where ω is the driving frequency, and F is the amplitude of the forcing (both ω and F are positive). Assuming $u(0) = u'(0) = 0$, the resulting solution is

$$u = \begin{cases} \dfrac{F}{k - m\omega^2}\Big(\cos(\omega t) - \cos(\omega_0 t)\Big), & \text{if } \omega \neq \omega_0, \\[2mm] \dfrac{F}{2\sqrt{km}}\, t\sin(\omega_0 t), & \text{if } \omega = \omega_0, \end{cases} \tag{3.65}$$

where ω_0 is given in (3.50).

What is of interest here is that, when the system is driven at its natural frequency ω_0, the solution is an oscillatory function whose amplitude becomes unbounded as t increases. This happens even though the amplitude of the forcing is constant. This is an example of what is called **resonance**. An example of a resonant solution is shown in Figure 3.7, upper.

Resonance is a particularly important phenomena in science and engineering, and it is often something that is to be avoided. As an example, a wing on an airplane can go into a flapping motion. This can be modeled as a simple harmonic oscillator, and under certain conditions the wing can start to go into resonance. This is known as flutter, and the resulting large oscillations can lead to the wing breaking off (which can be upsetting

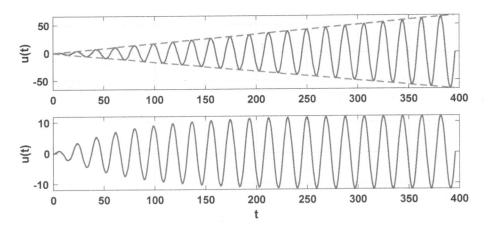

Figure 3.7. *Upper: Resonant solution given in (3.65) when $\omega = \omega_0 = 1/3$, $F = 1$, $m = 9$ and $k = 1$. The red dashed lines correspond to $\pm Ft/2\sqrt{km}$. Lower: Solution when a dashpot, with $c = 1/4$, is included.*

to those in the airplane). What is a concern is that this will happen no matter what the value of F, as long as it's nonzero. So, even a very small force, what would normally be considered to be inconsequential, can lead to extremely large oscillations.

One way to avoid resonance is to include a damping mechanism in the system. With the dashpot we introduced earlier, the equation to solve is

$$mu'' + cu' + ku = F \cos \omega t. \tag{3.66}$$

The forcing no longer contains a solution of the associated homogeneous equation, and so resonance will not occur. However, it is often the case that the damping is weak. This means that if $\omega = \omega_0$, then the solution will start out like it's going into resonance, but eventually the damping will stop this. An example of what happens is shown in Figure 3.7, lower.

This brings us to the question to be considered. Using the flutter example, the question is: we don't want the wings to break off, so just how large do the oscillations get before the damping stops this? To answer this, it is the particular solution that is responsible for the growing oscillations. So, for the weakly damped case we are considering, only the particular solution is considered. To find the particular solution of (3.66), the assumption that $u = A \cos \omega t + B \sin \omega t$ leads to the requirement that A and B satisfy

$$m(\omega_0^2 - \omega^2)A + c\omega B = F,$$
$$-c\omega A + m(\omega_0^2 - \omega^2)B = 0.$$

From this one obtains

$$A = \frac{m(\omega_0^2 - \omega^2)}{c^2\omega^2 + m^2(\omega_0^2 - \omega^2)^2}F, \qquad B = \frac{c\omega}{c^2\omega^2 + m^2(\omega_0^2 - \omega^2)^2}F.$$

Now, to determine the amplitude of the resulting oscillation, it makes things easier to write the solution in the form $u = R \cos(\omega t - \varphi)$. This requires that $R \cos \varphi = A$ and $R \sin \varphi = B$, and therefore

$$R = \sqrt{A^2 + B^2} = \frac{1}{\sqrt{c^2\omega^2 + m^2(\omega_0^2 - \omega^2)^2}}F. \tag{3.67}$$

The amplitude R is plotted in Figure 3.8 as a function of the driving frequency ω in the particular case of when $F = 1$, $m = 1$, and $k = 1/2$. What is seen is that the smaller the damping coefficient c, the more peaked the response becomes. Also, the peak response occurs at a frequency smaller than the natural frequency ω_0, but this difference decreases as c is reduced.

Our flutter question is answered by determining what driving frequency ω gives the largest value for R. Taking the derivative of R with

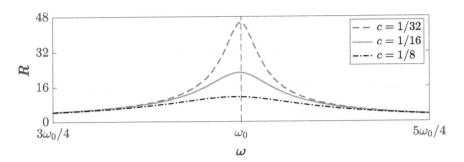

Figure 3.8. *The amplitude (3.67) of the forced, but damped, oscillator, as a function of the driving frequency. Note that ω_0 is the natural frequency of the undamped oscillator.*

respect to ω, and setting it to zero gives us that $\omega = \omega_M$, where

$$\omega_M = \sqrt{\omega_0^2 - \omega_c^2} \tag{3.68}$$

and $\omega_c = c/(\sqrt{2}m)$. The resulting maximum for R is therefore

$$R_M = \frac{1}{c\sqrt{\omega_0^2 - \frac{1}{2}\omega_c^2}}F. \tag{3.69}$$

Now, suppose that for the flutter problem it is found experimentally that the wings won't break off if the amplitude of the oscillation satisfies $R \leq R_b$. Based on our calculations, this means that the damping coefficient c must be large enough that $R_M \leq R_b$.

Reality Check: The resonance phenomena considered here is not possible for the mass-spring system envisioned in Figure 3.2. As the oscillations grow, as predicted by (3.65), they will eventually get to the point that the mass will start banging up against the upper support. Presumably, as the amplitude grows, our simple linear model is no longer valid, and a more physically realistic, nonlinear, model is necessary. Even so, the simple model is useful as it provides information about the onset of resonance.

Units and Values: In the exercises, the value to use for g is usually stated. If it is not given, then you should leave g unevaluated. Whatever value is used, it is only approximate. If a more physically realistic value is needed, then you should probably use the Somigliana equation. Finally, weight is a force, so for an object that weighs w lbs, its mass can be determined from the equation $w = mg$.

Exercises

In answering the following questions, do not numerically evaluate numbers such as $\sqrt{2}$, $\pi/3$, e^2, $\ln(4/3)$, etc. The exception to this is when the question explicitly asks you to *compute* the answer.

1. Write the following in the form $u = R\cos(\omega_0 t - \varphi)$.

   a) $u = \cos 3t + \sin 3t$ c) $u = -\frac{1}{3}\sqrt{3}\cos t + \sin t$

   b) $u = \sqrt{3}\cos \pi t - \sin \pi t$ d) $u = -4\cos 2t - 4\sin 2t$

2. A block weighing 2 lb stretches a spring 6 in. Assume that the mass is pulled down an additional 3 in and then released from rest. Assume that $g = 32\,\text{ft/s}^2$.

   a) What IVP does $u(t)$ satisfy?

   b) What is the solution of the IVP?

   c) What is the natural frequency, period, and amplitude of the motion?

   d) Sketch the solution for $0 \le t \le 3T$.

   e) Is the restoring force in the spring ever zero? What is the minimum value of the force in the spring?

3. A mass of 100 gm stretches a spring $\frac{5}{6}$ m. Assume that the mass is pulled down a distance of 1 m, and then set in motion with an upward velocity of 2 m/s. Assume that $g = 10\,\text{m/s}^2$.

   a) What IVP does $u(t)$ satisfy?

   b) What is the solution of the IVP?

   c) What is the natural frequency, period, and amplitude of the motion?

   d) When does the mass first return to its steady state position?

   e) Sketch the solution for $0 \le t \le 3T$.

   f) What is the first time the force F is zero?

4. A mass of 1 kg stretches a spring 10 cm. Assume that the mass is pushed upward a distance of 5 cm, and then set in motion with a downward velocity of 50 cm/s. Assume that $g = 10\,\text{m/s}^2$.

   a) What IVP does $u(t)$ satisfy?

   b) What is the solution of the IVP?

   c) What is the natural frequency, period, and amplitude of the motion?

   d) Sketch the solution for $0 \le t \le 3T$.

   e) What is the largest value of the restoring force in the spring? When is the first time it equals this value?

5. According to Archimedes' principle, an object that is completely or partially submerged in water is acted on by an upward (buoyant) force equal to the weight of the displaced water. You are to use this for the following situation: A cubic block of wood, with side l and mass density ρ, is floating in water. If the block is slightly depressed and then released, it oscillates in the vertical direction. Derive the differential equation of motion and determine the period of the motion. In doing this let ρ_0 be the mass density of the water, and assume that $\rho_0 > \rho$.

6. In a mass-spring system, suppose the mass is pulled down a distance
   d and released from rest.

   a) If the resulting natural frequency is $10\,\mathrm{s}^{-1}$ when $d = 0.1\,\mathrm{m}$, what is
      the natural frequency when $d = 0.2\,\mathrm{m}$?

   b) Suppose the amplitude of the motion is $0.1\,\mathrm{m}$. Is it possible to
      change the initial velocity, keeping d unchanged, so the amplitude
      of the motion is $0.2\,\mathrm{m}$?

   c) Suppose the natural frequency is $10\,\mathrm{s}^{-1}$ when $d = 0.1\,\mathrm{m}$. Is it
      possible to change the initial velocity, keeping d unchanged, so the
      natural frequency is $20\,\mathrm{s}^{-1}$?

Damping

7. A block weighing $16\,\mathrm{lb}$ stretches a spring $6\,\mathrm{in}$. The mass is attached
   to a viscous damper with a damping constant of $2\,\mathrm{lbs\cdot s/ft}$. Assume
   that the mass is set in motion from its equilibrium position with a
   downward velocity of $4\,\mathrm{in/s}$. Also, assume that $g = 32\,\mathrm{ft/s}^2$.

   a) What IVP does $u(t)$ satisfy?

   b) What is the solution of the IVP?

   c) Sketch the solution for $0 \le t \le \pi\sqrt{15}/5$.

   d) What is the largest value of $u(t)$?

8. Suppose you construct a mass-spring-dashpot system as shown in Figure 3.1. In this problem assume that $g = 10\,\mathrm{m/s}^2$.

   a) If the spring is stretched $\frac{1}{10}\,\mathrm{m}$ by a force of $\frac{1}{2}\,\mathrm{N}$, what is the spring
      constant?

   b) If the dashpot exerts a force of $-3\,\mathrm{N}$ when the velocity is $1\,\mathrm{m/s}$,
      what is the damping constant?

   c) Suppose the mass is $\frac{1}{2}\,\mathrm{kg}$, and it is pulled up $1\,\mathrm{m}$ from its rest
      position and given an initial downward velocity of $2\,\mathrm{m/s}$. What
      IVP does $u(t)$ satisfy?

   d) What is the solution of the IVP?

   e) Sketch the solution for $0 \le t \le 10\pi$.

9. The general solution for the under-damped case is given in (3.62).
   Suppose the initial conditions are $u(0) = u_0$ and $u'(0) = u'_0$.

   a) Show that

   $$R = \sqrt{u_0^2 + \left(\frac{u'_0 - \lambda u_0}{\mu}\right)^2}.$$

   b) How does Figure 3.3 change?

   c) What are R and φ if $u'_0 = 0$?

10. It is often stated that "the key difference between critical damping and overdamping is that critical damping provides the quickest approach to zero amplitude." However, this statement is not true. This problem investigates this for the case of when $m = 1$, $k = 4$, $u(0) = 1$, and $u'(0) = -4$.

   a) Find the solution when $c = 5$, which is the over-damped case, and when $c = 4$, which is the critically damped case. Sketch both solutions on the same axes. Explain why the statement is not true.

   b) Solve the two problems in part (a) but use the general initial conditions $u(0) = u_0$ and $u'(0) = u_0'$. Use this to explain how to modify the statement so that it is true.

11. It is usually stated that negative damping is unstable. For the mass-spring-dashpot system, negative damping means that c is negative. From the solution, explain why the system is unstable for any nonzero initial conditions.

Resonance and Forced Motion

12. A block weighing 4 lb stretches a spring 1.5 in. Assume that the block is acted on by a periodic forcing as in (3.64), with $F = 3$ lb and $\omega = 16$ /sec. At the start, the block is not moving and it is at its rest position. Assume that $g = 32\,\text{ft/s}^2$.

   a) What IVP does $u(t)$ satisfy?

   b) What is the solution of the IVP?

   c) Sketch the solution for $0 \le t \le \pi$.

13. Suppose that a spring-mass system is at rest but, starting at $t = 0$, the mass is subjected to a force of $5\cos 3t$ N. Assume that the mass is 2 kg, and the spring constant is $18\,\text{kg/s}^2$.

   a) What IVP does $u(t)$ satisfy?

   b) What is the solution of the IVP?

   c) Sketch the solution for $0 \le t \le 4\pi$.

14. Suppose the forcing in (3.66) is replaced with $F \sin \omega t$. Does this change (3.67)?

15. This exercise considers what happens when the forcing in (3.66) consists of a combination of driving frequencies.

   a) Suppose the forcing is

   $$F_0 \cos \omega_0 t + F_1 \cos \omega_1 t + F_2 \cos \omega_2 t,$$

   where the F_i's are nonzero, and the ω_i's are all different, with ω_0 given in (3.50). Does resonance still occur?

   b) Suppose the forcing is $F_0 \cos \omega_0 t \cos \omega_1 t$, where F_0 is nonzero, $\omega_1 \ne \omega_0$, and ω_0 given in (3.50). Does resonance still occur?

3.11 ▪ Euler Equation

Although second-order equations with constant coefficients are the ones that most often arise in applications, there is a notable exception to this statement. This is the Euler equation, which is

$$x^2 \frac{d^2 y}{dx^2} + bx \frac{dy}{dx} + cy = 0, \tag{3.70}$$

where b and c are constants. The reason this equation arises as often as it does is that it comes from using polar coordinates when solving what is known as Laplace's equation (see Section 7.8.2).

A complication that arises with (3.70) is that it is not a second-order differential equation when $x = 0$. For this reason, $x = 0$ is referred to as a *singular point* for the equation. This is an issue as it is often the case that the interval used when solving Euler's equation has the form $0 \leq x < L$. What condition, if any, you can impose at $x = 0$ is a question we will consider below.

In what follows it is assumed that $x > 0$. Solving (3.70) is rather easy, as one just assumes a solution of the form $y = x^r$. Since $y' = rx^{r-1}$ and $y'' = r(r-1)x^{r-2}$, then from (3.70) we get that

$$r(r-1) + br + c = 0, \tag{3.71}$$

The solutions of this quadratic equation are

$$r = \frac{1}{2}\left(1 - b \pm \sqrt{(1-b)^2 - 4c}\right). \tag{3.72}$$

Just as in Section 3.3, what happens next depends on the values of r obtained from this solution.

Two Real Roots

When there are two real-valued roots, say, r_1 and r_2, then the two corresponding solutions of (3.14) are $y_1 = x^{r_1}$ and $y_2 = x^{r_2}$. It is left as an exercise to show they are independent. Therefore, the resulting general solution of (3.14) is

$$y = c_1 x^{r_1} + c_2 x^{r_2}, \tag{3.73}$$

where c_1 and c_2 are arbitrary constants.

One Real Root

When there is only one root, then you use reduction of order. This means that to find a second solution, assume that $y = w(x)x^r$. Proceeding as in Section 3.3.2, one finds that $w = \ln x$. Therefore, the resulting general solution of (3.14) is

$$y = c_1 x^r + c_2 \ln(x)x^r,$$

where c_1 and c_2 are arbitrary constants.

Complex Roots

In this case, the roots can be written as $r = \lambda \pm i\mu$, where

$$\lambda = \frac{1}{2}(1 - b), \tag{3.74}$$

and

$$\mu = \frac{1}{2}\sqrt{4c - (1 - b)^2}. \tag{3.75}$$

It is assumed here that $4c > (1 - b)^2$. Writing the general solution as in (3.73), and then separating into real and complex parts using Euler's formula, one finds that the resulting general solution can be written as

$$y = d_1 x^\lambda \cos(\mu \ln x) + d_2 x^\lambda \sin(\mu \ln x), \tag{3.76}$$

where d_1 and d_2 are arbitrary constants.

3.11.1 ▪ Examples

Example 1: Find the solution of $x^2 y'' + 2xy' - 6y = 0$, for $0 < x < 2$, that is bounded for $0 < x < 2$ and satisfies $y(2) = 1$.

Answer: Substituting in $y = x^r$, one gets the equation $r^2 + r - 6 = 0$. The solutions of this are $r = -3$, and $r = 2$. So, the general solution of the differential equation is

$$y = c_1 x^{-3} + c_2 x^2.$$

The requirement that y is bounded means that $c_1 = 0$. As for $y(2) = 1$, we need $c_2 = 1/4$. Therefore, the solution is

$$y(x) = \frac{1}{4}x^2. \quad \blacksquare$$

Example 2: Find the general solution of $4x^2 y'' + 17y = 0$, for $0 < x < \infty$.

Answer: Substituting in $y = x^r$, one gets the equation $4r^2 - 4r + 17 = 0$. The solutions of this are $r = \frac{1}{2} \pm 2i$. So, from (3.76), the general solution is

$$y = d_1 \sqrt{x} \cos(2 \ln x) + d_2 \sqrt{x} \sin(2 \ln x). \quad \blacksquare$$

Exercises

1. Assuming $x > 0$, find the general solution of the following Euler equations.

a) $x^2y'' - 3xy' + 4y = 0$

b) $x^2y'' - 5xy' + 10y = 0$

c) $6x^2y'' + 7xy' - y = 0$

d) $x^2y'' + y = 0$

e) $x^2y'' - 3xy' + 13y = 0$

f) $5x^2y'' + 12xy' + 2y = 0$

g) $x^2y'' + xy' = 0$

h) $x^2y'' - 2xy' = 0$

i) $x^2y'' - xy' - n(n+2)y = 0$,
   where n is a positive integer

2. Find the solution of the following problems. Before doing these problems, you might want to review Exercise 3, on page 63.

a) $x^2y'' - 2xy' + 2y = x^3e^x$, where $y(1) = 0$, and $y'(1) = 0$

b) $x^2y'' - 4xy' + 4y = -2x^2 + 1$, where $y(1) = 0$, and $y'(1) = 0$

c) $x^2y'' - xy' + y = \ln x$, where $y(1) = 0$, and $y'(1) = 0$

d) $xy'' + y' = x$, where $y(1) = 1$, and $y'(1) = -1$

e) $(x-1)^2y'' + (x-1)y' - y = 0$, where $y(2) = 1$, and $y'(2) = 0$

3.12 ▪ Guessing the Title of the Next Chapter

Since Chapter 2 is about first-order equations, and this chapter is about second-order equations, you might expect the next chapter to be about third-order equations. This was often how older textbooks were written, where the next chapter would be titled Higher-Order Equations, or something similar. Although it is possible to find applications that involve higher-order equations, such as viscoelasticity, they are not that common. Moreover, the usual method for solving higher-order equations is to first rewrite them in system form. This is certainly the approach used when solving them numerically. Well, as it turns out, the next chapter is about linear systems and the following chapter is on nonlinear systems. So, although third-order and higher equations are not considered in this text, the methods used to solve them are.

Chapter 4

Linear Systems

This chapter, and the one that follows, consider problems that involve two or more first-order ordinary differential equations. Together the equations form what is called a first-order system. These are very common. To explain why, it is worth considering a couple of examples.

Example 1: Mechanics

As stated on several occasions earlier in this text, one of the biggest generators of differential equations is Newton's second law, which states that $F = ma$. To demonstrate its connection with a system of differential equations, let $x(t)$ denote the position of an object. The velocity is then $v = x'(t)$, and the acceleration is $a = x''(t)$. So, $F = ma$ can be written as $mv' = F$. Along with the equation $x' = v$, the resulting system is

$$
\frac{dx}{dt} = v,
$$
$$
\frac{dv}{dt} = \frac{1}{m}F.
$$

As an example, for a uniform gravitation field, and including air resistance, then $F = -mg - cv$ (see Section 2.3.2). In this case, the system becomes

$$
x' = v,
$$
$$
v' = -g - \frac{c}{m}v.
$$

This is a linear first-order system for x and v. It is also inhomogeneous since $x \equiv 0$ and $v \equiv 0$ is not a solution. ∎

Introduction to Differential Equations, M. H. Holmes, 2020

Example 2: Epidemics

Epidemics, such as the black death and cholera, have come and gone throughout human history. Given the catastrophic nature of these events there is a long history of scientific study trying to predict how and why they occur. One of particular prominence is the Kermack-McKendrick model for epidemics. This assumes the population can be separated into three groups. One is the population $S(t)$ of those susceptible to the disease, another is the population $I(t)$ that is ill, and the third is the population $R(t)$ of individuals that have recovered. A model that accounts for the susceptible group getting sick, the subsequent increase in the ill population, and the eventual increase in the recovered population is the following set of equations [Holmes, 2019]

$$\frac{dS}{dt} = -k_1 SI,$$
$$\frac{dI}{dt} = -k_2 I + k_1 SI,$$
$$\frac{dR}{dt} = k_2 I.$$

Given the three groups, and the letters used to designate them, this is an example of what is known as a SIR model in mathematical epidemiology. For us, this is an example of a nonlinear first-order system for S, I, and R. The reason it is nonlinear is the SI term that appears in the first two equations.

As you might expect, solving a nonlinear system can be challenging. So, in this chapter, we will concentrate on linear systems. In the next chapter, nonlinear problems are considered.

4.1 ▪ Linear Systems

To get things started, consider the problem of solving

$$x' = ax + by, \tag{4.1}$$
$$y' = cx + dy. \tag{4.2}$$

This is a first-order, linear, homogeneous system. In these equations, $x(t)$ and $y(t)$ are the dependent variables, and a, b, c, and d are constants. This can be written in system form as

$$\frac{d}{dt}\begin{pmatrix} x \\ y \end{pmatrix} = \begin{pmatrix} a & b \\ c & d \end{pmatrix}\begin{pmatrix} x \\ y \end{pmatrix}.$$

A simpler way to write this is as

$$\frac{d}{dt}\mathbf{x} = \mathbf{A}\mathbf{x}, \tag{4.3}$$

where the vector is

$$\mathbf{x} = \begin{pmatrix} x \\ y \end{pmatrix},$$

and the matrix is

$$\mathbf{A} = \begin{pmatrix} a & b \\ c & d \end{pmatrix}. \tag{4.4}$$

The equation in (4.3) plays a central role throughout this chapter. Written in this way, we could be dealing with 20 equations, or 200 equations, and not just the two in (4.1) and (4.2).

For those a bit rusty on the basic rules for working with matrices and vectors, a short summary is provided in Appendix A.

Before getting into the discussion of how to solve (4.3), it is worth considering what we already know about the solution.

4.1.1 ▪ Example: Transforming to System Form

In Section 3.5, Example 1, we found that for

$$y'' + 2y' - 3y = 0 \tag{4.5}$$

the roots of the characteristic equation are $r_1 = -3$ and $r_2 = 1$. The resulting independent solutions are $y_1 = e^{-3t}$ and $y_2 = e^t$. In this example, the differential equation, along with its solutions, are translated into vector form.

a) Write (4.5) as a linear first-order system as in (4.3).

The standard way to do this is to let $v = y'$, so the differential equation can be written as $v' + 2v - 3y = 0$, or equivalently, $v' = 3y - 2v$. This, along with the equation $y' = v$, gives us the system

$$y' = v,$$
$$v' = 3y - 2v.$$

In other words, we have an equation of the form (4.3), where

$$\mathbf{x} = \begin{pmatrix} y \\ v \end{pmatrix}, \quad \text{and} \quad \mathbf{A} = \begin{pmatrix} 0 & 1 \\ 3 & -2 \end{pmatrix}.$$

b) Write the two linearly independent solutions in vector form.

For $y_1 = e^{-3t}$, then $v_1 = y_1' = -3e^{-3t}$. Letting $\mathbf{x}_1$ be the solution vector coming from y_1, then

$$\mathbf{x}_1 = \begin{pmatrix} y_1 \\ v_1 \end{pmatrix} = \begin{pmatrix} e^{-3t} \\ -3e^{-3t} \end{pmatrix} = \begin{pmatrix} 1 \\ -3 \end{pmatrix} e^{-3t} = \mathbf{a}_1 e^{r_1 t},$$

where $r_1 = -3$ and

$$\mathbf{a}_1 = \begin{pmatrix} 1 \\ -3 \end{pmatrix}.$$

Similarly, since $v_2 = y_2' = e^t$, then letting $\mathbf{x}_2$ be the vector version of y_2,

$$\mathbf{x}_2 = \begin{pmatrix} y_2 \\ v_2 \end{pmatrix} = \begin{pmatrix} e^t \\ e^t \end{pmatrix} = \begin{pmatrix} 1 \\ 1 \end{pmatrix} e^t = \mathbf{a}_2 e^{r_2 t},$$

where $r_2 = 1$ and

$$\mathbf{a}_2 = \begin{pmatrix} 1 \\ 1 \end{pmatrix}.$$

c) Write the general solution in vector form.

The general solution for the second-order equation is $y = c_1 y_1 + c_2 y_2$. From this, we get that $v = y' = c_1 y_1' + c_2 y_2'$. Therefore, the general solution vector is

$$\mathbf{x} = \begin{pmatrix} y \\ v \end{pmatrix} = \begin{pmatrix} c_1 y_1 + c_2 y_2 \\ c_1 y_1' + c_2 y_2' \end{pmatrix} = \begin{pmatrix} c_1 y_1 \\ c_1 y_1' \end{pmatrix} + \begin{pmatrix} c_2 y_2 \\ c_2 y_2' \end{pmatrix}$$

$$= c_1 \mathbf{x}_1 + c_2 \mathbf{x}_2. \quad \blacksquare \qquad\qquad (4.6)$$

A very useful observation to make about the above example is that the linearly independent solutions have the form $\mathbf{x} = \mathbf{a}e^{rt}$, where $\mathbf{a}$ is a constant vector. In fact, when the time comes to solve (4.3) we will simply assume that $\mathbf{x} = \mathbf{a}e^{rt}$, and then find r and $\mathbf{a}$. Also, note that for the single linear equation $x' = ax$, there is one linearly independent solution. As the above example shows, for two linear first-order equations there are two linearly independent solutions. Consequently, it should not be a surprise to find out that for n linear first-order equations there are n linearly independent solutions.

4.1.2 ▪ General Version

We are going to consider solving homogeneous linear first-order systems. Assuming there are n dependent variables, then the system can be written as

$$\begin{aligned} x_1' &= a_{11}x_1 + a_{12}x_2 + \cdots a_{1n}x_n \\ x_2' &= a_{21}x_1 + a_{22}x_2 + \cdots a_{2n}x_n \\ &\vdots \qquad\qquad \vdots \qquad\qquad \vdots \\ x_n' &= a_{n1}x_1 + a_{n2}x_2 + \cdots a_{nn}x_n, \end{aligned}$$

where the a_{ij}'s are constants. This can be written as

$$\frac{d}{dt}\mathbf{x} = \mathbf{Ax}, \qquad (4.7)$$

where $\mathbf{A}$ is an $n \times n$ matrix, and $\mathbf{x}$ is an n-vector, given, respectively, as

$$\mathbf{A} = \begin{pmatrix} a_{11} & a_{12} & \cdots & a_{1n} \\ a_{21} & a_{22} & \cdots & a_{2n} \\ \vdots & \vdots & \cdots & \vdots \\ a_{n1} & a_{n2} & \cdots & a_{nn} \end{pmatrix} \quad \text{and} \quad \mathbf{x} = \begin{pmatrix} x_1 \\ x_2 \\ \vdots \\ x_n \end{pmatrix}.$$

For an initial value problem, an n-vector $\mathbf{x}_0$ would be given, and the condition to be satisfied would be $\mathbf{x}(0) = \mathbf{x}_0$.

Because (4.7) is linear and homogeneous, the principle of superposition holds (see page 5). Therefore, if $\mathbf{x}_1$ and $\mathbf{x}_2$ are solutions of (4.7), then

$$\mathbf{x} = c_1 \mathbf{x}_1 + c_2 \mathbf{x}_2$$

is a solution for any values of the constants c_1 and c_2.

As a final comment, the inhomogeneous equation $\frac{d}{dt}\mathbf{x} = \mathbf{Ax} + \mathbf{f}$ is not considered in this chapter, but it is considered in Section 6.6.

Exercises

1. Write the following as $\mathbf{x}' = \mathbf{Ax}$, making sure to identify the entries in $\mathbf{x}$ and $\mathbf{A}$. If initial conditions are given, write them as $\mathbf{x}(0) = \mathbf{x}_0$.

   a) $u' = u - v$
      $v' = 2u - 3v$
   b) $2u' = -u$
      $3v' = u + v$
   c) $u' = u - v + 2w$
      $v' = u$
      $w' = -u + 5v$

   d) $u' = u - v$
      $v' = 2u - 3v$
      $u(0) = -1, \ v(0) = 0$
   e) $u' = 2u - w$
      $v' = u + v + w$
      $3w' = 2v + 6w$
      $u(0) = -1, \ v(0) = 0, \ w(0) = 3$

2. For the following: a) Write the equation in the form $\mathbf{x}' = \mathbf{Ax}$. b) Find the general solution of the second-order equation and then write it in vector form as $\mathbf{x} = c_1 \mathbf{x}_1 + c_2 \mathbf{x}_2$, where $\mathbf{x}_1 = \mathbf{a}_1 e^{r_1 t}$ and $\mathbf{x}_2 = \mathbf{a}_2 e^{r_2 t}$. Make sure to identify $\mathbf{a}_1$, $\mathbf{a}_2$, r_1 and r_2.

   a) $y'' + 2y' - 3y = 0$
   b) $4y'' + 3y' - y = 0$
   c) $3y'' + 4y' + 3y = 0$
   d) $y'' + 4y' = 0$

3. Show that the given vector $\mathbf{x}$ is a solution of the differential equation. Also, what initial condition does $\mathbf{x}$ satisfy?

a)
$$\mathbf{x}' = \begin{pmatrix} 1 & 2 \\ 2 & -2 \end{pmatrix} \mathbf{x}, \quad \mathbf{x} = \begin{pmatrix} 4 \\ 2 \end{pmatrix} e^{2t}$$

b)
$$\mathbf{x}' = \begin{pmatrix} 3 & 1 \\ 2 & 2 \end{pmatrix} \mathbf{x}, \quad \mathbf{x} = 3 \begin{pmatrix} 1 \\ -2 \end{pmatrix} e^{t}$$

c)
$$\mathbf{x}' = \begin{pmatrix} 2 & 0 \\ 0 & -3 \end{pmatrix} \mathbf{x}, \quad \mathbf{x} = \begin{pmatrix} 1 \\ 0 \end{pmatrix} e^{2t} + \begin{pmatrix} 0 \\ 2 \end{pmatrix} e^{-3t}$$

d)
$$\mathbf{x}' = \begin{pmatrix} \frac{1}{2} & 1 \\ -1 & \frac{1}{2} \end{pmatrix} \mathbf{x}, \quad \mathbf{x} = \begin{pmatrix} \cos t \\ -\sin t \end{pmatrix} e^{t/2}$$

4. This problem considers other possibilities for transforming a second-order equation into a first-order system.

a) Assuming that $c \neq 0$, show that (4.1), (4.2) can be reduced to the second-order linear equation

$$y'' - (a + d)y' + (ad - bc)y = 0.$$

b) Using the result from part (a), transform $y'' + 2y' - 3y = 0$ into a first-order system where none of the entries in $\mathbf{A}$ are zero.

4.2 ▪ General Solution of a Homogeneous Equation

The problem considered here is

$$\frac{d}{dt}\mathbf{x} = \mathbf{A}\mathbf{x}, \quad \text{for } t > 0. \tag{4.8}$$

From (4.6), as well as Exercise 2 in the previous section, we have an idea of what the general solution of this equation looks like. Namely, if we are able to find n linearly independent solutions $\mathbf{x}_1(t)$, $\mathbf{x}_2(t)$, ..., $\mathbf{x}_n(t)$, then the general solution can be written as

$$\mathbf{x}(t) = c_1\mathbf{x}_1(t) + c_2\mathbf{x}_2(t) + \cdots + c_n\mathbf{x}_n(t), \tag{4.9}$$

where c_1, c_2, ..., c_n are arbitrary constants.

The requirement to be linearly independent is a simple generalization of the definition given in Section 3.2. Namely, $\mathbf{x}_1(t)$, $\mathbf{x}_2(t)$, ..., $\mathbf{x}_n(t)$ are

linearly independent if, and only if, the only constants c_1, c_2, ..., c_n that satisfy

$$c_1\mathbf{x}_1 + c_2\mathbf{x}_2 + \cdots + c_n\mathbf{x}_n = \mathbf{0}, \quad \forall\, t \geq 0, \tag{4.10}$$

are $c_1 = 0$, $c_2 = 0$, ..., $c_n = 0$. In the above equation, $\mathbf{0}$ is the **zero vector**, which means that all of its components are zero. Also, the symbol $\forall$ is a mathematical shorthand for "for all" or "for every."

In the last chapter the Wronskian was used to determine independence. It is possible to also use the Wronskian with (4.8), but this is not particularly useful for larger n. There is an easier way to show independence, and this will be explained in Section 4.4.

The general solution of (4.8) is found by assuming that $\mathbf{x} = \mathbf{a}e^{rt}$, where $\mathbf{a}$ is a constant vector. Differentiating this expression, $\mathbf{x}' = r\mathbf{a}e^{rt}$, and so (4.8) becomes $r\mathbf{a}e^{rt} = \mathbf{A}(\mathbf{a}e^{rt})$. Since e^{rt} is never zero we can divide by it, which gives us the equation

$$\mathbf{A}\mathbf{a} = r\mathbf{a}. \tag{4.11}$$

What we want are nonzero solutions of this equation, and so we require that $\mathbf{a} \neq \mathbf{0}$. This problem for r and $\mathbf{a}$ is called an **eigenvalue problem**, where r is an **eigenvalue**, and $\mathbf{a}$ is an **associated eigenvector**. This is one of the core topics covered in linear algebra. We do not need to know the more theoretical aspects of this problem, but we certainly need to know how to solve it. So, for completeness, the more pertinent aspects of an eigenvalue problem are reviewed next.

It is worth pointing out that it is possible to solve (4.8) without using eigenvalues and eigenvectors, and how this is done is explained in Section 6.6.

4.3 ▪ Review of Eigenvalue Problems

Given an $n \times n$ matrix $\mathbf{A}$, its eigenvalues r and the associated eigenvectors $\mathbf{a}$ are found by solving

$$\mathbf{A}\mathbf{a} = r\mathbf{a}. \tag{4.12}$$

It is required that $\mathbf{a}$ is not the zero vector. There are no conditions placed on r, and it can be real or complex valued.

In preparation for solving the above equation, it is first rewritten as $\mathbf{A}\mathbf{a} - r\mathbf{a} = \mathbf{0}$, or equivalently as

$$(\mathbf{A} - r\mathbf{I})\mathbf{a} = \mathbf{0}. \tag{4.13}$$

The $n \times n$ matrix $\mathbf{I}$ is known as the **identity matrix** and it is defined as

$$\mathbf{I} \equiv \begin{pmatrix} 1 & 0 & \cdots & 0 \\ 0 & 1 & \cdots & 0 \\ \vdots & \vdots & \cdots & \vdots \\ 0 & 0 & \cdots & 1 \end{pmatrix}.$$

For example, when $n = 2$ and $n = 3$,

$$\mathbf{I} = \begin{pmatrix} 1 & 0 \\ 0 & 1 \end{pmatrix} \quad \text{and} \quad \mathbf{I} = \begin{pmatrix} 1 & 0 & 0 \\ 0 & 1 & 0 \\ 0 & 0 & 1 \end{pmatrix}.$$

In linear algebra it is shown that for the equation (4.13) to have a nonzero solution, it is necessary that the matrix $\mathbf{A} - r\mathbf{I}$ be singular, or non-invertible. What this means is that the determinant of this matrix is zero. This gives rise to the following method for solving the eigenvalue problem.

Eigenvalue Algorithm. *The procedure used to solve the eigenvalue problem consists of two steps:*

1. *Find the r's by solving*

$$\det(\mathbf{A} - r\mathbf{I}) = 0. \tag{4.14}$$

*This is known as the **characteristic equation**, and the left-hand-side of this equation is an nth degree polynomial in r.*

2. *For each eigenvalue r, find the associated eigenvectors by finding the nonzero solutions of*

$$(\mathbf{A} - r\mathbf{I})\mathbf{a} = \mathbf{0}. \tag{4.15}$$

In this textbook we are mostly interested in systems involving two equations. For those who might not remember, the determinant of a 2×2 matrix is defined as

$$\det \begin{pmatrix} a_{11} & a_{12} \\ a_{21} & a_{22} \end{pmatrix} \equiv a_{11}a_{22} - a_{12}a_{21}.$$

In the second step of the algorithm, when solving (4.15), we are interested in finding the vectors that can be used to form the general solution of this equation. To say this more mathematically, we want to find linearly independent solutions. For those you might not remember what this is, the definition is given next.

Linearly Independent. *The vectors $\mathbf{a}_1$, $\mathbf{a}_2$, $\cdots$, $\mathbf{a}_k$ are linearly independent if, and only if, the only numbers c_1, c_2, ..., c_k that satisfy*

$$c_1\mathbf{a}_1 + c_2\mathbf{a}_2 + \cdots + c_k\mathbf{a}_k = \mathbf{0}, \tag{4.16}$$

are $c_1 = c_2 = \cdots = c_k = 0$. If it is possible for any of the c_i's to be nonzero, then the vectors are linearly dependent.

In n dimensions, it is not possible to have more than n linearly independent vectors. Consequently, n is the maximum number of linearly independent eigenvectors you can find for an $n \times n$ matrix $\mathbf{A}$. Finally, as will be seen in one of the examples to follow, eigenvectors can contain complex numbers. When this happens, the c_i's in the above equation must be allowed to be complex-valued.

The following examples all involve 2×2 matrices. What is illustrated are the various situations that can arise with eigenvalue problems. In these examples, the eigenvector will be written in component form as

$$\mathbf{a} = \begin{pmatrix} a \\ b \end{pmatrix}. \tag{4.17}$$

Example 1: Two Real Eigenvalues

For

$$\mathbf{A} = \begin{pmatrix} 2 & 1 \\ 1 & 2 \end{pmatrix},$$

we get that

$$\mathbf{A} - r\mathbf{I} = \begin{pmatrix} 2 & 1 \\ 1 & 2 \end{pmatrix} - r \begin{pmatrix} 1 & 0 \\ 0 & 1 \end{pmatrix} = \begin{pmatrix} 2-r & 1 \\ 1 & 2-r \end{pmatrix}.$$

Since $\det(\mathbf{A} - r\mathbf{I}) = (2 - r)^2 - 1 = r^2 - 4r + 3$, then the characteristic equation (4.14) is $r^2 - 4r + 3 = 0$. Solving this we get that the eigenvalues are $r_1 = 3$ and $r_2 = 1$. For r_1, (4.15) takes the form

$$\begin{pmatrix} -1 & 1 \\ 1 & -1 \end{pmatrix} \begin{pmatrix} a \\ b \end{pmatrix} = \begin{pmatrix} 0 \\ 0 \end{pmatrix}.$$

In component form, we have that

$$-a + b = 0,$$
$$a - b = 0.$$

The solution is $b = a$, and so the eigenvectors are

$$\mathbf{a} = \begin{pmatrix} a \\ b \end{pmatrix} = \begin{pmatrix} a \\ a \end{pmatrix} = a\,\mathbf{a}_1, \tag{4.18}$$

where

$$\mathbf{a}_1 = \begin{pmatrix} 1 \\ 1 \end{pmatrix}. \tag{4.19}$$

For the second eigenvalue $r_2 = 1$, one finds that the eigenvectors have the form $\mathbf{a} = a\mathbf{a}_2$, where a is an arbitrary nonzero constant and

$$\mathbf{a}_2 = \begin{pmatrix} 1 \\ -1 \end{pmatrix}.$$

The eigenvectors $\mathbf{a}_1$ and $\mathbf{a}_2$ are independent. To show this, note that

$$c_1 \mathbf{a}_1 + c_2 \mathbf{a}_2 = c_1 \begin{pmatrix} 1 \\ 1 \end{pmatrix} + c_2 \begin{pmatrix} 1 \\ -1 \end{pmatrix} = \begin{pmatrix} c_1 + c_2 \\ c_1 - c_2 \end{pmatrix}.$$

So, from (4.16), if $c_1 \mathbf{a}_1 + c_2 \mathbf{a}_2 = \mathbf{0}$, then $c_1 + c_2 = 0$ and $c_1 - c_2 = 0$. From the last equation, $c_1 = c_2$, and inserting this into the first equation yields $2c_2 = 0$. So, $c_2 = 0$, and this also means that $c_1 = 0$. Therefore, $\mathbf{a}_1$ and $\mathbf{a}_2$ are independent. ∎

There is an important observation that needs to be made here. In the above example, it was shown that eigenvectors for different eigenvalues are linearly independent. This is always true, and this is important enough that it needs to be stated more prominently.

Different Eigenvalues Test. *If* $\mathbf{a}_1$, $\mathbf{a}_2$, $\cdots$, $\mathbf{a}_k$ *are eigenvectors corresponding to different eigenvalues for a matrix* $\mathbf{A}$, *then these vectors are linearly independent.*

The above test applies irrespective of whether the eigenvalues are real or complex valued. It also is not limited to a 2×2 matrix, and holds in the general case of when the matrix is $n \times n$.

Example 2: One Eigenvalue But Two Independent Eigenvectors

When

$$\mathbf{A} = \begin{pmatrix} 3 & 0 \\ 0 & 3 \end{pmatrix},$$

the characteristic equation is $(r - 3)^2 = 0$. So the only eigenvalue is $r_1 = 3$. In this case,

$$\mathbf{A} - r\mathbf{I} = \begin{pmatrix} 0 & 0 \\ 0 & 0 \end{pmatrix}. \tag{4.20}$$

This means that all vectors are solutions of (4.15). In other words, the solutions are

$$\mathbf{a} = \begin{pmatrix} a \\ b \end{pmatrix} = \begin{pmatrix} a \\ 0 \end{pmatrix} + \begin{pmatrix} 0 \\ b \end{pmatrix} = a\,\mathbf{a}_1 + b\,\mathbf{a}_2,$$

where

$$\mathbf{a}_1 = \begin{pmatrix} 1 \\ 0 \end{pmatrix} \quad \text{and} \quad \mathbf{a}_2 = \begin{pmatrix} 0 \\ 1 \end{pmatrix}. \tag{4.21}$$

To check on independence, we are not able to use the Different Eigenvalues Test given above because $\mathbf{a}_1$ and $\mathbf{a}_2$ are eigenvectors for the same eigenvalue. To use the definition, note that

$$c_1\mathbf{a}_1 + c_2\mathbf{a}_2 = c_1 \begin{pmatrix} 1 \\ 0 \end{pmatrix} + c_2 \begin{pmatrix} 0 \\ 1 \end{pmatrix} = \begin{pmatrix} c_1 \\ c_2 \end{pmatrix}.$$

So, if $c_1\mathbf{a}_1 + c_2\mathbf{a}_2 = \mathbf{0}$, then we conclude that $c_1 = c_2 = 0$. Therefore, $\mathbf{a}_1$ and $\mathbf{a}_2$ are independent. ■

Example 3: Complex-Valued Eigenvalues

For the matrix

$$\mathbf{A} = \begin{pmatrix} 1 & 2 \\ -\frac{1}{2} & 1 \end{pmatrix},$$

the characteristic equation is $r^2 - 2r + 2 = 0$. The resulting eigenvalues are $r = 1 + i$ and $r = 1 - i$. Proceeding as usual, for r_1,

$$\mathbf{A} - r_1\mathbf{I} = \begin{pmatrix} i & 2 \\ -\frac{1}{2} & i \end{pmatrix}.$$

This means that (4.15) requires that $-ia + 2b = 0$, or equivalently, $a = -2ib$. So, the eigenvectors are

$$\mathbf{a} = \begin{pmatrix} a \\ b \end{pmatrix} = b \begin{pmatrix} -2i \\ 1 \end{pmatrix} = b\,\mathbf{a}_1,$$

where

$$\mathbf{a}_1 = \begin{pmatrix} -2i \\ 1 \end{pmatrix}.$$

Similarly, for $r_2 = 1 - i$, one finds that the eigenvectors are

$$\mathbf{a} = b\,\mathbf{a}_2,$$

where

$$\mathbf{a}_2 = \begin{pmatrix} 2i \\ 1 \end{pmatrix}.$$

Finally, because $\mathbf{a}_1$ and $\mathbf{a}_2$ are eigenvectors for different eigenvalues, they are independent. ■

There is an observation that needs to be made here. In the above example, the eigenvalues have the form $r_1 = \lambda + i\mu$ and $r_2 = \lambda - i\mu$, where λ and μ are real numbers, with $\mu \neq 0$. Because of this, the eigenvalues are said to be **complex conjugates**. When a matrix only contains real numbers, as in the last example, and it has complex eigenvalues, they must occur as complex conjugates. Moreover, you should notice that the respective eigenvectors $\mathbf{a}_1$ and $\mathbf{a}_2$ are also complex conjugates (if you change i to $-i$ in $\mathbf{a}_1$, you get $\mathbf{a}_2$). This is useful information as it means that once you know $\mathbf{a}_1$, you immediately know $\mathbf{a}_2$.

Example 4: Only One Independent Eigenvector

The matrix

$$\mathbf{A} = \begin{pmatrix} 3 & 1 \\ 0 & 3 \end{pmatrix},$$

has one eigenvalue $r = 3$ (similar to Example 2). In this case (4.15) becomes

$$\mathbf{A} - r\mathbf{I} = \begin{pmatrix} 0 & 3 \\ 0 & 0 \end{pmatrix}. \tag{4.22}$$

This means that $b = 0$. Consequently, the eigenvectors have the form

$$\mathbf{a} = \begin{pmatrix} a \\ 0 \end{pmatrix} = a \begin{pmatrix} 1 \\ 0 \end{pmatrix} = a\, \mathbf{a}_1,$$

where

$$\mathbf{a}_1 = \begin{pmatrix} 1 \\ 0 \end{pmatrix}.$$

In the previous three examples involving 2×2 matrices we found two linearly independent eigenvectors. This matrix is different as there is only one. An $n \times n$ matrix that has fewer than n independent eigenvectors is said to be **defective**. So, the matrix of this example is defective, while the matrices for the three previous examples are not defective. ∎

A semi-useful observation can be made here. The only 2×2 matrices that have only one eigenvalue, and are not defective, have the form $\mathbf{A} = a\mathbf{I}$. In this case, the eigenvalue is $r = a$ and the eigenvectors are given in (4.21). This is what happened in Example 2, where $a = 3$. So, if you have a 2×2 matrix with only one eigenvalue, and $\mathbf{A} \neq a\mathbf{I}$, then the matrix is defective. This is what happened in Example 4.

Exercises

1. Determine whether the following pairs of vectors are linearly independent.

a) $\mathbf{a}_1 = \begin{pmatrix} 1 \\ 2 \end{pmatrix}$, $\mathbf{a}_2 = \begin{pmatrix} 2 \\ 1 \end{pmatrix}$

c) $\mathbf{a}_1 = \begin{pmatrix} 2 \\ -8 \end{pmatrix}$, $\mathbf{a}_2 = \begin{pmatrix} -1 \\ 4 \end{pmatrix}$

b) $\mathbf{a}_1 = \begin{pmatrix} 1 \\ -1 \end{pmatrix}$, $\mathbf{a}_2 = \begin{pmatrix} -3 \\ 3 \end{pmatrix}$

d) $\mathbf{a}_1 = \begin{pmatrix} -5 \\ 10 \end{pmatrix}$, $\mathbf{a}_2 = \begin{pmatrix} 1 \\ 2 \end{pmatrix}$

2. The following matrices have two real-valued eigenvalues. Find the eigenvalues, and two linearly independent eigenvectors.

a) $\begin{pmatrix} 2 & 1 \\ 4 & -1 \end{pmatrix}$

b) $\begin{pmatrix} -2 & -7 \\ 1 & 6 \end{pmatrix}$

3. The following matrices have complex-valued eigenvalues. Find the eigenvalues, and two linearly independent eigenvectors.

a) $\begin{pmatrix} 2 & -4 \\ 1 & 2 \end{pmatrix}$

b) $\begin{pmatrix} 2 & 13 \\ -1 & -4 \end{pmatrix}$

4. Show that the following matrices are defective.

a) $\begin{pmatrix} 3 & -2 \\ 2 & -1 \end{pmatrix}$

b) $\begin{pmatrix} -1 & 1 \\ -9 & 5 \end{pmatrix}$

4.4 ▪ Solving a Homogeneous Equation

As stated earlier, given an $n \times n$ matrix $\mathbf{A}$, to find the general solution of

$$\frac{d}{dt}\mathbf{x} = \mathbf{Ax}, \tag{4.23}$$

you start by assuming that $\mathbf{x} = \mathbf{a}e^{rt}$, where $\mathbf{a}$ is a constant vector. Substituting this into the differential equation, and simplifying, leads to the eigenvalue problem

$$\mathbf{Aa} = r\mathbf{a}. \tag{4.24}$$

If $\mathbf{A}$ is not defective, then there are n linearly independent eigenvectors $\mathbf{a}_1, \mathbf{a}_2, \ldots, \mathbf{a}_n$. Letting $r_1, r_2, \ldots, r_n$ be their respective eigenvalues, then the general solution of (4.23) can be written as

$$\mathbf{x} = c_1\mathbf{a}_1 e^{r_1 t} + c_2\mathbf{a}_2 e^{r_2 t} + \cdots + c_n\mathbf{a}_n e^{r_n t}, \tag{4.25}$$

where the c_i's are arbitrary constants.

The vectors $\mathbf{x}_j = \mathbf{a}_j e^{r_j t}$ used in the above formula for the general solution are linearly independent. The reason is that the test for independence in (4.10) must hold at $t = 0$, and for $t = 0$ the equation reduces to (4.16). Since the $\mathbf{a}_j$'s are independent, it follows that the c_j's are all zero. Consequently, the vectors $\mathbf{x}_j$ are linearly independent.

With the formula for the general solution in (4.25), all that is left to do is consider how to rewrite it when the eigenvalues are complex and to also determine what to do when the matrix is defective. A summary of what follows in given in Section 4.5.

4.4.1 ▪ Complex-Valued Eigenvalues

As usual, when the roots are complex-valued there are options as to how the general solution can be written. It is certainly possible to just use the expression in (4.25). However, it is often easier to rewrite the solution so as to avoid the use of complex variables. It is easiest to explain how this is done using an example.

Example

The matrix in the differential equation,

$$\mathbf{x}' = \begin{pmatrix} 1 & 2 \\ -\frac{1}{2} & 1 \end{pmatrix} \mathbf{x},$$

is the one considered in Example 3 of the previous section. The eigenvalues are $r = 1 + i$ and $r = 1 - i$. Using the eigenvectors found earlier, the general solution can be written as

$$\mathbf{x} = c_1 \begin{pmatrix} -2i \\ 1 \end{pmatrix} e^{(1+i)t} + c_2 \begin{pmatrix} 2i \\ 1 \end{pmatrix} e^{(1-i)t}.$$

Because complex numbers are used for the r's, both c_1 and c_2 must be allowed to be complex-valued.

Given that $\mathbf{x}$ is real-valued, the coefficients c_1 and c_2 must be complex conjugates. In other words, if $c_1 = \alpha + i\beta$, where α and β are real-valued, then it must be that $c_2 = \alpha - i\beta$. We are going to separate the solution into real and imaginary parts, which for the eigenvectors means that

$$\begin{pmatrix} -2i \\ 1 \end{pmatrix} = \begin{pmatrix} 0 \\ 1 \end{pmatrix} + i \begin{pmatrix} -2 \\ 0 \end{pmatrix}, \quad \text{and} \quad \begin{pmatrix} 2i \\ 1 \end{pmatrix} = \begin{pmatrix} 0 \\ 1 \end{pmatrix} - i \begin{pmatrix} -2 \\ 0 \end{pmatrix}.$$

It makes things a bit easier to write these as

$$\begin{pmatrix} -2i \\ 1 \end{pmatrix} = \mathbf{p} + i\mathbf{q}, \quad \text{and} \quad \begin{pmatrix} 2i \\ 1 \end{pmatrix} = \mathbf{p} - i\mathbf{q},$$

where

$$\mathbf{p} = \begin{pmatrix} 0 \\ 1 \end{pmatrix}, \quad \text{and} \quad \mathbf{q} = \begin{pmatrix} -2 \\ 0 \end{pmatrix}.$$

Now, using Euler's formula (3.14), we have that

$$\mathbf{x} = (\alpha + i\beta)(\mathbf{p} + i\mathbf{q})e^t(\cos t + i \sin t) + (\alpha - i\beta)(\mathbf{p} - i\mathbf{q})e^t(\cos t - i \sin t)$$

$$= d_1(\mathbf{p} \cos t - \mathbf{q} \sin t)e^t + d_2(\mathbf{p} \sin t + \mathbf{q} \cos t)e^t$$

$$= d_1 \begin{pmatrix} 2 \sin t \\ \cos t \end{pmatrix} e^t + d_2 \begin{pmatrix} -2 \cos t \\ \sin t \end{pmatrix} e^t,$$

where $d_1 = 2\alpha$ and $d_2 = -2\beta$ are arbitrary real-valued constants.   ∎

General Formula

To summarize what was done in the above example, suppose that $\mathbf{A}$ is a 2×2 matrix with complex-valued eigenvalues $r_1 = \lambda + i\mu$ and $r_2 = \lambda - i\mu$, where λ and μ are real-valued with $\mu \neq 0$. Also, assume that their respective eigenvectors are $\mathbf{a}_1 = \mathbf{p} + i\mathbf{q}$ and $\mathbf{a}_2 = \mathbf{p} - i\mathbf{q}$, where $\mathbf{p}$ and $\mathbf{q}$ are vectors containing only real numbers. In this case, instead of writing the general solution as

$$\mathbf{x} = c_1 \mathbf{a}_1 e^{r_1 t} + c_2 \mathbf{a}_2 e^{r_2 t},$$

it can be written as

$$\mathbf{x}(t) = d_1 \mathbf{b}_1 e^{\lambda t} + d_2 \mathbf{b}_2 e^{\lambda t},$$

where

$$\mathbf{b}_1 = \mathbf{p} \cos(\mu t) - \mathbf{q} \sin(\mu t),$$
$$\mathbf{b}_2 = \mathbf{p} \sin(\mu t) + \mathbf{q} \cos(\mu t),$$

and d_1 and d_2 are arbitrary real-valued constants. As a labor saving observation, it should be noted that $\mathbf{p}$ and $\mathbf{q}$ are known once the eigenvector for r_1 is found, which means you do not also need to find the eigenvector for r_2.

4.4.2 ▪ Defective Matrix

The other case to consider is what to do when there are not enough linearly independent eigenvectors, which means that $\mathbf{A}$ is defective. So, suppose that $\mathbf{A}$ is a 2×2 matrix that has one eigenvalue r, and $\mathbf{a}$ is its associated eigenvector. Based on the way we fixed the single root solution in Chapter 3, you might expect for the vector version you should assume a solution of the form $\mathbf{x} = \mathbf{b}te^{rt}$. However, this does not work, and to find a second independent solution, the assumption is that

$$\mathbf{x} = \mathbf{a}te^{rt} + \mathbf{b}e^{rt}.$$

To find $\mathbf{b}$, the above expression is substituted into the differential equation to obtain

$$\mathbf{A}\mathbf{b} = r\mathbf{b} + \mathbf{a},$$

or equivalently

$$(\mathbf{A} - r\mathbf{I})\mathbf{b} = \mathbf{a}. \tag{4.26}$$

It is useful to know that we don't need all solutions of this equation. Rather, all we need is just one of them. Once this is determined, the general solution is

$$\mathbf{x} = c_1\mathbf{a}e^{rt} + c_2(t\mathbf{a} + \mathbf{b})e^{rt}.$$

4.5 ▪ Summary for Solving a Homogeneous Equation

Assuming that $\mathbf{A}$ is 2×2, then the general solution of $\mathbf{x}' = \mathbf{A}\mathbf{x}$ is as given below.

- When $\mathbf{A}$ is not defective.

  - If $\mathbf{A}$ has real eigenvalues r_1 and r_2, with respective eigenvectors $\mathbf{a}_1$ and $\mathbf{a}_2$, then

    $$\mathbf{x} = c_1\mathbf{a}_1e^{r_1t} + c_2\mathbf{a}_2e^{r_2t}. \tag{4.27}$$

    This expression can be used when $r_1 = r_2$ (in this case, just make sure $\mathbf{a}_1$ and $\mathbf{a}_2$ are independent).

  - If $\mathbf{A}$ has complex eigenvalues $r = \lambda \pm i\mu$ (with $\mu \neq 0$), with respective eigenvectors $\mathbf{p} \pm i\mathbf{q}$, then

    $$\mathbf{x}(t) = d_1\mathbf{b}_1e^{\lambda t} + d_2\mathbf{b}_2e^{\lambda t}, \tag{4.28}$$

    where

    $$\mathbf{b}_1 = \mathbf{p}\cos(\mu t) - \mathbf{q}\sin(\mu t),$$
    $$\mathbf{b}_2 = \mathbf{p}\sin(\mu t) + \mathbf{q}\cos(\mu t).$$

- When $\mathbf{A}$ is defective, with eigenvalue r and eigenvector $\mathbf{a}$, then

  $$\mathbf{x} = c_1\mathbf{a}e^{rt} + c_2(t\mathbf{a} + \mathbf{b})e^{rt}, \tag{4.29}$$

  where $\mathbf{b}$ is any solution of

  $$(\mathbf{A} - r\mathbf{I})\mathbf{b} = \mathbf{a}. \tag{4.30}$$

Example 1 (real eigenvalues): Find the general solution of

$$\mathbf{x}' = \begin{pmatrix} 0 & 1 \\ 2 & 1 \end{pmatrix} \mathbf{x}.$$

Step 1: Find the eigenvalues and eigenvectors. Using the eigenvalue algorithm, from (4.14),

$$\det(\mathbf{A} - r\mathbf{I}) = 0 \quad \Rightarrow \quad \det \begin{pmatrix} -r & 1 \\ 2 & 1-r \end{pmatrix} = 0$$

$$\Rightarrow \quad r^2 - r - 2 = 0$$

$$\Rightarrow \quad r = -1, 2.$$

For $r = -1$, then from (4.15),

$$(\mathbf{A} - r\mathbf{I})\mathbf{a} = \mathbf{0} \quad \Rightarrow \quad \begin{pmatrix} 1 & 1 \\ 2 & 2 \end{pmatrix} \mathbf{a} = \mathbf{0} \quad \Rightarrow \quad a + b = 0.$$

So, $b = -a$, and this means that

$$\mathbf{a} = \begin{pmatrix} a \\ b \end{pmatrix} = \begin{pmatrix} a \\ -a \end{pmatrix} = a \, \mathbf{a}_1,$$

where

$$\mathbf{a}_1 = \begin{pmatrix} 1 \\ -1 \end{pmatrix}.$$

In a similar manner, one finds that for $r = 2$, an eigenvector is

$$\mathbf{a}_2 = \begin{pmatrix} 1 \\ 2 \end{pmatrix}.$$

Step 2: Since this is a non-defective matrix with real eigenvalues, the general solution is

$$\mathbf{x} = c_1 \begin{pmatrix} 1 \\ -1 \end{pmatrix} e^{-t} + c_2 \begin{pmatrix} 1 \\ 2 \end{pmatrix} e^{2t}. \quad \blacksquare$$

Example 2 (complex eigenvalues): Find the solution of the IVP:

$$\mathbf{x}' = \begin{pmatrix} 2 & 1 \\ -2 & 0 \end{pmatrix} \mathbf{x}, \quad \text{where} \quad \mathbf{x}(0) = \begin{pmatrix} 0 \\ 1 \end{pmatrix}.$$

Step 1: Find the eigenvalues and eigenvectors. Using the eigenvalue algorithm, from (4.14), you find that the eigenvalues are $r_1 = 1 + i$ and $r_2 = 1 - i$. To determine the eigenvector for r_1, we have that

$$\mathbf{A} - r_1\mathbf{I} = \begin{pmatrix} 2 - (1+i) & 1 \\ -2 & -(1+i) \end{pmatrix} = \begin{pmatrix} 1 - i & 1 \\ -2 & -(1+i) \end{pmatrix}.$$

So, writing $\mathbf{a}$ as in (4.17), then $(\mathbf{A} - r_1\mathbf{I})\mathbf{a} = \mathbf{0}$ can be written in component form as

$$(1 - i)a + b = 0$$
$$-2a - (1 + i)b = 0.$$

Both equations lead to the conclusion that $b = -(1-i)a$. So, the eigenvectors are

$$\mathbf{a} = \begin{pmatrix} a \\ b \end{pmatrix} = a\begin{pmatrix} 1 \\ -1 + i \end{pmatrix} = a\,\mathbf{a}_1.$$

As explained earlier, it makes things easier to write $\mathbf{a}_1 = \mathbf{p} + i\mathbf{q}$, which means that

$$\begin{pmatrix} 1 \\ -1 + i \end{pmatrix} = \mathbf{p} + i\mathbf{q},$$

where

$$\mathbf{p} = \begin{pmatrix} 1 \\ -1 \end{pmatrix}, \quad \text{and} \quad \mathbf{q} = \begin{pmatrix} 0 \\ 1 \end{pmatrix}.$$

Moreover, because the eigenvector for $r_2 = 1 - i$ is the complex conjugate of $\mathbf{a}_1$, then $\mathbf{a}_2 = \mathbf{p} - i\mathbf{q}$.

Step 2: Find the general solution. Since there are complex eigenvalues, from (4.28), the general solution is

$$\mathbf{x} = d_1\mathbf{b}_1 e^t + d_2\mathbf{b}_2 e^t,$$

where

$$\mathbf{b}_1 = \begin{pmatrix} 1 \\ -1 \end{pmatrix}\cos t - \begin{pmatrix} 0 \\ 1 \end{pmatrix}\sin t,$$

and

$$\mathbf{b}_2 = \begin{pmatrix} 1 \\ -1 \end{pmatrix}\sin t + \begin{pmatrix} 0 \\ 1 \end{pmatrix}\cos t.$$

Step 3: Satisfy the initial condition. Setting $t = 0$ in the general solution, we get that

$$d_1\begin{pmatrix} 1 \\ -1 \end{pmatrix} + d_2\begin{pmatrix} 0 \\ 1 \end{pmatrix} = \begin{pmatrix} 0 \\ 1 \end{pmatrix}.$$

This can be written in component form as

$$d_1 = 0$$
$$-d_1 + d_2 = 1.$$

So, $d_1 = 0$ and $d_2 = 1$.

Step 4: The resulting solution is

$$\mathbf{x}(t) = \left[\begin{pmatrix} 1 \\ -1 \end{pmatrix} \sin t + \begin{pmatrix} 0 \\ 1 \end{pmatrix} \cos t \right] e^t. \quad \blacksquare$$

Example 3 (defective matrix): Find the solution of the IVP:

$$\mathbf{x}' = \begin{pmatrix} 1 & 1 \\ -1 & 3 \end{pmatrix} \mathbf{x}, \quad \text{where} \quad \mathbf{x}(0) = \begin{pmatrix} -1 \\ 2 \end{pmatrix}.$$

Step 1: Find the eigenvalues and eigenvectors. Using the eigenvalue algorithm, from (4.14), you find the single eigenvalue $r = 2$, with eigenvector

$$\mathbf{a} = \begin{pmatrix} 1 \\ 1 \end{pmatrix}.$$

To find a second independent solution, from (4.30) we must solve

$$\begin{pmatrix} -1 & 1 \\ -1 & 1 \end{pmatrix} \mathbf{b} = \begin{pmatrix} 1 \\ 1 \end{pmatrix}.$$

A solution of this is

$$\mathbf{b} = \begin{pmatrix} 0 \\ 1 \end{pmatrix}.$$

Step 2: Find the general solution. Using (4.29), the general solution is

$$\mathbf{x} = c_1 \begin{pmatrix} 1 \\ 1 \end{pmatrix} e^{2t} + c_2 \left[t \begin{pmatrix} 1 \\ 1 \end{pmatrix} + \begin{pmatrix} 0 \\ 1 \end{pmatrix} \right] e^{2t}.$$

Step 3: Satisfy the initial condition. Setting $t = 0$ in the general solution, we get that

$$c_1 \begin{pmatrix} 1 \\ 1 \end{pmatrix} + c_2 \begin{pmatrix} 0 \\ 1 \end{pmatrix} = \begin{pmatrix} -1 \\ 2 \end{pmatrix}.$$

This gives us $c_1 = -1$ and $c_1 + c_2 = 2$. So, $c_2 = 3$.

Step 4: The resulting solution is

$$\mathbf{x} = \left[3t \begin{pmatrix} 1 \\ 1 \end{pmatrix} + \begin{pmatrix} -1 \\ 2 \end{pmatrix} \right] e^{2t}. \quad \blacksquare$$

Exercises

1. Find a general solution of the following differential equations.

a) $\mathbf{x}' = \begin{pmatrix} -1 & 6 \\ 1 & 0 \end{pmatrix} \mathbf{x}$

f) $\mathbf{x}' = \begin{pmatrix} 0 & -9 \\ 1 & 0 \end{pmatrix} \mathbf{x}$

b) $\mathbf{x}' = \begin{pmatrix} 0 & \frac{1}{4} \\ 1 & 0 \end{pmatrix} \mathbf{x}$

g) $\mathbf{x}' = \begin{pmatrix} 1 & 5 \\ -\frac{1}{4} & -1 \end{pmatrix} \mathbf{x}$

c) $\mathbf{x}' = \begin{pmatrix} 2 & 1 \\ 6 & 3 \end{pmatrix} \mathbf{x}$

h) $\mathbf{x}' = \begin{pmatrix} 1 & \frac{1}{4} \\ -5 & 0 \end{pmatrix} \mathbf{x}$

d) $\mathbf{x}' = \begin{pmatrix} 2 & 0 \\ -1 & 2 \end{pmatrix} \mathbf{x}$

i) $\mathbf{x}' = \begin{pmatrix} 1 & 3 \\ -1 & 3 \end{pmatrix} \mathbf{x}$

e) $\mathbf{x}' = \begin{pmatrix} -2 & 0 \\ 0 & -2 \end{pmatrix} \mathbf{x}$

j) $\mathbf{x}' = \begin{pmatrix} 0 & 0 \\ 0 & 0 \end{pmatrix} \mathbf{x}$

2. Find the solution of the initial value problem $\mathbf{x}' = \mathbf{A}\mathbf{x}$, where the differential equation is given in the previous problem, and the initial condition is $\mathbf{x}(0) = \begin{pmatrix} 4 \\ -1 \end{pmatrix}$.

3. A solution of $\mathbf{x}' = \mathbf{A}\mathbf{x}$ is given below. What are the eigenvalues of $\mathbf{A}$, and what are corresponding eigenvectors?

a) $\mathbf{x}(t) = \begin{pmatrix} 1 \\ 1 \end{pmatrix} e^{3t} + 2\begin{pmatrix} 1 \\ -1 \end{pmatrix} e^{t}$
   c) $\mathbf{x}(t) = \begin{pmatrix} e^{-2t} \\ 3e^{4t} \end{pmatrix}$

b) $\mathbf{x}(t) = \begin{pmatrix} 1 \\ 0 \end{pmatrix} e^{-5t} + \begin{pmatrix} 1 \\ 3 \end{pmatrix}$
   d) $\mathbf{x}(t) = \begin{pmatrix} e^{-8t} - e^{-t} \\ 3e^{-t} \end{pmatrix}$

4. The general solution (4.25), and the eigenvalue algorithm given in Section 4.3, can be used for any dimension n. In this exercise you are to find the general solution for the case of when $n = 3$.

a) $\mathbf{x}' = \begin{pmatrix} 0 & 1 & 1 \\ 1 & 0 & 1 \\ 1 & 1 & 0 \end{pmatrix} \mathbf{x}$

c) $\mathbf{x}' = \begin{pmatrix} -2 & 2 & 0 \\ 0 & 1 & 0 \\ 4 & 2 & -1 \end{pmatrix} \mathbf{x}$

b) $\mathbf{x}' = \begin{pmatrix} 1 & 1 & 2 \\ 0 & 2 & 0 \\ 0 & 1 & 1 \end{pmatrix} \mathbf{x}$

d) $\mathbf{x}' = \begin{pmatrix} -1 & 0 & 0 \\ 0 & 1 & 2 \\ 0 & 2 & -1 \end{pmatrix} \mathbf{x}$

4.6 ▪ Phase Plane

For differential equations involving 2×2 matrices, there are different ways the solution can be portrayed. As an example, the general solution of the differential equation

$$\mathbf{x}' = \begin{pmatrix} 2 & 1 \\ 1 & 2 \end{pmatrix} \mathbf{x},$$

is

$$\mathbf{x}(t) = c_1 \begin{pmatrix} 1 \\ 1 \end{pmatrix} e^{3t} + c_2 \begin{pmatrix} 1 \\ -1 \end{pmatrix} e^t, \tag{4.31}$$

or, in component form,

$$x(t) = c_1 e^{3t} + c_2 e^t,$$
$$y(t) = c_1 e^{3t} - c_2 e^t.$$

Given values for c_1 and c_2, using the component form, graphing the solution simply involves plotting x and y as functions of t. In contrast, with the vector version (4.31), the solution traces out a curve in the x,y-plane, with t being the parameter that generates the curve. The x,y-plane is referred to as the **phase plane**, and the curves that can be generated using (4.31) are known as **integral curves**.

4.6.1 ▪ Examples

Two Positive Eigenvalues.

The solution (4.31) involves two positive eigenvalues, $r_1 = 3$ and $r_2 = 1$. The resulting integral curves generated by (4.31) are shown in Table 4.1(a). Each curve corresponds to a specific choice for c_1 and c_2, and the arrows indicate the direction for increasing t. Together, the integral curves provide what is called a **phase portrait** for the equation. Any equation with two positive eigenvalues will produce a phase portrait that is roughly similar to the one for this example. A non-defective matrix with only one eigenvalue, which is positive, will also have a roughly similar phase plane, except the blue curves will be straight lines.

To explain how the phase portrait is constructed, you start by considering the $c_2 = 0$ and the $c_1 = 0$ cases first.

$c_2 = 0$: Since $\mathbf{x} = c_1 \begin{pmatrix} 1 \\ 1 \end{pmatrix} e^{3t}$, then $x = c_1 e^{3t}$ and $y = c_1 e^{3t}$. In other words, $y = x$. This is the red line in Table 4.1(a) with positive slope. Because e^{3t} increases with t, the solution moves outward, away from the origin. So, the arrows on the line point outward. Note that the line is determined by the eigenvector $\mathbf{a}_1 = \begin{pmatrix} 1 \\ 1 \end{pmatrix}$, and the direction on the line is determined by the positivity of the corresponding eigenvalue $r_1 = 3$.

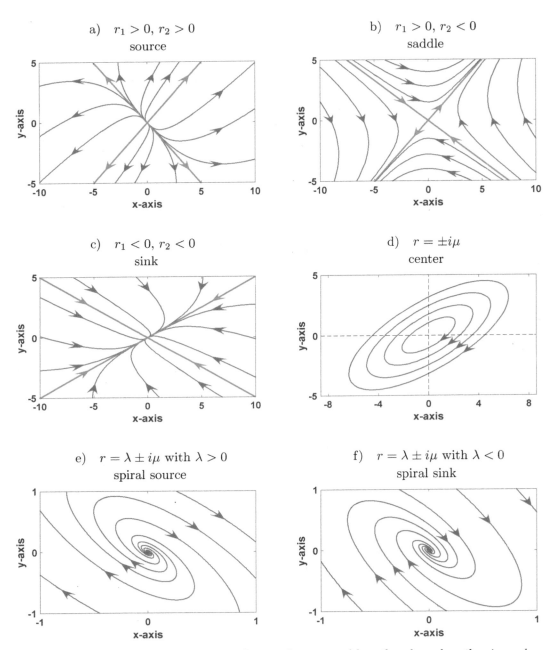

Table 4.1. *Examples of integral curves and how they depend on the eigenvalues of* **A**. *Each curve corresponds to a specific choice for the constants appearing in the general solution. The arrows indicate the direction for increasing t. It is assumed here that $\mu \neq 0$.*

$c_1 = 0$: Since $\mathbf{x} = c_2\begin{pmatrix} 1 \\ -1 \end{pmatrix}e^t$, then $x = c_2 e^t$ and $y = -c_2 e^t$. In other words, $y = -x$. This is the red line in Table 4.1(a) with negative slope. Because e^t increases with t, the solution moves outward, away from the origin. So, the arrows on the line point outward. Note that the line is determined by the eigenvector $\mathbf{a}_2 = \begin{pmatrix} 1 \\ -1 \end{pmatrix}$, and the direction on the line is determined by the positivity of the corresponding eigenvalue $r_2 = 1$.

$c_1 \neq 0$ and $c_2 \neq 0$: The general solution (4.31) consists of the addition of the two components we just considered, and some of the resulting integral curves are shown with the blue curves in Table 4.1(a). The arrows on the curves point outward, away from the origin, because both eigenvalues are positive. Also, since $r_1 > r_2$, each solution curve increases faster in the direction determined by $\mathbf{a}_1$, and this is the reason that the blue curves bend the way they do. Finally, note that if you run time backwards, so $t \to -\infty$, then, from (4.31), $\mathbf{x} \to \mathbf{0}$. That is why all of the blue curves look like they are emanating from the origin. ■

One Positive and One Negative Eigenvalue.

An example of this arises with the differential equation

$$\mathbf{x}' = \begin{pmatrix} -1 & 3 \\ 2 & 0 \end{pmatrix}\mathbf{x},$$

which has eigenvalues $r_1 = 2$ and $r_2 = -3$. The general solution is found to be

$$\mathbf{x}(t) = c_1\begin{pmatrix} 1 \\ 1 \end{pmatrix}e^{2t} + c_2\begin{pmatrix} 3 \\ -2 \end{pmatrix}e^{-3t}. \tag{4.32}$$

The resulting integral curves are shown in Table 4.1(b). Any equation with one positive, and one negative, eigenvalue will produce a phase portrait that is roughly similar to the one for this example.

As with the previous example, the phase portrait is constructed by considering the $c_2 = 0$ and the $c_1 = 0$ cases first.

$c_2 = 0$: Since $\mathbf{x} = c_1\begin{pmatrix} 1 \\ 1 \end{pmatrix}e^{2t}$, then $x = c_1 e^{2t}$ and $y = c_1 e^{2t}$. In other words, $y = x$. This is the red line in Table 4.1(b) with positive slope. Because e^{2t} increases with t, the solution moves outward, away from the origin. So, the arrows on the line point outward. Note that the line is determined by the eigenvector $\mathbf{a}_1 = \begin{pmatrix} 1 \\ 1 \end{pmatrix}$, and the outward direction on the line is determined by the positivity of the corresponding eigenvalue $r_1 = 2$.

$c_1 = 0$: Since $\mathbf{x} = c_2 \begin{pmatrix} 3 \\ -2 \end{pmatrix} e^{-3t}$, then $x = 3c_2 e^t$ and $y = -2c_2 e^t$. In other words, $y = -2x/3$. This is the red line in Table 4.1(b) with negative slope. Because e^{-3t} decreases with t, the solution moves inward, toward from the origin. So, the arrows on the line point inward. Note that the line is determined by the eigenvector $\mathbf{a}_2 = \begin{pmatrix} 3 \\ -2 \end{pmatrix}$, and the inward direction on the line is determined by the negativity of the corresponding eigenvalue $r_2 = -3$.

$c_1 \neq 0$ and $c_2 \neq 0$: The general solution (4.31) consists of the addition of the two components we just considered, and some of the resulting integral curves are shown with the blue curves in Table 4.1(b). To explain the arrows, the contribution of $c_2 \mathbf{a}_2 e^{-3t}$ goes to zero as t increases, but $c_1 \mathbf{a}_1 e^{2t}$ becomes unbounded. A consequence is that a solution curve will asymptotically approach the red line $y = x$.   ■

Two Negative Eigenvalues.

An example of this arises with the differential equation

$$\mathbf{x}' = \begin{pmatrix} -2 & 2 \\ \frac{1}{2} & -2 \end{pmatrix} \mathbf{x},$$

which has eigenvalues $r_1 = -1$ and $r_2 = -3$. The general solution is found to be

$$\mathbf{x}(t) = c_1 \begin{pmatrix} 2 \\ 1 \end{pmatrix} e^{-t} + c_2 \begin{pmatrix} -2 \\ 1 \end{pmatrix} e^{-3t}. \tag{4.33}$$

The resulting phase portrait is shown in Table 4.1(c). Any equation with two negative eigenvalues will produce a phase portrait that is roughly similar to the one for this example. A non-defective matrix with one eigenvalue, which is negative, will also have a roughly similar phase plane, except the blue curves will be straight lines.

The construction of the phase portrait is very similar to what was done for the two positive eigenvalues case. The principal difference is that the eigenvalues are now negative, so the movement along the integral curves is towards the origin.   ■

Imaginary Eigenvalues.

When the eigenvalues are imaginary, the integral curves are concentric ellipses centered at the origin (see Exercise 5). To demonstrate this, consider the differential equation

$$\mathbf{x}' = \begin{pmatrix} -2 & 4 \\ -2 & 2 \end{pmatrix} \mathbf{x}.$$

The eigenvalues are $r_1 = 2i$ and $r_2 = -2i$, and the general solution, from (4.28), is

$$\mathbf{x}(t) = d_1\left[\begin{pmatrix}2\\1\end{pmatrix}\cos 2t - \begin{pmatrix}0\\1\end{pmatrix}\sin 2t\right] + d_2\left[\begin{pmatrix}2\\1\end{pmatrix}\sin 2t + \begin{pmatrix}0\\1\end{pmatrix}\cos 2t\right]. \quad (4.34)$$

The ellipses generated by this solution are shown in Table 4.1(d).

The question is, is the movement around each ellipse clockwise, or counter-clockwise? This can be determined from the differential equation. For this example, $x' = -2x + 4y$, which means that when the ellipse crosses the y-axis (so $x = 0$), $x' = 4y$. Consequently, along the positive y-axis, $x' > 0$. The direction of the arrows must be consistent with this, and so the rotation is clockwise. ■

Complex Eigenvalues.

When the eigenvalues have nonzero real and imaginary parts the integral curves are spirals centered at the origin (see Exercise 5). As an example,

$$\mathbf{x}' = \begin{pmatrix}2 & 1\\-10 & 0\end{pmatrix}\mathbf{x},$$

has eigenvalues $r_1 = 1 + 3i$ and $r_2 = 1 - 3i$. The general solution, from (4.28), is

$$\mathbf{x}(t) = d_1\left[\begin{pmatrix}1\\-1\end{pmatrix}\cos 3t - \begin{pmatrix}0\\3\end{pmatrix}\sin 3t\right]e^t + d_2\left[\begin{pmatrix}1\\-1\end{pmatrix}\sin 3t + \begin{pmatrix}0\\3\end{pmatrix}\cos 3t\right]e^t.$$
$$(4.35)$$

Similarly, for the differential equation

$$\mathbf{x}' = \begin{pmatrix}-2 & 1\\-10 & 0\end{pmatrix}\mathbf{x},$$

the eigenvalues are $r_1 = -1 + 3i$ and $r_2 = -1 - 3i$. The general solution is

$$\mathbf{x}(t) = d_1\left[\begin{pmatrix}1\\1\end{pmatrix}\cos 3t - \begin{pmatrix}0\\3\end{pmatrix}\sin 3t\right]e^{-t} + d_2\left[\begin{pmatrix}1\\1\end{pmatrix}\sin 3t + \begin{pmatrix}0\\3\end{pmatrix}\cos 3t\right]e^{-t}.$$
$$(4.36)$$

The resulting integral curves for these two examples are shown in Table 4.1 (lower row). The one on the left comes from (4.35). The outward motion in this case is because the real part of the eigenvalue is positive. The one of the right comes from (4.36), and the inward motion is because the real part of the eigenvalue is negative.

The spiral curves seen in these two graphs are explainable from the formula for the solution. The solution contains $\cos \mu t$ and $\sin \mu t$ terms, and these are responsible for the motion around the origin. This is similar to what happens when $r = \pm i\mu$. However, these terms are multiplied by $e^{\lambda t}$, and this causes the radial distance from the origin to either increase, when $\lambda > 0$, or decrease, when $\lambda < 0$. ∎

4.6.2 ▪ Connection with an IVP

To illustrate the role the phase plane can play when solving an initial value problem, suppose the problem to solve is

$$\mathbf{x}' = \begin{pmatrix} -1 & 3 \\ 2 & 0 \end{pmatrix}\mathbf{x}, \tag{4.37}$$

where

$$\mathbf{x}(0) = \begin{pmatrix} 6 \\ -3 \end{pmatrix}. \tag{4.38}$$

This is the same differential equation used for the phase plane example in Table 4.1(b), and the general solution is given in (4.32). From the initial condition, the solution is found to be

$$\mathbf{x}(t) = \frac{3}{5}\begin{pmatrix} 1 \\ 1 \end{pmatrix}e^{2t} + \frac{9}{5}\begin{pmatrix} 3 \\ -2 \end{pmatrix}e^{-3t}. \tag{4.39}$$

The plot of this curve in the phase plane is shown in Figure 4.1. The integral curves for the differential equation, which appear in Table 4.1, are also included in the figure. As this shows, the solution of the initial value problem is simply a portion of one of its integral curves. The starting

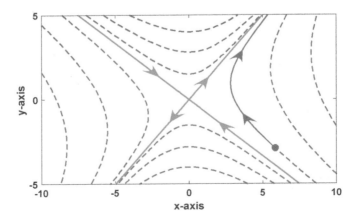

Figure 4.1. *The solid blue curve is the solution (4.39), and the solid blue dot is the location of the initial condition (4.38). The dashed blue curves, and the red lines, are integral curves for (4.37).*

point is determined by the initial condition, and the resulting solution follows the respective integral curve for increasing t.

The above observation is true in general. Namely, the integral curves in Table 4.1 are illustrations of the various solutions you can get with the respective differential equation. Which curve, or how much of the curve, you get depends on the location of the initial condition.

Exercises

1. Phase portraits are shown in Figure 4.2, with arrows on some of the curves. Do, or answer, the following: (i) Draw arrows on the other curves. (ii) What properties of the eigenvalues result in the integral curves shown in the phase portrait? (iii) Three different initial conditions are shown by the black dots. For each one, sketch the solution for the resulting IVP.

2. The eigenvalues for the following equations are real-valued. You are to sketch the phase portrait as follows: (i) Draw the (red) lines that are determined from the eigenvectors, and include the four arrows. (ii) In each of the four quadrants determined by the red lines, include two integral curves, with arrows.

   a) $\mathbf{x}' = \begin{pmatrix} 3 & -1 \\ -1 & 3 \end{pmatrix} \mathbf{x}$ c) $\mathbf{x}' = \begin{pmatrix} 3 & 2 \\ -4 & -3 \end{pmatrix} \mathbf{x}$

   b) $\mathbf{x}' = \begin{pmatrix} -6 & 3 \\ -4 & 1 \end{pmatrix} \mathbf{x}$ d) $\mathbf{x}' = \begin{pmatrix} 4 & -2 \\ 3 & -3 \end{pmatrix} \mathbf{x}$

3. The eigenvalues for the following equations are imaginary. You are to sketch the phase portrait as follows: draw three concentric ellipses centered at the origin with arrows indicating the direction of motion. It is useful to know that for $\mathbf{A}$ given in (4.4), when the eigenvalues are imaginary, the elliptical integral curves are tilted right, as in Table 4.1(d), if $ab < 0$, and they are tilted left, as in Figure 4.2(e), if $ab > 0$.

   a) $\mathbf{x}' = \begin{pmatrix} -1 & 2 \\ -2 & 1 \end{pmatrix} \mathbf{x}$ c) $\mathbf{x}' = \begin{pmatrix} 2 & 1 \\ -6 & -2 \end{pmatrix} \mathbf{x}$

   b) $\mathbf{x}' = \begin{pmatrix} 3 & 6 \\ -3 & -3 \end{pmatrix} \mathbf{x}$ d) $\mathbf{x}' = \begin{pmatrix} -3 & -1 \\ 12 & 3 \end{pmatrix} \mathbf{x}$

4. Spirals are either left (sinistral) or right (dextral) handed as shown in Figure 4.3. For the matrix $\mathbf{A}$ given in (4.4), assume the eigenvalues are $\lambda \pm i\mu$, with $\mu \neq 0$.

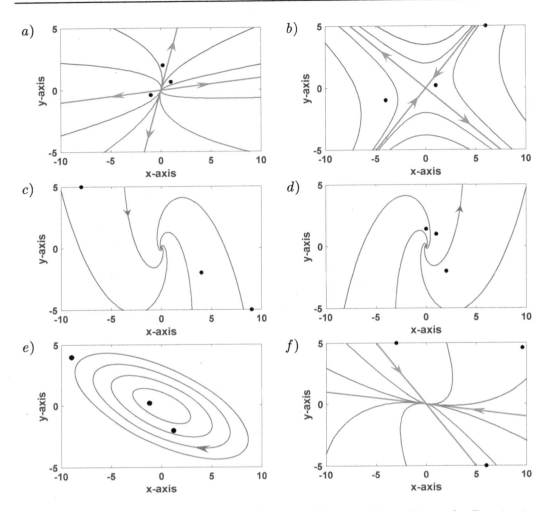

Figure 4.2. *Integral curves, and location of three initial conditions, for Exercise 1.*

   a) Suppose that $\lambda > 0$. Using the same approach used to determine
      clockwise or counter-clockwise motion for imaginary eigenvalues,
      explain why a spiral integral curve is left-handed if $b < 0$ and it is
      right-handed if $b > 0$. Also, explain why this reverses if $\lambda < 0$.

   b) Determine if b for Figure 4.2(c) is positive or negative. What about
      for Figure 4.2(d)?

5. This exercise involves the derivation of the formulas for the elliptical
   and spiral curves obtained when the eigenvalues are complex-valued.
   The matrix $\mathbf{A}$ is given in (4.4), and it is assumed that $\mu \neq 0$.

   a) Assuming that d_1 and d_2 are not both zero, from (4.28) and the
      identity $\cos^2(\mu t) + \sin^2(\mu t) = 1$, show that

$$p_2^2 x^2 - 2p_1 p_2 xy + (p_1^2 + q_1^2)y^2 = k^2 e^{2\lambda t},$$

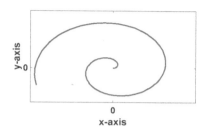 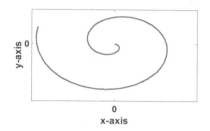

Figure 4.3. *Left-handed (on the left) and right-handed (on the right) spirals.*

where $p_1 = b(\lambda - a)$, $p_2 = (\lambda - a)^2 + \mu^2$, $q_1 = -b\mu$, and k is a positive constant.

b) In the equation in part (a), if $\lambda = 0$ you get an ellipse centered at the origin. Explain why the movement along the ellipse is clockwise if $b > 0$ and it is counter-clockwise if $b < 0$.

c) Show that to have a circular curve requires $b \neq 0$ and $c = -b$.

d) Explain why you get a spiral in the case of when $\lambda \neq 0$.

4.7 • Stability

The phase plane can be useful for visualizing stability or instability of a steady state solution. To explain how, recall from Section 2.4 that a **steady state** is a constant that satisfies the differential equation. So, for the equation $\mathbf{x}' = \mathbf{A}\mathbf{x}$, a steady state is a constant vector $\mathbf{x}_s$ that satisfies $\mathbf{A}\mathbf{x}_s = \mathbf{0}$. To avoid complications, it will be assumed that $\mathbf{A}$ is invertible, which means that the only steady state solution is $\mathbf{x}_s = \mathbf{0}$. It is useful to know that $\mathbf{A}$ is invertible if, and only if, $r = 0$ is not an eigenvalue for $\mathbf{A}$.

The definitions of unstable and asymptotically stable are effectively the same as in Section 2.4. Namely, a steady state $\mathbf{x}_s$ is **asymptotically stable** if any initial value $\mathbf{x}(0)$ chosen near $\mathbf{x}_s$ results in

$$\lim_{t \to \infty} \mathbf{x}(t) = \mathbf{x}_s. \tag{4.40}$$

The steady state is **unstable** if, no matter how close to $\mathbf{x}_s$ you restrict the choice for $\mathbf{x}(0)$, it is always possible to find an initial value $\mathbf{x}(0)$ that results in the solution $\mathbf{x}(t)$ becoming unbounded as t increases.

It is easy to determine stability using the phase plane. For example, in Table 4.1(a), when $r_1 > 0$ and $r_2 > 0$, the arrows on the integral curves indicate movement out away from the origin. Consequently, this is an example of when $\mathbf{x}_s = \mathbf{0}$ is unstable. Conversely, when $r_1 < 0$ and $r_2 < 0$, the flow in towards the origin, and this means $\mathbf{x}_s = \mathbf{0}$ is asymptotically stable. In fact, looking at the various possibilities in Table 4.1, you conclude that if $\mathbf{A}$ has an eigenvalue with $\text{Re}(r) > 0$, then the steady state in unstable. Similarly, if the eigenvalues of $\mathbf{A}$ are both negative, or if $\text{Re}(r) < 0$, then the steady state is asymptotically stable.

The conclusions in the previous paragraph were made using the phase portraits in Table 4.1. For those that prefer more rigorous derivations, then the formulas for the general solutions given in Section 4.5 can be used.

Our classification of a steady state being unstable or asymptotically stable does not include what happens when the eigenvalues are imaginary. As shown in Table 4.1(d), the solution does not decay to zero, or blowup, but simply encircles the origin. In this case, the steady state is said to be **neutrally stable**.

The other case we are missing here is what happens when the matrix is defective. From (4.29), the conclusion we had earlier still holds. Namely, if $r < 0$, then we have asymptotically stability, and if $r > 0$, then we have instability.

The above discussion is summarized in the following theorem.

Stability Theorem for a Linear System. *For $\mathbf{x}' = \mathbf{A}\mathbf{x}$, if $r = 0$ is not an eigenvalue for $\mathbf{A}$, then the following hold:*

1. *If all of the eigenvalues of $\mathbf{A}$ satisfy $\mathrm{Re}(r) < 0$, then $\mathbf{x}_s = \mathbf{0}$ is an asymptotically stable steady state.*

2. *If $\mathbf{A}$ has one or more eigenvalues with $\mathrm{Re}(r) > 0$, then $\mathbf{x}_s = \mathbf{0}$ is an unstable steady state.*

3. *If the eigenvalues of $\mathbf{A}$ are imaginary, then $\mathbf{x}_s = \mathbf{0}$ is a neutrally stable steady state.*

It is worth pointing out that the first two conclusions in the above theorem hold when $\mathbf{A}$ is $n \times n$. The third one also holds for the $n \times n$ case if you make the additional assumption that $\mathbf{A}$ is not defective. For those who might be wondering what happens when $r = 0$ is an eigenvalue, the solution of $\mathbf{A}\mathbf{x} = \mathbf{0}$ is no longer just $\mathbf{x}_s = \mathbf{0}$. In fact, any and all eigenvectors for $r = 0$ are steady state solutions. It is possible to examine the various cases that arise in this situation related to stability, but this will not be considered in this text.

In addition to their stability, steady states are often identified by the geometric properties of the solution near the steady state. So, for example, because of the outward direction of the flow in Figure 4.1(a), the steady state is called a **source**. In contrast, because of the inward flow in Figure 4.1(c), the steady state is called a **sink**. For similar reasons, the flow in Figure 4.1(e) is a **spiral source**, and the one in Figure 4.1(f) is a **spiral sink**. Finally, the steady state in Figure 4.1(b) is a **saddle**, and the one in Figure 4.1(d) is a **center**.

Example 1: Determine the stability of the steady state $\mathbf{x}_s = \mathbf{0}$ for

$$\mathbf{x}' = \begin{pmatrix} 1 & 3 \\ 2 & -4 \end{pmatrix} \mathbf{x}.$$

Answer: The characteristic equation for the matrix is $r^2 + 3r - 10 = 0$, and from this it follows that the eigenvalues are $r = -5$ and $r = 2$. Given that there is at least one eigenvalue that is positive, $\mathbf{x}_s = \mathbf{0}$ is unstable. Moreover, since it has one positive, and one negative, eigenvalue, the steady state is a saddle point. ∎

Example 2: Determine the stability of the steady state $\mathbf{x}_s = \mathbf{0}$ for

$$\mathbf{x}' = \begin{pmatrix} -1 & -2 \\ 2 & 0 \end{pmatrix}\mathbf{x}.$$

Answer: The characteristic equation for the matrix is $r^2 + r + 4 = 0$, and from this it follows that the eigenvalues are $r = \frac{1}{2}(-1 \pm i\sqrt{15})$. Given that both have negative real part, then $\mathbf{x}_s = \mathbf{0}$ is asymptotically stable. Moreover, since the eigenvalues are complex with negative real part, the steady state is a spiral sink. ∎

Example 3: Find the steady state, and determine its stability for

$$\mathbf{u}' = \begin{pmatrix} 1 & 1 \\ 1 & -1 \end{pmatrix}\mathbf{u} + \begin{pmatrix} 2 \\ 4 \end{pmatrix}. \tag{4.41}$$

Steady State: Since a steady state is a constant vector that satisfies the differential equation, then we require that

$$\begin{pmatrix} 1 & 1 \\ 1 & -1 \end{pmatrix}\mathbf{u} = -\begin{pmatrix} 2 \\ 4 \end{pmatrix}.$$

Solving this for $\mathbf{u}$, one finds the steady state

$$\mathbf{u}_s = \begin{pmatrix} -3 \\ 1 \end{pmatrix}.$$

Stability: Letting $\mathbf{u} = \mathbf{u}_s + \mathbf{x}$, and substituting this into the differential equation, one finds that $\mathbf{x}' = \mathbf{A}\mathbf{x}$, where $\mathbf{A}$ is the matrix in (4.41). If $\mathbf{x}_s = \mathbf{0}$ is unstable, then so is $\mathbf{u}_s$. Similarly, if $\mathbf{x}_s = \mathbf{0}$ is asymptotically stable, then $\mathbf{u}_s$ asymptotically stable. Now, the characteristic equation for $\mathbf{A}$ is $r^2 - 2 = 0$. From this, the eigenvalues are found to be $r = \pm\sqrt{2}$. Given that one is positive, $\mathbf{x}_s$ is unstable, and therefore $\mathbf{u}_s$ is unstable. Moreover, since it has one positive, and one negative, eigenvalue, $\mathbf{u}_s$ is a saddle point. ∎

Exercises

1. Determine whether $\mathbf{x}_s = \mathbf{0}$ is an asymptotically stable, unstable, or neutrally stable steady state for the following differential equations. Also, state whether the steady state is a sink, source, spiral sink, spiral source, saddle, or center.

a) $\mathbf{x}' = \begin{pmatrix} -1 & 6 \\ 1 & 0 \end{pmatrix} \mathbf{x}$

d) $\mathbf{x}' = \begin{pmatrix} 2 & 1 \\ 3 & 4 \end{pmatrix} \mathbf{x}$

g) $\mathbf{x}' = \begin{pmatrix} 2 & 5 \\ -5 & -6 \end{pmatrix} \mathbf{x}$

b) $\mathbf{x}' = \begin{pmatrix} 1 & 2 \\ -3 & -4 \end{pmatrix} \mathbf{x}$

e) $\mathbf{x}' = \begin{pmatrix} -1 & -1 \\ 6 & -6 \end{pmatrix} \mathbf{x}$

h) $\mathbf{x}' = \begin{pmatrix} 0 & -9 \\ 1 & 0 \end{pmatrix} \mathbf{x}$

c) $\mathbf{x}' = \begin{pmatrix} 3 & 1 \\ 1 & 3 \end{pmatrix} \mathbf{x}$

f) $\mathbf{x}' = \begin{pmatrix} 1 & \frac{1}{4} \\ -5 & 0 \end{pmatrix} \mathbf{x}$

i) $\mathbf{x}' = \begin{pmatrix} 1 & -4 \\ 1 & -1 \end{pmatrix} \mathbf{x}$

2. Write the following as $\mathbf{x}' = \mathbf{A}\mathbf{x}$, and then determine whether $\mathbf{x}_s = \mathbf{0}$ is an asymptotically stable, unstable, or neutrally stable steady state.

   a) The simple harmonic oscillator given in (3.49).

   b) The damped oscillator given in (3.57).

3. Find the steady state $\mathbf{u}_s$, and determine its stability, for the following differential equations. Also, state whether the steady state is a sink, source, spiral sink, spiral source, saddle, or center.

a) $\mathbf{u}' = \begin{pmatrix} 1 & 3 \\ 0 & -1 \end{pmatrix} \mathbf{u} + \begin{pmatrix} 1 \\ 0 \end{pmatrix}$

c) $\mathbf{u}' = \begin{pmatrix} -3 & -1 \\ 2 & -1 \end{pmatrix} \mathbf{u} - \begin{pmatrix} 1 \\ 2 \end{pmatrix}$

b) $\mathbf{u}' = \begin{pmatrix} -2 & 1 \\ 1 & -2 \end{pmatrix} \mathbf{u} + \begin{pmatrix} -2 \\ 1 \end{pmatrix}$

d) $\mathbf{u}' = \begin{pmatrix} 1 & -1 \\ 4 & 1 \end{pmatrix} \mathbf{u} + \begin{pmatrix} 1 \\ -1 \end{pmatrix}$

4. This exercise contains useful information to determine the stability of $\mathbf{x}_s = \mathbf{0}$ without having to calculate eigenvalues. Assume that $\mathbf{A}$ is given in (4.4) and that $\det(\mathbf{A}) \neq 0$. Also, the *trace of a matrix* is the sum of the numbers on the diagonal. The formula is $\mathrm{tr}(\mathbf{A}) = a + d$.

   a) Show that the eigenvalues of $\mathbf{A}$ are $\frac{1}{2}\left[\mathrm{tr}(\mathbf{A}) \pm \sqrt{[\mathrm{tr}(\mathbf{A})]^2 - 4\det(\mathbf{A})}\right]$.

   b) Explain why $r = 0$ is not an eigenvalue for $\mathbf{A}$.

   c) Show that if $\mathrm{tr}(\mathbf{A}) > 0$, then $\mathbf{x}_s$ is unstable.

   d) Show that if $\det(\mathbf{A}) < 0$, then $\mathbf{x}_s$ is unstable.

   e) Show that if $\mathrm{tr}(\mathbf{A}) = 0$, and $\det(\mathbf{A}) > 0$, then $\mathbf{x}_s$ is neutrally stable.

   f) Show that if $\mathrm{tr}(\mathbf{A}) < 0$ and $\det(\mathbf{A}) > 0$, then $\mathbf{x}_s$ is asymptotically stable.

Chapter 5

Nonlinear Systems

This chapter considers problems that involve two first-order ordinary differential equations, at least one of which is nonlinear. These problems are usually difficult enough that finding a formula for the solution is not possible. Consequently, most of the chapter does not concern solving these problems, but instead concentrates on developing ways to determine the properties of the solution. What this means exactly will be explained as the methods are derived. We begin with examples that illustrate the problems we will be considering.

Example 1: Pendulum

The equation for the angular deflection of a pendulum is (see Figure 5.1)

$$\ell\frac{d^2\theta}{dt^2} = -g\sin\theta, \qquad (5.1)$$

where the initial angle $\theta(0)$ and the initial angular velocity $\theta'(0)$ are assumed to be given. Also, ℓ is the length of the pendulum and g is the gravitational acceleration constant. Introducing the angular velocity $v = \theta'$ then the equation can be written as the first-order system

$$\theta' = v, \qquad (5.2)$$
$$v' = -\alpha\sin\theta, \qquad (5.3)$$

where $\alpha = g/\ell$. Although (5.2) is linear, (5.3) is nonlinear because of the $\sin\theta$ term. Consequently, together (5.2), (5.3) form a nonlinear first-order system for θ and v. ■

Introduction to Differential Equations, M. H. Holmes, 2020

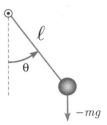

Figure 5.1. *Angular deflection of a pendulum.*

Example 2: Measles

A model for the spread of a disease, like measles, is

$$\frac{dS}{dt} = \alpha N - (\beta I + \alpha)S,$$

$$\frac{dI}{dt} = \beta IS - (\alpha + \gamma)I.$$

In these equations, $S(t)$ is the number of people susceptible to the disease, and $I(t)$ is number that are ill. The nonlinearity, which is due to the term IS, appears in both equations. ■

The equations for the pendulum and the spread of measles are not solvable using elementary functions. What is possible it to ask questions about the solution that are significant and answerable. As an example, with measles, a reasonable question would be: what would it take to eliminate the disease from the population? This requires that $I \to 0$ as $t \to \infty$ (and the faster this happens the better). In more mathematical terms, we want $I = 0$ to be an asymptotically stable steady state. How to modify the stability of $I = 0$, with the goal of quickly eliminating the disease, will be considered in Section 5.2.2.

A question arising with the pendulum is, does it ever stop moving? Given the physical assumptions used in the derivation of the equation it is reasonable to expect that it does not stop and, in fact, the solution is expected to be periodic. So, we would like to know if it is possible to show that the solution is periodic, and in the process determine the period (without actually solving the problem).

5.1 ▪ Non-Linear Systems

The problems in this chapter can be written in component form as

$$u' = f(u, v), \tag{5.4}$$

$$v' = g(u, v). \tag{5.5}$$

In these equations, $u(t)$ and $v(t)$ are the dependent variables, and f and g are given functions of u and v. It is assumed that the equations are *autonomous*, which means that f and g do not depend explicitly on t.

The vector form of (5.4), (5.5) is

$$\frac{d\mathbf{y}}{dt} = \mathbf{f}(\mathbf{y}), \tag{5.6}$$

where

$$\mathbf{y} = \begin{pmatrix} u \\ v \end{pmatrix}, \quad \text{and} \quad \mathbf{f} = \begin{pmatrix} f(u,v) \\ g(u,v) \end{pmatrix}.$$

For an initial value problem, an initial condition of form

$$\mathbf{y}(0) = \begin{pmatrix} u_0 \\ v_0 \end{pmatrix}. \tag{5.7}$$

would also be given.

Example: For the nonlinear system

$$u' = v - \frac{1}{2}u, \tag{5.8}$$

$$v' = -\frac{1}{2}v + 2u(2 - u^2), \tag{5.9}$$

we have that

$$\mathbf{f} = \begin{pmatrix} v - \frac{1}{2}u \\ -\frac{1}{2}v + 2u(2 - u^2) \end{pmatrix}.$$

There are no known mathematical methods that can be used to find the solution of this system (by hand). However, it is easily solved using a computer, and four example curves are shown in Figure 5.2. In all four cases, the solution ends up at one of two points. In this chapter we will not attempt to find the solution curves but we will be very interested in determining these two points and finding the reason why the solution approaches them. ∎

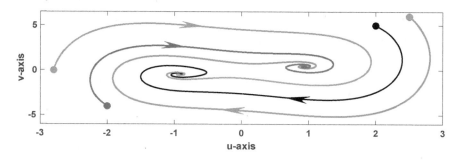

Figure 5.2. *Solution curves of (5.8), (5.8) in the u,v-plane for four different initial conditions (shown with the solid dots). The arrows indicate the direction for increasing t.*

5.1.1 ▪ Steady-State Solutions

For $\mathbf{y}' = \mathbf{f}(\mathbf{y})$, a **steady state solution** $\mathbf{y}_s$ is a constant vector that satisfies $\mathbf{f}(\mathbf{y}_s) = \mathbf{0}$. In component form, the requirements are that

$$f(u_s, v_s) = 0, \tag{5.10}$$
$$g(u_s, v_s) = 0. \tag{5.11}$$

Solving for u_s and v_s is not straightforward. In fact, given that $f(u, v)$ and $g(u, v)$ can be almost anything, there is no method that always works for solving these equations. The recommendation is to pick one of the equations, and use it to solve for u in terms of v, or v in terms of u. The equation to pick for this is usually the one that is easiest to solve. This solution is then substituted into the other equation, and you then have one equation and one unknown (see Example 1). It is also not uncommon that you need to be opportunistic, and take advantage of certain terms in the equation to help simply the equations (see Example 2).

Example 1: Find the steady states of

$$\frac{du}{dt} = 3 - u - v - uv,$$
$$\frac{dv}{dt} = uv - 2v.$$

Answer: The equations to solve are

$$3 - u - v - uv = 0,$$
$$uv - 2v = 0.$$

The second equation looks the easiest to work with. Factoring it as $v(u - 2) = 0$, we get two solutions: $v = 0$ and $u = 2$. Taking $v = 0$, then from the first equation we get that $u = 3$. For $u = 2$, from the first equation we get that $v = 1/3$. Therefore, we have found two steady states: $(u_s, v_s) = (3, 0)$, and $(u_s, v_s) = (2, 1/3)$. ∎

Example 2: Assuming α is a positive constant, find the steady states of

$$\frac{du}{dt} = 1 - (1 + \alpha)u + u^2 v,$$
$$\frac{dv}{dt} = u - u^2 v.$$

Answer: The equations to solve are

$$1 - (1 + \alpha)u + u^2 v = 0,$$
$$u - u^2 v = 0.$$

It is possible to use the approach from the previous example, but it is easier to look a little closer at these equations. They both contain the term $u^2 v$. In fact, from the second equation $u^2 v = u$. Using this information in the first equation, we get that $u = 1/\alpha$. From the second equation, it follows that $v = \alpha$. Therefore, we have found that the only steady state is: $(u_s, v_s) = (1/\alpha, \alpha)$. ∎

Example 3: Find the steady states of

$$x' = x - x^2 - xy,$$
$$y' = 2y - y^2 - 3xy.$$

Answer: The equations to solve are

$$x - x^2 - xy = 0,$$
$$2y - y^2 - 3xy = 0.$$

Factoring the first equation as $x(1 - x - y) = 0$, then either $x = 0$ or $x = 1 - y$. If $x = 0$, then from the second equation $y = 0$ or $y = 2$, giving us the two steady states $(0, 0)$ and $(0, 2)$. When $x = 1 - y$, the second equation reduces to $y(1 - 2y) = 0$, which has solutions $y = 0$ and $y = 1/2$. This gives us two more steady states, which are $(1/2, 1/2)$ and $(1, 0)$. ∎

Example 4: For the system

$$x' = x - y,$$
$$y' = (x - y)^3,$$

the steady states are any points that satisfy $y = x$. ∎

We are going to avoid the situation in Example 4. Specifically, in the problems we will consider, there can be multiple steady states, but they are discrete points as in Examples 1, 2, and 3. The way this will be stated is that the **steady states are isolated**, which means that there is a nonzero distance d so that the distance between any two steady states for the problem is at least d.

Exercises

1. Write the following as $\mathbf{y}' = \mathbf{f}(\mathbf{y})$, making sure to identify the entries in $\mathbf{y}$ and $\mathbf{f}$. If initial conditions are given, write them as $\mathbf{y}(0) = \mathbf{y}_0$.

a) $u' = u^2 - v$
   $v' = 2u - 3v$

b) $u' = u^2 + v^2$
   $2v' = \sin(u)$

c) $u' = e^u - v$
   $v' = uv$
   $u(0) = -1,\ v(0) = 0$

d) Van der Pol oscillator
   $u'' + (1 - u^2)u' + u = 0$

e) Toda oscillator
   $u'' + e^u - 1 = 0$

f) Duffing oscillator
   $u'' + u + u^3 = 0$
   $u(0) = 1,\ u'(0) = -1$

g) Michaelis-Menten system
   $S' = -k_1 ES + k_{-1}(E_0 - E),$
   $E' = -k_1 ES + (k_2 + k_{-1})(E_0 - E)$
   $S(0) = 1,\ E(0) = 2$

h) Predator-prey
   $x' = ax - bxy$
   $y' = -cy + dxy$

i) Projectile (nonuniform field)
   $$y'' = -\frac{gR^2}{(R + y)^2}$$
   $y(0) = 0,\ y'(0) = 3$

j) Orbital motion
   $$r'' = \frac{\alpha^2}{r^3} - \frac{\mu}{r^2}$$
   $r(0) = 1,\ r'(0) = 2$

2. Find the steady state solutions of the following.

a) $\begin{cases} u' = 1 - 2u - v - uv \\ v' = 3uv - v \end{cases}$

b) $\begin{cases} u' = v - u^2 \\ v' = v + u^3 \end{cases}$

c) $\begin{cases} u' = 4 - uv^2 \\ v' = -v + uv^2 \end{cases}$

d) $\begin{cases} S' = 2S - S^2 - \frac{2SP}{1+S} \\ P' = \frac{2SP}{1+S} - P \end{cases}$

e) $\begin{cases} S' = -IS + 5 - I - S \\ I' = IS - I \end{cases}$

f) $\begin{cases} s' = c - s^2 \\ c' = 1 + sc \end{cases}$

g) $\begin{cases} x' = \sin(y) + \sin(x) \\ y' = 3y^2 + x^4 \end{cases}$

h) $\begin{cases} x' = xy \\ y' = (2 - x - y)(1 + y) \end{cases}$

5.2 ▪ Stability

The question considered now is central to this chapter, and it is whether a steady state is achievable. What this means is that the steady state is asymptotically stable. To explain how we are going to determine stability, consider the problem of solving

$$x' = x - x^2 - xy, \tag{5.12}$$

$$y' = 2y - y^2 - 3xy. \tag{5.13}$$

This is the problem from Example 3 in the previous section, and we found that there are four steady states: $(0, 0)$, $(0, 2)$, $(1, 0)$, and $(1/2, 1/2)$. One approach for providing insight about stability is to solve the problem numerically. This is easy to do, and two computed solution curves are shown in Figure 5.3. The curves are consistent with what is expected if

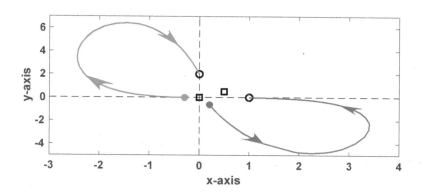

Figure 5.3. *Solution of (5.12),(5.13) for different initial conditions. The blue curve approaches the steady state $(1,0)$, while the red curve approaches the steady state $(0,2)$.*

$(0,2)$ and $(1,0)$ are asymptotically stable. Also, since both curves start near $(0,0)$, yet move away from it, it would not be a surprise to find out that $(0,0)$ is an unstable steady state.

Solving the problem numerically is so easy that it possible to solve the problem for many different initial conditions, and check if the solution approaches one of the various steady states. The results from such a calculation are shown in Figure 5.4. What is found is that there are, apparently, two asymptotically stable steady states, $(0,2)$ and $(1,0)$. The calculations also identity the regions for the initial conditions that result in the solution ending up at the respective steady state. The two regions determined from this computation are called the *domain of attraction* for the respective steady state.

Our goal is not to be able to determine the shaded regions shown in Figure 5.4, but, rather, to show that there is a small region around the respective steady state with the same property as the shaded region. Namely, for any initial condition in that small region, the solution of the resulting IVP will end up at the steady state. In this case, the steady state is said to be **asymptotically stable**. What we are doing now is the two dimensional version of what we did in Section 2.4, and the nonlinear version of what was done in Section 4.7.

5.2.1 ▪ Derivation of the Stability Conditions

The differential equation is $\mathbf{y}' = \mathbf{f}(\mathbf{y})$, and this can be written in component form as

$$u' = f(u,v), \tag{5.14}$$
$$v' = g(u,v). \tag{5.15}$$

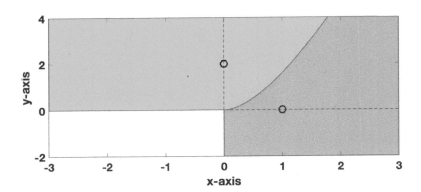

Figure 5.4. *An initial condition $(x(0), y(0))$ located in one of the shaded regions results in the solution of (5.12),(5.13) ending up at the steady state in that shaded region. The two steady states are shown by the dark circles.*

Assume that (u_s, v_s) is a steady-state, which means that u_s and v_s are constants that satisfy

$$f(u_s, v_s) = 0,$$
$$g(u_s, v_s) = 0.$$

The reason for considering stability comes from this question: If we start the solution near (u_s, v_s), what happens?

There are three possible conclusions coming from this question: the steady state is unstable, it is asymptotically stable, or it is neutrally stable. What these are can be explained using a ball and bowl (see Figure 5.5). The force on the ball is gravity. For the bowl, the steady state is at the bottom, and for the inverted bowl it is at the top. For the inverted bowl, if you release the ball from rest, no matter where you place it (other than exactly at the top), the ball will roll away. The conclusion is that the steady state is **unstable**. For the bowl, you can control how far the ball will get from the steady state (the bottom) by placing it close to the bottom and giving it only a small initial velocity. Consequently, the steady state is *stable*. Because the only force is gravity, the ball will roll around in the bowl forever. This means the steady state is **neutrally stable**. If the problem also includes damping, such as friction, then the ball will slow down and eventually come to rest at the bottom. In this case the steady state is **asymptotically stable**. Note that including

Figure 5.5. *Ball in a bowl, on the left, and a ball on an inverted bowl, on the right.*

damping for the inverted bowl will not change the fact that the top is an unstable steady state.

For those that prefer a more mathematical definition, the idea underlying asymptotic stability is that if $\mathbf{y}(0)$ is any point close to the steady state $\mathbf{y}_s$, then

$$\lim_{t \to \infty} \mathbf{y}(t) = \mathbf{y}_s. \tag{5.16}$$

As stated above, a steady state is stable if you can control how far the solution gets from $\mathbf{y}_s$ by picking $\mathbf{y}(0)$ close to $\mathbf{y}_s$. Specifically, given any $\varepsilon > 0$, you can find a $\delta > 0$ so that if $||\mathbf{y}(0) - \mathbf{y}_s|| < \delta$, then $||\mathbf{y}(t) - \mathbf{y}_s|| < \varepsilon$. If this is not possible then $\mathbf{y}_s$ is unstable. If $\mathbf{y}_s$ is stable, and (5.16) holds, then it is asymptotically stable. Otherwise it is said to be neutrally stable. Note that this version of the definition of stability requires that u and v have the same physical dimensions so that $||\mathbf{y}|| = \sqrt{u^2 + v^2}$ is defined.

To answer the stability question, assume that the initial position $(u(0), v(0))$ is very close to (u_s, v_s). To determine what happens, we will use what is called the linear approximation in multivariable calculus. This states that if $f(u, v)$ and $g(u, v)$ are differentiable at (u_s, v_s), then each can approximated using their respective tangent plane. In particular,

$$f(u, v) \approx f(u_s, v_s) + f_u(u_s, v_s)(u - u_s) + f_v(u_s, v_s)(v - v_s),$$
$$g(u, v) \approx g(u_s, v_s) + g_u(u_s, v_s)(u - u_s) + g_v(u_s, v_s)(v - v_s).$$

In the above expressions, $f_u = \frac{\partial f}{\partial u}$, $f_v = \frac{\partial f}{\partial v}$, $g_u = \frac{\partial g}{\partial u}$, $g_v = \frac{\partial g}{\partial v}$. It should be pointed out that this approximation is also a direct consequence of Taylor's theorem, and this can be used to derive more accurate approximations if needed.

By assumption, $f(u_s, v_s) = 0$ and $g(u_s, v_s) = 0$. Consequently, the **linear approximation of** (5.14) **and** (5.15) **near the steady state** is

$$u' = f_u(u_s, v_s)(u - u_s) + f_v(u_s, v_s)(v - v_s),$$
$$v' = g_u(u_s, v_s)(u - u_s) + g_v(u_s, v_s)(v - v_s).$$

This can be written in system form as

$$\mathbf{y}' = \mathbf{J}(\mathbf{y} - \mathbf{y}_s), \tag{5.17}$$

where

$$\mathbf{y} = \begin{pmatrix} u \\ v \end{pmatrix}, \quad \mathbf{y}_s = \begin{pmatrix} u_s \\ v_s \end{pmatrix},$$

and

$$\mathbf{J}_s = \begin{pmatrix} f_u(u_s, v_s) & f_v(u_s, v_s) \\ g_u(u_s, v_s) & g_v(u_s, v_s) \end{pmatrix}.$$

The matrix $\mathbf{J}_s$ is known as the **Jacobian matrix** of $\mathbf{f}$ evaluated at $\mathbf{y}_s$.

To put the problem into the form covered in the last chapter, let $\mathbf{x} = \mathbf{y} - \mathbf{y}_s$. With this, (5.17) becomes

$$\mathbf{x}' = \mathbf{A}\mathbf{x}, \tag{5.18}$$

where $\mathbf{A} = \mathbf{J}_s$. The general solution of this is given in Section 4.5. For what we are doing it is not necessary to distinguish between real or complex valued eigenvalues. Using the formulas in Section 4.5, and remembering that $\mathbf{y} = \mathbf{y}_s + \mathbf{x}$, we conclude that if $\mathbf{J}_s$ is not defective, then

$$\mathbf{y} = \mathbf{y}_s + c_1 \mathbf{a}_1 e^{r_1 t} + c_2 \mathbf{a}_2 e^{r_2 t}, \tag{5.19}$$

and if it is defective, then

$$\mathbf{y} = \mathbf{y}_s + c_1 \mathbf{a} e^{rt} + c_2 (t\mathbf{a} + \mathbf{b}) e^{rt}. \tag{5.20}$$

Whether the e^{rt} terms in (5.19) or (5.20) go to zero, or blow up, as $t \to \infty$, depends on whether $\text{Re}(r)$ is positive or negative. To determine this, it is easiest to go through the various possibilities individually.

- If all of the eigenvalues of $\mathbf{J}_s$ satisfy $\text{Re}(r) < 0$, then the exponentials in (5.19) and (5.20) go to zero as $t \to \infty$. So, $\mathbf{y}_s$ is asymptotically stable

- If one, or more, of the eigenvalues of $\mathbf{J}_s$ satisfies $\text{Re}(r) > 0$, then at least one of the exponentials in (5.19) and (5.20) blows up as $t \to \infty$. So, $\mathbf{y}_s$ is unstable.

There is a notable hole in the above list in that there is no conclusion for the case of when the eigenvalues are imaginary. In the theorem in Section 4.7, this is referred to as being neutrally stable. There are neutrally stable steady states for nonlinear systems, as illustrated with the ball and bowl example earlier, but the tangent plane approximation is inadequate to determine this. One approach to show neutral stability is to use the ideas developed in Section 5.3.

As a final comment, the only assumption needed to guarantee that the above conclusions hold is that the first and second partial derivatives of $f(u, v)$ and $g(u, v)$ are continuous. Those interested in a mathematically rigorous proof of this should consult Stuart and Humphries [1998] or Perko [2001].

Phase Plane

The above derivation for the stability conditions can provide us with information about the solution curves near a steady state. The reason is that the reduced equation in (5.18) is the same one considered in the last chapter. This enables us, in certain cases, to apply the phase plane solutions shown in Table 4.1 (page 100) to the nonlinear system. To explain how, suppose you have a steady state that the above test determines is unstable or asymptotically stable. As stated earlier, we are only considering isolated steady states, and to guarantee this happens it is assumed that $r = 0$ is not an eigenvalue. Now, in the vicinity of the steady state, we have that $\mathbf{y} \approx \mathbf{y}_s + \mathbf{x}$. This means that the phase portrait for $\mathbf{y}$ is similar to one of those in Table 4.1, but it is centered at $\mathbf{y} = \mathbf{y}_s$ rather than at $\mathbf{x} = \mathbf{0}$. Which one is determined by the eigenvalues of $\mathbf{J}_s$. Demonstrations of this will be included in the examples that follow.

5.2.2 ▪ Summary

For the nonlinear system

$$u' = f(u, v)$$
$$v' = g(u, v),$$

the associated **Jacobian matrix J** is given as

$$\mathbf{J} = \begin{pmatrix} \dfrac{\partial f}{\partial u} & \dfrac{\partial f}{\partial v} \\ \dfrac{\partial g}{\partial u} & \dfrac{\partial g}{\partial v} \end{pmatrix}.$$

The eigenvalues of $\mathbf{J}$ are used to determine stability, as explained in the next theorem.

Linearized Stability Theorem. *Given a steady state* $\mathbf{y}_s$, *and letting* $\mathbf{J}_s$ *be the Jacobian matrix evaluated at* $\mathbf{y}_s$:

- *If all of the eigenvalues of* $\mathbf{J}_s$ *satisfy* $Re(r) < 0$, *then* $\mathbf{y}_s$ *is asymptotically stable.*

- *If one, or more, of the eigenvalues of* $\mathbf{J}_s$ *satisfies* $Re(r) > 0$, *then* $\mathbf{y}_s$ *is unstable.*

This assumes that the second partial derivatives of $f(u, v)$ *and* $g(u, v)$ *are continuous at, and in the immediate vicinity of,* $\mathbf{y}_s$.

Not every possibility is included in the above theorem. As an example, no conclusion can be made when there are only imaginary eigenvalues. Any case that is not covered by the theorem will be referred to as *indeterminate* in this chapter.

For those with good memories, there are a few easy to use shortcuts that avoid computing eigenvalues. If you are interested in what they are, see Exercise 4.

It is worth pointing out that even though we are considering systems with two equations (so, $n = 2$), the above theorem holds when there are n equations. In fact, for $n = 1$ the above theorem reduces to the one given in Section 2.4.1 (page 35).

Finally, if the above theorem determines that a steady state is unstable or asymptotically stable, and $r = 0$ is not an eigenvalue, then the eigenvalues and eigenvectors of $\mathbf{J}_s$ can be used to determine the phase portrait of the solution near the steady state. This is done in the same way as for the examples shown in Table 4.1. The principal difference now is that it is centered at $\mathbf{y} = \mathbf{y}_s$ rather than at $\mathbf{x} = \mathbf{0}$. Therefore, the classification of steady states into a source, sink, spiral source, spiral sink, or saddle, as given on page 108, is applicable to the nonlinear systems considered here.

5.2.3 ▪ Examples

Example 1: Determine the stability of the steady states of

$$u' = v - \frac{1}{2}u,$$

$$v' = -\frac{1}{2}v + 2u(2 - u^2).$$

This is the system that produced the solution curves shown in Figure 5.2.

Step 1: Find the steady states. The equations to solve are

$$v - \frac{1}{2}u = 0,$$

$$-\frac{1}{2}v + 2u(2 - u^2) = 0.$$

One finds that there are three steady states, and they are: $(u, v) = -(2\alpha, \alpha)$, $(0, 0)$, $(2\alpha, \alpha)$, where $\alpha = \frac{1}{8}\sqrt{30}$.

Step 2: Determine the Jacobian matrix.

$$\mathbf{J} = \begin{pmatrix} \dfrac{\partial f}{\partial u} & \dfrac{\partial f}{\partial v} \\ \dfrac{\partial g}{\partial u} & \dfrac{\partial g}{\partial v} \end{pmatrix} = \begin{pmatrix} -\frac{1}{2} & 1 \\ 2(2 - 3u^2) & -\frac{1}{2} \end{pmatrix}.$$

Step 3: Check each steady state.

$(2\alpha, \alpha)$: In this case

$$\mathbf{J}_s = \begin{pmatrix} -\frac{1}{2} & 1 \\ -\frac{29}{4} & -\frac{1}{2} \end{pmatrix},$$

and this has eigenvalues $r_1 = (-1 + i\sqrt{29})/2$ and $r_2 = (-1 - i\sqrt{29})/2$. Since both satisfy $\text{Re}(r) < 0$, this steady state is asymptotically stable. In addition, since the eigenvalues are complex, and $\text{Re}(r) < 0$, the phase portrait near this steady state should be a spiral sink. To check, the region in Figure 5.2 that is near $(2\alpha, \alpha)$ is shown in Figure 5.6. As expected, the solution curves spiral into the steady state, as they should for a spiral sink.

$(0, 0)$: In this case

$$\mathbf{J}_s = \begin{pmatrix} -\frac{1}{2} & 1 \\ 4 & -\frac{1}{2} \end{pmatrix},$$

and this has eigenvalues $r_1 = 3/2$ and $r_2 = -5/2$. Since $r_1 > 0$ then this steady state is unstable. Also, since $r_2 < 0 < r_1$, then this is a saddle point and the phase portrait near $(0, 0)$ will resemble the one in Figure 4.1(b) or in Figure 4.2(b).

$-(2\alpha, \alpha)$: In this case

$$\mathbf{J}_s = \begin{pmatrix} -\frac{1}{2} & 1 \\ -\frac{29}{4} & -\frac{1}{2} \end{pmatrix},$$

and this has eigenvalues $r_1 = (-1 + i\sqrt{29})/2$ and $r_2 = (-1 + i\sqrt{29})/2$. Since both satisfy $\text{Re}(r) < 0$, this steady state is asymptotically stable. As with $(2\alpha, \alpha)$, this is a spiral sink. ■

Example 2: Determine the stability of the steady states of

$$x' = x - x^2 - xy,$$
$$y' = 2y - y^2 - 3xy.$$

This is the system that produced the solution curves shown in Figure 5.3.

Answer: In Section 5.1.1, Example 3, we found that there are four

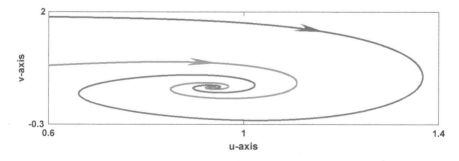

Figure 5.6. *Solution curves of (5.8), (5.8) in the u,v-plane near the steady state $(2\alpha, \alpha)$.*

steady states: $(0,0)$, $(0,2)$, $(1/2,1/2)$ and $(1,0)$. To determine their stability, the Jacobian is

$$
\mathbf{J} = \begin{pmatrix} \dfrac{\partial f}{\partial x} & \dfrac{\partial f}{\partial y} \\[2mm] \dfrac{\partial g}{\partial x} & \dfrac{\partial g}{\partial y} \end{pmatrix} = \begin{pmatrix} 1 - 2x - y & -x \\ -3y & 2 - 2y - 3x \end{pmatrix}.
$$

$(0,2)$: In this case

$$
\mathbf{J}_s = \begin{pmatrix} -1 & 0 \\ -6 & -2 \end{pmatrix}.
$$

The eigenvalues are $r_1 = -1$ and $r_2 = -2$, and since they are both negative, the steady state is asymptotically stable. Moreover, since both are negative, the phase portrait near this steady state will resemble those for a sink. Sketching the phase portrait was explained in Section 4.6. Briefly, eigenvectors of $\mathbf{J}_s$, for r_1 and r_2 are, respectively,

$$
\mathbf{a}_1 = \begin{pmatrix} -1 \\ 6 \end{pmatrix}, \quad \text{and} \quad \mathbf{a}_2 = \begin{pmatrix} 0 \\ 1 \end{pmatrix}.
$$

The two red lines shown in Figure 5.7 are determined by these eigenvectors. The arrows point toward the steady state as both eigenvalues are negative. Typical integral curves are shown in blue. The result is a phase portrait for a sink.

$(1/2,1/2)$: In this case

$$
\mathbf{J}_s = \begin{pmatrix} -1/2 & -1/2 \\ -3/2 & -1/2 \end{pmatrix},
$$

and this has eigenvalues $r_1 = (-1+\sqrt{3})/2$ and $r_2 = (-1-\sqrt{3})/2$. Since $r_1 > 0$, it follows that this steady state is unstable. As for the phase portrait near this steady state, since $r_2 < 0 < r_1$, then this steady

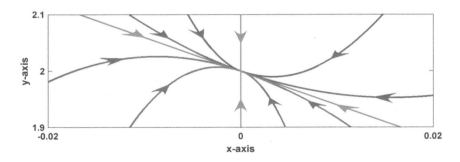

Figure 5.7. *Phase portrait near the steady state $(0,2)$ for Example 2.*

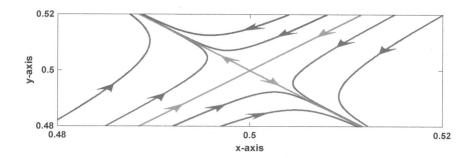

Figure 5.8. *Solution curves of Example 2 in the x,y-plane near the steady state* $(1/2, 1/2)$.

state is a saddle point. To sketch the phase portrait, the eigenvectors of $\mathbf{J}_s$, for r_1 and r_2 are, respectively,

$$\mathbf{a}_1 = \begin{pmatrix} -\frac{1}{3}\sqrt{3} \\ 1 \end{pmatrix}, \quad \text{and} \quad \mathbf{a}_2 = \begin{pmatrix} \frac{1}{3}\sqrt{3} \\ 1 \end{pmatrix}.$$

The two red lines determined by these vectors are shown in Figure 5.8. Typical integral curves are shown in blue. So, the curves have the pattern expected for a saddle.

Determining the stability of the remaining two steady states is left as an exercise. ■

Example 3: As introduced at the beginning of the chapter, a model for the spread of a disease, like measles, is

$$\frac{dS}{dt} = \alpha N - (\beta I + \alpha)S,$$

$$\frac{dI}{dt} = \beta IS - (\alpha + \gamma)I,$$

where N is the total number of individuals in the population (it is constant). The coefficients, α, β, and γ, are positive constants. It is not hard to show that the two steady states are $(S, I) = (N, 0)$ and $(S, I) = (S_e, I_e)$, where

$$S_e = \frac{\alpha + \gamma}{\beta} \quad \text{and} \quad I_e = \frac{\alpha}{\alpha + \gamma}(N - S_e).$$

The first steady state, $(N, 0)$, corresponds to the case of when the disease is eliminated, and everyone ends up in the S group. The other steady state, (S_e, I_e), is an example of what is known as an epidemic equilibrium, and this is something that is usually avoided if at all possible. Said another way, we want this steady state to be unstable.

To determine the stability of the steady states, note that

$$
\mathbf{J} = \begin{pmatrix} \dfrac{\partial f}{\partial S} & \dfrac{\partial f}{\partial I} \\[2ex] \dfrac{\partial g}{\partial S} & \dfrac{\partial g}{\partial I} \end{pmatrix} = \begin{pmatrix} -(\beta I + \alpha) & -\beta S \\[1ex] \beta I & \beta S - (\alpha + \gamma) \end{pmatrix}.
$$

$(S, I) = (N, 0)$: In this case

$$
\mathbf{J}_s = \begin{pmatrix} -\alpha & -\beta N \\[1ex] 0 & \beta N - (\alpha + \gamma) \end{pmatrix}.
$$

The eigenvalues of this matrix are $-\alpha$ and $\beta(N - S_e)$. Therefore, if $N < S_e$, then this steady state is asymptotically stable, and if $N > S_e$, then it is unstable.

$(S, I) = (S_e, I_e)$: One finds that this steady state is unstable if $N < S_e$, and it is asymptotically stable if $N > S_e$.

Measles: According to the model, to eradicate the disease, which means that (S_e, I_e) is unstable, it is required that

$$
N < \frac{\alpha + \gamma}{\beta}. \tag{5.21}
$$

The parameter α is the birth rate in the population and γ is associated with the rate at which people get well, both of which you can do little to change. As for β, it reflects how contagious the disease is (a larger β means it is more contagious). For measles, $\alpha = 1/50$, $\gamma = 100$, and $\beta = 1800/N$ [Engbert and Drepper, 1994], in which case

$$
\frac{\alpha + \gamma}{\beta} \approx \frac{1}{18} N.
$$

Clearly, (5.21) is not even close to being satisfied. This is a reflection of that fact that measles is one of the most contagious diseases known. What is needed is to reduce β by a factor of 20 (or more). It is possible to make β smaller by taking actions that limit the propagation of the disease, but finding effective ways to do this is challenging. ■

Exercises

1. For the following find the steady states, and then determine whether they are asymptotically stable, unstable, or indeterminate. Also, except for the indeterminate cases, state whether the steady state is a sink, source, spiral sink, spiral source, or saddle. Any parameters appearing in the equations should be assumed to be positive.

a) $\begin{cases} u' = 1 - 2u - v - uv \\ v' = 3uv - v \end{cases}$

g) $\begin{cases} x' = e^x - y \\ y' = xy \end{cases}$

b) $\begin{cases} u' = v - u \\ v' = v + u^3 \end{cases}$

h) $\begin{cases} x' = ax - bxy \\ y' = -cy + dxy \end{cases}$

c) $\begin{cases} u' = 1 + v \\ v' = u + v^3 \end{cases}$

i) $\begin{cases} S' = 2S - S^2 - \frac{2SP}{1+S} \\ P' = \frac{2SP}{1+S} - P \end{cases}$

d) $\begin{cases} u' = 4 - uv^2 \\ v' = -v + uv^2 \end{cases}$

j) $\begin{cases} S' = -\frac{1}{2}IS + 1 - I - S \\ I' = \frac{1}{2}IS - I \end{cases}$

e) $\begin{cases} x' = x^2 - y \\ y' = 2x - 3y \end{cases}$

k) $\begin{cases} r' = s - r \\ s' = (2 - r - s)(1 + s^2) \end{cases}$

f) $\begin{cases} x' = x^2 + y^2 \\ 2y' = \sin(x) \end{cases}$

l) $\begin{cases} S' = -2ES + E_0 - E \\ E' = -2ES + 2(E_0 - E) \end{cases}$

2. For the following: (i) find the steady state, (ii) find the linear approximation of the system near the steady state, and then (iii) sketch the phase portrait in the vicinity of the steady state as follows: draw the (red) lines that are determined from the eigenvectors of $\mathbf{J}_s$, including the arrows for these lines, then in each of the four quadrants determined by the red lines, include two integrals curves, with arrows.

a) $\begin{cases} u' = v - u \\ v' = v + u^3 \end{cases}$

c) $\begin{cases} r' = s - r \\ s' = (2 - r - s)(1 + s^2) \end{cases}$

b) $\begin{cases} u' = 1 + v \\ v' = u + v^3 \end{cases}$

d) $\begin{cases} S' = -2ES + E_0 - E \\ E' = -2ES + 2(E_0 - E) \end{cases}$

3. Suppose that $y = Y$ is a steady state solution of $y'' + cy' + g(y) = 0$. So, $y = Y$ is a constant and $g(Y) = 0$.

a) Show that Y is unstable if $c < 0$.

b) Show that Y is asymptotically stable if $c > 0$ and $g'(Y) > 0$, and it is unstable if $c > 0$ and $g'(Y) < 0$.

4. In this problem, assume that

$$\mathbf{J}_s = \begin{pmatrix} a & b \\ c & d \end{pmatrix}.$$

The *trace of a matrix* is the sum of the numbers on the diagonal. The formula is $\text{tr}(\mathbf{J}_s) = a + d$. Also, the determinant is $\det(\mathbf{J}_s) = ad - bc$.

a) Show that the eigenvalues of $\mathbf{J}_s$ are $\frac{1}{2}\left[\text{tr}(\mathbf{J}_s)\pm\sqrt{[\text{tr}(\mathbf{J}_s)]^2 - 4\det(\mathbf{J}_s)}\right]$.

b) Show that if $\text{tr}(\mathbf{J}_s) > 0$, then $\mathbf{y}_s$ is unstable.

c) Show that if $\det(\mathbf{J}_s) < 0$, then $\mathbf{y}_s$ is unstable.

d) Show that if $\det(\mathbf{J}_s) > 0$ and $\text{tr}(\mathbf{J}_s) < 0$, then $\mathbf{y}_s$ is asymptotically stable.

5. This exercise considers the curve, in the first quadrant, that separates the red and blue regions in Figure 5.4.

a) Explain why the curve must contain the point $(1/2, 1/2)$.

b) Suppose that the initial point $(x(0), y(0))$ is on the curve. Explain why the resulting solution $(x(t), y(t))$ must remain on the curve.

6. A model for how a joke moves through a population involves three groups: S is the population that either has not heard the joke, or does not remember it, T is the population of those who know the joke and they will tell it to others, and R is the population who know the joke but will not tell it to others (they are not good joke tellers or they don't think it's all that funny). As shown in Holmes [2019],

$$\frac{dS}{dt} = -2\alpha ST + \beta(N - S),$$
$$\frac{dT}{dt} = \alpha ST - \beta T,$$

where N is the total number of individuals in the population (it is constant). The coefficients α and β are positive constants. Also, once S and T are determined, then $R = N - T - S$.

a) There are two steady states, what are they?

b) One of the steady states has $T = 0$. When is it asymptotically stable?

c) One of the steady states has $T \neq 0$. When is it asymptotically stable?

d) The α is the telling parameter, so a larger α means the joke is being told more often. Similarly, β is the forgetting parameter, so a larger β means the joke is being forgotten faster. Based on your answers from parts (b) and (c), under what conditions will the joke disappear from the population?

5.3 ▪ Periodic Solutions

With the stability test derived in the previous section, we have a fairly good tool for determining if, and when, the solution of a nonlinear system will come to rest. The next question concerns what can be learned about periodic solutions. This is needed as periodicity plays an important role in our lives, and examples are the sleep-wake cycle and the periodic events associated with the Earth's rotation.

To begin, it's best to define what is meant by periodicity. A solution of $\mathbf{y}' = \mathbf{f}(\mathbf{y})$ is **periodic** if there is a positive number T so that

$$\mathbf{y}(t + T) = \mathbf{y}(t), \ \forall t \geq 0. \tag{5.22}$$

The smallest positive T, if it exists, is **the period**.

We will only consider problems that come from Newton's second law. Specifically, if $u(t)$ is the displacement, and F is a function of u, then $F = ma$ gives us the differential equation

$$mu'' = F(u). \tag{5.23}$$

Letting $v = u'$, then the above equation can be written in system form as

$$u' = v, \tag{5.24}$$

$$v' = \frac{1}{m}F(u). \tag{5.25}$$

It is not hard to show that if $u(t)$ is periodic with period T, then the velocity $v(t)$ is also periodic with period T. Consequently, (5.22) is satisfied, and so the solution is periodic. Examples of what are, or are not, periodic are explored in more depth in Exercise 2.

We will first find a way to determine the solution curve in the phase plane directly from the differential equation and initial conditions. Once that is done, we will then be able to determine the period T, as well as other properties of the solution.

Example: Mass-Spring

In Section 3.10, it was shown that the displacement $u(t)$ of a mass in a spring-mass system satisfies $mu'' + ku = 0$. The general solution of this equation can be written as $u = R\cos(\omega_0 t - \varphi)$, and $v = u' = -\omega_0 R\sin(\omega_0 t - \varphi)$, where $\omega_0 = \sqrt{k/m}$. Consequently, the solution is periodic, with period $T = 2\pi/\omega_0$. The key observation here is that, using the identity $\cos^2\theta + \sin^2\theta = 1$,

$$\left(\frac{u}{R}\right)^2 + \left(\frac{v}{\omega_0 R}\right)^2 = 1,$$

or equivalently

$$u^2 + \frac{1}{\omega_0^2}v^2 = R^2. \tag{5.26}$$

This is an equation for an ellipse in the u,v-plane. As an example, suppose that $m = 1$, $k = 4$, and the initial conditions are $u(0) = 1$ and $v(0) = 0$. In this case, $u = \cos(2t)$, $v = -2\sin(2t)$, and from (5.26), the ellipse is

$$u^2 + \frac{1}{4}v^2 = 1. \tag{5.27}$$

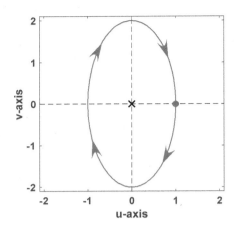

Figure 5.9. *Elliptical path, given in (5.27), that is followed by the solution of the mass-spring IVP. The blue dot is the location of the initial condition.*

This curve is shown in Figure 5.9. Because the period is $T = \pi$, the solution goes around the ellipse and returns to the starting point $(1, 0)$ at $t = \pi, 2\pi, 3\pi, \ldots$.

To see what can be learned from the system form of the problem, the equations are

$$u' = v,$$
$$v' = -\omega_0^2 u.$$

This can be used to determine the direction of the arrows in Figure 5.9. Since $v' = -\omega_0^2 u$, using the initial condition given earlier, $v'(0) = -\omega_0^2$. The fact that this is negative means that v must decrease as it leaves the initial point, and so the direction of motion is clockwise around the curve. Note that it is not possible for the solution to reverse direction on the curve because this would require that there is a point on the curve where $u' = 0$ and $v' = 0$. Such a point corresponds to a steady state, and the only steady state for this problem is the origin. ∎

The important conclusion coming from the above example is that, no matter what time t you select, the solution is located somewhere on the curve shown in Figure 5.9. Having a closed curve like this is a requirement for the solution to be periodic. The reason is that a solution traces out a curve in the phase plane, whether the solution is periodic or not (see Table 4.1 for examples). For the solution to be periodic, it must return to its original position, and that is why a closed curve as in Figure 5.9 is required. What is shown below is how to determine this curve without actually knowing what the solution is.

5.3.1 ▪ Closed Solution Curves and Hamiltonians

It is possible to find the equation for the closed curve without too much trouble if the differential equation comes from Newton's second law, $F = ma$. To explain, if $u(t)$ is the displacement, and F is a function of u, then $F = ma$ gives us the differential equation $mu'' = F(u)$. Multiplying this by the velocity u', and remembering that $v = u'$, we get that

$$mvv' = F(u)u'. \tag{5.28}$$

The key is to observe that the left hand side can be written as

$$\frac{d}{dt}\left(\frac{1}{2}mv^2\right).$$

To do the same for the right hand side, let $V(u)$ be such that $V'(u) = -F(u)$. In this case, the right hand side of (5.28) can be written as

$$F(u)u' = -\frac{dV}{du}\frac{du}{dt} = -\frac{d}{dt}V(u).$$

What we have done is to rewrite (5.28) as

$$\frac{d}{dt}\left(\frac{1}{2}mv^2 + V(u)\right) = 0. \tag{5.29}$$

Integrating this equation,

$$\frac{1}{2}mv^2 + V(u) = c. \tag{5.30}$$

The value of the constant c is determined from the initial condition.

There is a physical interpretation of the equation we have derived that is worth knowing about. The left hand side of (5.30) is

$$H(u, v) = \frac{1}{2}mv^2 + V(u). \tag{5.31}$$

This function is a **Hamiltonian** for the differential equation. In this instance it is the total mechanical energy of the system, and it consists of the sum of the kinetic energy, $\frac{1}{2}mv^2$, and a potential energy, $V(u)$. What we have shown in (5.30) is that the total energy is constant. So, the solution moves along a constant energy curve determined by the Hamiltonian and the initial conditions.

Not every forcing function $F(u)$ will result in (5.30) being a closed curve. Moreover, it is typical that when $F(u)$ is nonlinear, that not all initial conditions, if any, will yield a closed curve. Examples of these situations are given below.

Finally, as is often the case in mathematics, it is not recommended that you memorize the formula given in (5.30). It is better that you remember how it is derived. Namely, you multiply the second-order equation by the velocity, and then rewrite the terms as derivatives.

Example: Mass-Spring Revisited

Starting with the equation

$$mu'' + ku = 0,$$

we multiply by u' and obtain

$$mvv' + kuu' = 0.$$

This can be written as

$$\frac{d}{dt}\left(\frac{1}{2}mv^2 + \frac{1}{2}ku^2\right) = 0.$$

This means that

$$\frac{1}{2}mv^2 + \frac{1}{2}ku^2 = c,$$

where c is an arbitrary constant. Taking, as in the last example, $u(0) = 1$, $v(0) = 0$, $m = 1$, and $k = 4$, and substituting these values into the above equation we find that $c = 2$. Consequently, the above equation becomes

$$u^2 + \frac{1}{4}v^2 = 1. \tag{5.32}$$

This is exactly the same equation (5.27) we derived earlier using the known solution to the problem. What is significant is that we have found this curve without first finding the solution of the problem. ∎

It was mentioned earlier that not every forcing function will result in a closed curve. For the above mass-spring problem the spring force is $F = -km$. This is attractive, in the sense that it pulls the mass back towards the rest position $u = 0$. If the force is repelling, so $F = km$, then instead of (5.32), you get $u^2 - \frac{1}{4}v^2 = 1$. This is an equation for a hyperbola, which is not a close curve.

Example: Pendulum

The equation for the angular deflection of a pendulum can be written as

$$\frac{d^2\theta}{dt^2} = -\alpha \sin\theta. \tag{5.33}$$

where $\alpha = g/\ell$. Introducing the angular velocity $v = \theta'$, then we obtain the first-order system

$$\theta' = v, \tag{5.34}$$

$$v' = -\alpha \sin\theta. \tag{5.35}$$

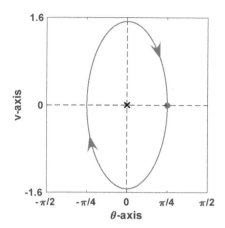

Figure 5.10. *Path followed by the solution of the pendulum example.*

In this example, assume that $\alpha = 4$, and that the initial conditions are $\theta(0) = \pi/4$ and $v(0) = 0$. To determine the closed solution curve, we multiply (5.33) by the velocity $v = \theta'$, giving us

$$vv' = -4\theta' \sin \theta.$$

Writing this as

$$\frac{d}{dt}\frac{1}{2}v^2 = \frac{d}{dt}(4\cos\theta),$$

and then integrating gives us the equation

$$\frac{1}{2}v^2 - 4\cos\theta = c.$$

With the initial conditions we find that $c = -2\sqrt{2}$, and so the equation for the curve takes the form

$$v^2 - 8\cos\theta = -4\sqrt{2}. \tag{5.36}$$

The curve obtained from this equation is shown in Figure 5.10.

The direction of the arrows can be determined from the v' equation (5.35). Namely, since $v'(0) = -\alpha\sin(\theta(0)) = -2\sqrt{2}$, and this is negative, then v must decrease as it leaves the initial point. Therefore, the direction of motion is clockwise around the curve.

It is possible to determine various properties of the solution from (5.36). For example, the maximum velocity v_M occurs when $v' = 0$. Since $v' = -4\sin\theta$, then from Figure 5.10 it is apparent that the only solution is $\theta = 0$. In this case, from (5.36), $v^2 = 4(2 - \sqrt{2})$. Therefore, $v_M = 2\sqrt{2 - \sqrt{2}}$.

Finally, to illustrate the periodicity of the individual components of the solution, both θ and v are plotted in Figure 5.11 as functions of t.

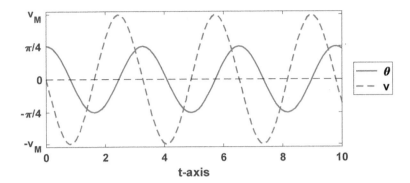

Figure 5.11. *Solution curves for* $\theta(t)$ *and* $v(t)$ *for the pendulum solution shown in Figure 5.10.*

An interesting question is whether it is possible to determine the period of these functions without knowing the solution. It is, and how this is possible will be explained in the next section ■

Example: Librating versus Circulating Motion

For a pendulum, if the initial velocity is large enough, then the mass will go all the way around, pass through $\theta = \pi$ (or, $\theta = -\pi$) and return to where it started. It will continue to do this indefinitely. This motion is periodic, but it does not satisfy the definition of a periodic solution given in (5.22). In mechanics it is called a circulating, or rotating, motion. In contrast, the tick-toc type of periodic motion considered in the previous example is referred to as libration.

The integral curves for the pendulum are shown in Figure 5.12. The closed, solid blue, curves correspond to the periodic solutions discussed earlier. The dashed curves are some of the possible circulating solutions. On these curves, the angular coordinate θ increases monotonically if $v > 0$,

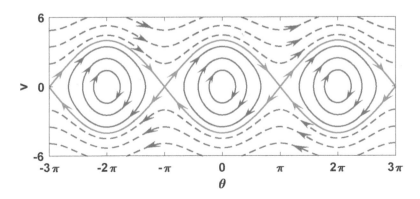

Figure 5.12. *Phase portrait for the pendulum equations (5.34), (5.35), when* $\alpha = 4$.

and decreases monotonically if $v < 0$. In the physical plane this corresponds to the mass continually making complete circuits around the pivot point (i.e., it is making a circulating motion).

The red curves in Figure 5.12 form what is known as the *separatrix* for the pendulum. If you start at a point on the separatrix, the solution will approach the vertical, unstable, steady state. ∎

5.3.2 ▪ Finding the Period

Once the closed curve formed by the periodic solution is known, it is possible to find the period. As usual, it is easiest to explained how this is done using examples.

Example: Mass-Spring

The equation for the curve is given in (5.32). Solving this for v yields $v = \pm 2\sqrt{1 - u^2}$. Which sign you use depends on what part of the curve you are considering. In Figure 5.9 the two u intercepts are $u = \pm 1$. So, for the lower part of the curve connecting $(1, 0)$ to $(-1, 0)$, v is negative, and so $v = -2\sqrt{1 - u^2}$. Since $v = u'$, then we have the first-order differential equation

$$\frac{du}{dt} = -2\sqrt{1 - u^2}.$$

This equation is separable, which yields

$$\int \frac{du}{\sqrt{1 - u^2}} = \int -2dt.$$

Carrying out the integrations,

$$\arcsin(u) = -2t + c.$$

Given that $u = 1$ at $t = 0$, then $c = \pi/2$.

To determine the period, we solve the above equation for t to obtain

$$t = \frac{1}{2}\left(\frac{\pi}{2} - \arcsin(u)\right).$$

It is now possible to determine how long it takes for the solution to move along the lower half of the curve and arrive at $(-1, 0)$. Namely, letting $u = -1$ in the above equation we get that

$$t = \frac{1}{2}\left(\frac{\pi}{2} - \arcsin(-1)\right) = \frac{\pi}{2}.$$

To compute the time to transverse the upper part of the curve, you can either use the separation of variables approach or you can use the symmetry of the solution curve. Both yield the result that the time is $\pi/2$. Therefore, the period is the sum, which means that $T = \pi$. This agrees with what we found earlier using the exact solution to the problem. ∎

Example: Pendulum

The equation for the curve is given in (5.36). Solving this for v yields $v = \pm 2\sqrt{2\cos\theta - \sqrt{2}}$. The lower part of the solution curve, shown in Figure 5.10, goes from $(\pi/4, 0)$ to $(-\pi/4, 0)$. On this part of the curve $v = -2\sqrt{2\cos\theta - \sqrt{2}}$, which gives us the first-order differential equation

$$\frac{d\theta}{dt} = -2\sqrt{2\cos\theta - \sqrt{2}}\,.$$

This equation is separable, which yields

$$\int \frac{d\theta}{\sqrt{2\cos\theta - \sqrt{2}}} = -2t + c.$$

In anticipation of imposing the initial condition, the above integral is written as

$$\int_{\theta_0}^{\theta} \frac{dr}{\sqrt{2\cos r - \sqrt{2}}} = -2t + c.$$

Now, given that $\theta(0) = \pi/4$, then $\theta_0 = \pi/4$ and $c = 0$. The above equation then takes the form

$$\int_{\pi/4}^{\theta} \frac{dr}{\sqrt{2\cos r - \sqrt{2}}} = -2t.$$

The time to reach $\theta = -\pi/4$ is therefore

$$\begin{aligned}
t &= -\frac{1}{2}\int_{\pi/4}^{-\pi/4} \frac{dr}{\sqrt{2\cos r - \sqrt{2}}} \\
&= \frac{1}{2}\int_{-\pi/4}^{\pi/4} \frac{dr}{\sqrt{2\cos r - \sqrt{2}}}\,.
\end{aligned}$$

Using the separation of variables approach, or using the symmetry of the solution curve, the time to transverse the upper part of the curve is the same as the above value. Therefore, the period T for the pendulum is

$$T = \int_{-\pi/4}^{\pi/4} \frac{dr}{\sqrt{2\cos r - \sqrt{2}}}\,. \tag{5.37}$$

So, we have a formula for the period that does not require knowing the solution. The complication is that it is an improper integral, of the type often referred to in a calculus textbook as "Type II," which means the integrand becomes infinite at the endpoints. It is not possible to carry out the integration in terms of elementary functions, but it is relatively simple to evaluate it using a computer. Doing so, one finds that $T = 3.267\ldots$.

∎

We have been able to determine a great deal about the properties of a periodic solution, without actually knowing what the solution is. As stated earlier, this is significant as most of the nonlinear problems that give rise to a periodic solution can not be solved using elementary functions. Consequently, they are almost always solved numerically. Our results complement what can be learned numerically, as we have been able to derive analytical formulas for the period, the closed curve, and other components of the solution. This makes it much easier to determine how the solution changes when the initial conditions, or the parameters appearing in the equations, are changed.

Exercises

1. Find a Hamiltonian function $H(u, v)$ for each of the following:

   a) $2u'' + 3e^{2u} - 3 = 0$

   b) $u'' + \dfrac{u}{1 + 5u^2} = 0$

   c) $5u'' + 7u + 6u^9 = 0$

   d) $u'' + 5u^3 \sqrt{1 + u^2} = 0$

2. This problem considers periodic, and non-periodic, solutions of $\mathbf{y}' = \mathbf{f}(\mathbf{y})$.

   a) Explain why any steady state is a periodic solution of this equation.

   b) Suppose that $\mathbf{y}_b$, given below, is a solution. Is it a periodic solution?

   $$\mathbf{y}_b = \begin{pmatrix} \sin t \\ \sin(3t) \end{pmatrix} \qquad \mathbf{y}_c = \begin{pmatrix} \sin t \\ \sin(\pi t) \end{pmatrix}$$

   c) Suppose that $\mathbf{y}_c$, given above, is a solution. Is it a periodic solution?

   d) Show that if $u(t)$ is periodic with period T, then $v(t) = u'(t)$ is also periodic with period T.

   e) Suppose that $v = u'$. Give an example where $v(t)$ is periodic, but $u(t)$ is not periodic.

3. In this problem assume that the curve coming from (5.30) has the form shown in Figure 5.13.

   a) Explain why the maximum, and minimum, velocities occur when $u = u_s$, where u_s is a steady state value.

   b) Use the fact that there are two u-intercepts to explain why it is not possible that $V(u) = u^3$.

4. The problem concerns a Duffing oscillator, and the differential equation is $u'' + u + u^3 = 0$. Assume the initial conditions are $u(0) = 1$ and $v(0) = 0$. This equation comes from a mass-spring system, as shown in Figure 3.2, where the restoring force of the spring is nonlinear (specifically, cubic) rather than the linear form assumed using Hooke's law.

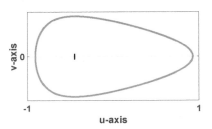

Figure 5.13. *Path followed by the solution for Exercise 3.*

a) The path followed by the solution is shown in Figure 5.14. Find the equation for this closed curve.

b) Find the steady-state, show that it is not on the curve you found in part (a).

c) Draw arrows on the curve indicating the direction of motion. Make sure to explain how you determine this.

d) What is the maximum velocity?

e) What is the minimum displacement?

f) Find a formula, similar to the one in (5.37), for the period.

5. The problem concerns what is known as a Morse oscillator, and the differential equation is

$$u'' + 2(1 - e^{-u})e^{-u} = 0.$$

Assume the initial conditions are $u(0) = 1$ and $v(0) = 0$. This equation arises when studying the vibrational energy of a diatomic molecule.

a) The path followed by the solution is shown in Figure 5.15. Find the equation for this closed curve.

b) Find the steady-state, show that it is not on the curve you found in part (a).

c) Draw arrows on the curve indicating the direction of motion. Make sure to explain how you determine this.

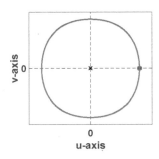

Figure 5.14. *Path followed by the solution of the Duffing oscillator in Exercise 4.*

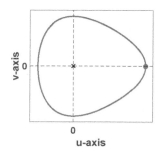

Figure 5.15. *Path followed by the solution of the Morse oscillator in Exercise 5.*

d) What is the maximum velocity?

e) What is the minimum displacement?

f) Find a formula, similar to the one in (5.37), for the period.

6. This problem concerns the generalization of the Hamiltonian to the general system in (5.4), (5.5). Assume that there is a function $H(u, v)$ so that

$$\frac{\partial H}{\partial v} = f(u, v) \quad \text{and} \quad \frac{\partial H}{\partial u} = -g(u, v). \tag{5.38}$$

Also, assume that f and g are smooth functions of u and v.

a) Explain why this requires that $f_u = -g_v$. If this holds then (5.4), (5.5) is said to be a *Hamiltonian system.*

b) Show that the $H(u, v)$ given in (5.31) satisfies (5.38).

c) Use (5.38) to show that $\frac{d}{dt} H = 0$. So, $H(u, v) = c$, where c is a constant, and in this sense $H(u, v)$ is a Hamiltonian for the system.

d) Find a Hamiltonian for $u' = v^2 - u$, $v' = v - 2u$.

e) Under what condition is the linear system $\mathbf{y}' = \mathbf{A}\mathbf{y}$, where

$$\mathbf{A} = \begin{pmatrix} a & b \\ c & d \end{pmatrix},$$

a Hamiltonian system? Assuming this holds, find $H(u, v)$.

5.4 ▪ Motion in a Central Force Field

The problem of interest concerns the motion in three dimensions of a particle that is subjected to a radial force $\mathbf{F}$. The specific assumption is that

$$\mathbf{F} = \frac{1}{r} f(r)\mathbf{x}, \tag{5.39}$$

where $\mathbf{x}(t)$ is the position of the particle and $r = \|\mathbf{x}\|$. From Newton's second law, the resulting differential equation is

$$m\mathbf{x}'' = \frac{1}{r} f(r)\mathbf{x}, \tag{5.40}$$

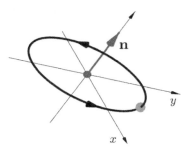

Figure 5.16. *A particle, the red dot, orbits a particle located at the origin. The orbit curve lies in a plane containing the origin and has normal* **n**, *where* **n** *is parallel to* $\mathbf{p} = \mathbf{x}_0 \times \mathbf{v}_0$.

where m is the mass of the particle. As for the initial conditions, it is assumed that the initial position $\mathbf{x}(0) = \mathbf{x}_0$ and the initial velocity $\mathbf{x}'(0) = \mathbf{v}_0$ are given. To avoid some uninteresting situations, it is assumed that $\mathbf{x}_0 \times \mathbf{v}_0 \neq \mathbf{0}$.

The force $\mathbf{F}$ can be thought of as coming from the interaction with a particle located at the center. For example, if the force is gravity, then $f(r) = -k/r^2$, where $k = GMm$. In contrast, if the particles are charged and the force is electrostatic, then $f(r) = -k/r^2$, where $k = -qQ/4\pi\varepsilon_0$. The definition of the various constants making up k is not important here, other than to know that it is possible for k to be positive or negative. In particular, it is positive for a gravitational force, and for an electrostatic force if the charges of the particles are opposite. It is negative for an electrostatic force if the charges of the particles are the same.

The solution of (5.39) can be shown to lie in a plane that has a normal vector $\mathbf{n}$ that is parallel to $\mathbf{p} = \mathbf{x}_0 \times \mathbf{v}_0$ (see Exercise 6). We will orient the coordinate system so the z-axis is in the $\mathbf{n}$ direction, which means that the solution of (5.40) is confined to the x,y-plane. To take advantage of this, we will use polar coordinates and write $x(t) = r(t)\cos\theta(t)$ and $y(t) = r(t)\sin\theta(t)$. After some routine change of variables calculations one finds that (5.40) reduces to

$$m\left[r'' - r(\theta')^2\right] = f(r), \tag{5.41}$$

$$\frac{d}{dt}\left[r^2(\theta')\right] = 0. \tag{5.42}$$

The last equation gives us that $r^2\theta' = p$, where p is a constant, and this means that the first equation reduces to

$$mr'' = f(r) + \frac{mp^2}{r^3}. \tag{5.43}$$

This is a force balance equation, where $f(r)$ is the force introduced earlier and mp^2/r^3 is an outward directed force due to angular momentum.

The second-order differential equation (5.43) can be written as a first-order nonlinear system by letting $v = r'$, giving

$$r' = v, \tag{5.44}$$

$$v' = \frac{1}{m}f(r) + \frac{p^2}{r^3}. \tag{5.45}$$

It is worth knowing that in the derivation of (5.43), it is found that $p = \|\mathbf{x}_0 \times \mathbf{v}_0\|$. So, p is a positive constant that is known from the initial conditions.

5.4.1 ▪ Steady States

The steady states, if there are any, satisfy $v = 0$ and $r^3 f(r) + mp^2 = 0$. Assuming that $f(r) = -k/r^2$, then to be a steady state it is required that $kr = mp^2$. This means we need $k > 0$, and the resulting steady state is $r = r_s$, where

$$r_s = \frac{mp^2}{k}.$$

Also, since $r^2\theta' = p$, then $\theta = \omega t + \theta_0$, where $\omega = k^2/m^2p^3$. The corresponding solution is a circular orbit in the x,y-plane, with radius $r = r_s$ and period $2\pi/\omega$.

To check the stability, note that

$$\mathbf{J} = \begin{pmatrix} 0 & 1 \\ \frac{2k}{mr_s^3} - 3\frac{p^2}{r_s^4} & 0 \end{pmatrix} = \begin{pmatrix} 0 & 1 \\ -p^2/r_s^4 & 0 \end{pmatrix}.$$

From this one finds that the eigenvalues are $\pm ip/r_s^2$, which means that the stability of the steady state is indeterminate using the Linearized Stability Theorem.

5.4.2 ▪ Periodic Orbit

The next question is whether the solution is periodic. Said another way, we would like to know if the particle orbits the particle that is located at the origin. To find the closed curve formed by the solution, if there is one, we multiply (5.43) by r'. From this, and remembering that we have taken $f(r) = -k/r^2$, it is found that

$$\frac{1}{2}mv^2 + \frac{mp^2}{2r^2} - \frac{k}{r} = c, \tag{5.46}$$

where c is a constant determined by the initial conditions. Completing the square, we get that

$$v^2 + p^2\left(\frac{1}{r} - \frac{1}{r_s}\right)^2 = c_0^2, \tag{5.47}$$

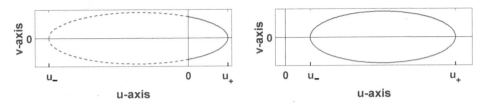

Figure 5.17. *Two possible elliptical curves coming from (5.48). The u-intercepts for each ellipse are u_- and u_+.*

where $c_0^2 = v_0^2 + p^2 \left(1/r_0 - 1/r_s \right)^2$, $r(0) = r_0$, and $v(0) = v_0$.

To answer the question about a periodic orbit, it will make things easier if we let $u = 1/r$. So, (5.47) takes the form

$$v^2 + p^2 \left(u - u_s \right)^2 = c_0^2, \tag{5.48}$$

where $u_s = 1/r_s$. This is an equation for an ellipse in the u,v-plane with center $(u, v) = (u_s, 0)$. Two representative elliptical paths obtained from this equation are shown in Figure 5.17. Since $u = 1/r$, then u must be positive. This means that the dashed portion of the ellipse on the left is not possible physically. To determine whether the ellipse has only positive values, we can use the u intercepts. Setting $v = 0$ in (5.48) yields $u_{\pm} = u_s \pm c_0/p$. As shown in Exercise 7, to have $u_- > 0$ it is required that $k > mr(0)^3 [\theta'(0)]^2$. Therefore, as long as the initial angular velocity $\theta'(0)$ is not too large, the particle will orbit the particle at the origin.

To demonstrate what a solution curve looks like, the numerical solution of the central force problem in (5.43) is shown in Figure 5.18. The orbital path in the r,v-plane is on the left. The physical path, in the x,y-plane, is shown on the right.

The question arises as what happens when you get an ellipse like the one on the left in Figure 5.17. Irrespective of which point you start at

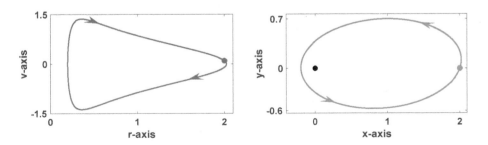

Figure 5.18. *Numerical solution of (5.43) in the case of when the solution is periodic. The initial position, and direction of motion, are shown on each curve. The two time points used to place the direction arrows on the left are the same time points used on the right.*

on the solid curve, and no matter which direction you go on the curve, u approaches zero. In other words, $r \to \infty$. Physically, what is happening is that the angular momentum is so large that an orbit is not possible, and the particle simply escapes whatever hold the particle at the origin might have on it. It is also evident from Figure 5.17, contrary to what is often shown in cartoons, that the particle does not make several orbits around the origin before escaping. In fact, the particle is incapable of making even one complete orbit.

Exercises

1. Suppose the law of gravity results in $f(r) = -k/r^3$, where $k > 0$. You can assume that $k \neq mp^2$.

    a) Are there any steady state solutions? If so, check on their stability.

    b) Assuming there is a periodic solution, determine its equation in the u,v-plane.

    c) Use your result from part (b) to explain why there is no periodic solution of this problem.

2. Suppose the law of gravity results in $f(r) = -kr$, where $k > 0$. Note that this is assuming that gravity acts like an elastic spring.

    a) Are there any steady state solutions? If so, check on their stability.

    b) Assuming there is a periodic solution, determine its equation in the r,v-plane.

    c) The solution curve is shown in Figure 5.19 in the case of when $r(0) = r_0$ and $v(0) = 0$. Show that the second r intercept is at $r_0(r_s/r_0)^2$, where r_s is the steady state you found in part (a).

    d) Where is the steady state located in Figure 5.19?

3. This problem concerns the solution shown in Figure 5.18.

    a) In Figure 5.18(left), where is r_s located?

    b) In Figure 5.18(right), sketch in the circular orbit derived in Section 5.4.1.

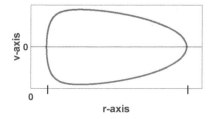

Figure 5.19. *Solution curve for the problem in Exercise 2.*

4. What initial conditions correspond to someone throwing a baseball so that it encircles the Earth at a constant height, and then returns to the person who threw it? Some of the results from Exercise 7 might be useful here. Assume the Earth is a smooth sphere with radius R.

5. This exercise explores the usefulness of making the change of variables from r, t to u, τ, where $u(\tau) = 1/r$ and $\tau = \theta(t)$. This is an approach often used in physics textbooks.

   a) Show that $r'(t) = -pu'(\tau)$, and $r''(t) = -p^2 u^2 u''(\tau)$.

   b) The mathematical requirement for the change of variables to be valid is that $\theta(t)$ is a strictly monotonic function of t. Explain why this holds in this problem.

   c) Using the results from part (a), show that (5.43) takes the form

   $$u'' + u = -\frac{1}{mp^2 u^2} f\left(\frac{1}{u}\right).$$

   d) Assuming that $f(r) = -k/r^2$, find the general solution of the resulting differential equation in part (c). In doing this, use (3.23) when writing down the general solution of the associated homogeneous equation. Also, what is the resulting formula for r?

   e) Use the results from Exercise 7 to show that $u(0) = 1/x_0$ and $u'(0) = -x_0'/(x_0 y_0')$. Use these to find the two arbitrary constants in your solution in (d).

6. Let $\mathbf{p} = \mathbf{x} \times \mathbf{x}'$. In this exercise you will likely need to review the properties of the cross product you learned in calculus.

   a) Show that $\mathbf{p}' = \mathbf{0}$. This means that $\mathbf{p}$ is a constant vector, and so, from the initial conditions, $\mathbf{p} = \mathbf{x}_0 \times \mathbf{v}_0$. It is assumed that $\mathbf{x}_0 \times \mathbf{v}_0 \neq \mathbf{0}$.

   b) Explain why $\mathbf{p} \cdot \mathbf{x} = 0$ and $\mathbf{p} \cdot \mathbf{x}' = 0$. Why does this mean that $\mathbf{x}$ and $\mathbf{x}'$ are in the plane that is perpendicular to $\mathbf{p}$, and which contains the origin?

   c) Assuming $\mathbf{x} = (r(t) \cos \theta(t), r(t) \sin \theta(t), 0)$, show that $\mathbf{p} = r^2 \theta' \mathbf{k}$, where $\mathbf{k}$ is the unit vector pointing in the positive z-direction.

   d) The plane has normal $\mathbf{p}$ as well as normal $-\mathbf{p}$. Which one is used when orientating the positive z-axis in such a way that $r^2 \theta' > 0$?

7. This problem determines how the initial conditions for (5.39) contribute to the reduced problem for the orbit. Assume that $\mathbf{x}_0 = (x_0, 0, 0)^T$ and $\mathbf{v}_0 = (x_0', y_0', 0)^T$, where x_0, x_0', and y_0' are given with x_0 and y_0' both positive. The superscript T indicates transpose. Also, assume that $f(r) = -k/r^2$ and $\theta(0) = 0$.

   a) Show that $p = x_0 y_0'$.

   b) Show that the initial conditions for (5.43) are $r(0) = x_0$, $r'(0) = x_0'$.

   c) Show that $u_- > 0$ reduces to the requirement that $k > m x_0 (y_0')^2$.

Chapter 6

Laplace Transform

We have found that to solve $y'' + by' + cy = 0$ you assume that $y = e^{rt}$, and for $\mathbf{x}' = \mathbf{A}\mathbf{x}$ you assume that $\mathbf{x} = \mathbf{a}e^{rt}$. What is notable here is the exponential dependence of the solution on t. It is possible to extend this assumption in such a way that it is possible to solve a wide variety of more complicated problems, such as those involving partial differential equations. The extension we are going to consider is called the Laplace transform.

It is recommended that if you are a bit fuzzy on integration by parts, or partial fractions, that you spend some time reviewing those integration methods as one or both are used in many of the examples and exercises in this chapter.

6.1 ▪ Definition

The generalization we are interested in called the Laplace transform, and its definition is given next.

Laplace Transform. *Given a function $y(t)$, for $0 \le t < \infty$, its Laplace transform $Y(s)$ is defined as*

$$Y(s) \equiv \int_0^\infty y(t)e^{-st}dt. \tag{6.1}$$

It will be useful to have a more compact notation for the integral in this expression, and this will be done by writing the above formula as

$$Y(s) \equiv \mathcal{L}(y). \tag{6.2}$$

Introduction to Differential Equations, M. H. Holmes, 2020

The Laplace variable s is analogous to the r used in the assumption $y = e^{rt}$ or $\mathbf{x} = \mathbf{a}e^{rt}$. Also, although it is not apparent from the definition, it is important to know that **the variable s is complex-valued.**

6.1.1 ▪ Requirements

There are a couple of ways to find the Laplace transform of a function. One is to carry out the integration in (6.1), just as you did in calculus. Much of the material in this section concerns the mathematical requirements needed to do this. However, it is also possible to find a Laplace transform by looking it up in a table, such as the one in Table 6.1 (on page 151). As demonstrated in Example 3 (version 2), this is very easy to do. Most, but not all, of the transforms in this chapter can be done using the given table (along with the formula in Exercise 4).

For the improper integral in (6.1) to exist, a condition must be imposed on the complex variable s. To explain, if $y(t) = e^{3t}$, then using the definition of an improper integral and (6.1)

$$Y(s) = \lim_{T \to \infty} \int_0^T e^{3t} e^{-st} dt = \lim_{T \to \infty} \int_0^T e^{(3-s)t} dt \tag{6.3}$$

$$= \lim_{T \to \infty} \left[\frac{1}{3-s} e^{(3-s)T} - \frac{1}{3-s} \right]. \tag{6.4}$$

Clearly, we need $s \neq 3$. As for the limit, it is useful to know that, given a nonzero complex number z,

$$\lim_{T \to \infty} e^{zT} = \begin{cases} 0 & \text{if } \operatorname{Re}(z) < 0, \\ \text{does not exist} & \text{if } \operatorname{Re}(z) \geq 0. \end{cases} \tag{6.5}$$

The proof of this comes directly from Euler's formula, as expressed in (3.15). For (6.4), $z = 3 - s$ and this means that for the limit to exist we need $\operatorname{Re}(3 - s) < 0$, or equivalently, we need $\operatorname{Re}(s) > 3$. In this case,

$$Y(s) = \frac{1}{s-3}.$$

The requirement that $\operatorname{Re}(s) > 3$ gives rise to what is known as the *half-plane of convergence* for the Laplace transform.

The second mathematical requirement concerns the smoothness of $y(t)$. For the problems considered in this textbook, it is enough to assume that $y(t)$ is continuous for $0 \leq t < \infty$, except possibly for jump discontinuities. What a **jump discontinuity** means is that $y(t)$ is not continuous at the point, but the limits of y from the left and right are defined and finite (the two limits do not need to be equal). A simple example, with a jump discontinuity at $t = 2$, is

$$y(t) = \begin{cases} 3 & \text{if } 0 \leq t \leq 2, \\ -1 & \text{if } 2 < t. \end{cases} \tag{6.6}$$

The specific requirement for the Laplace transform is that over any interval $0 \leq t \leq T$, $y(t)$ is continuous except for possibly a finite number of jump discontinuities. In this case, $y(t)$ is said to be **piecewise continuous** for $t \geq 0$.

The final requirement on $y(t)$ is to guarantee that the improper integral in (6.1) converges. Specifically, it is required that there is a constant α so that

$$\lim_{t \to \infty} y(t)e^{\alpha t} = 0.$$

If this holds, then $y(t)$ is said to have *exponential order*. As examples, any polynomial function in t, any linear combination of $\sin(\omega t)$ and $\cos(\omega t)$, and any linear combination of terms of the form $e^{\omega t}$ have exponential order. On the other hand, e^{t^2} and e^{t^3} do not. Throughout this chapter, whenever taking the Laplace transform, it is assumed that the function has exponential order.

In the above example it is stated that $\text{Re}(s) > 3$. This can *not* be written as $s > 3$. The reason is that the usual definition of inequality can not be used with complex numbers. For example, the rules of inequality require that $s^2 \geq 0$. So, taking $s = i$, you end up concluding that $-1 \geq 0$. In fact, it is possible to prove that the complex numbers cannot be made an ordered field no matter how you define the rule used for inequality.

6.1.2 ▪ Examples

With the technical details out of the way, we consider a few examples. As you will see, finding the Laplace transform of a function provides ample opportunity to practice using integration by parts. Also, in what follows the improper integral will be treated as a definite integral, with the upper endpoint being $t = \infty$ (see Example 1 below). It is understood that the evaluation at the upper endpoint involves a limit, as expressed in (6.3).

Example 1: If $y(t) = \sin 2t$, find $Y(s)$.

Answer: Using (6.1), and integration by parts (with $u = e^{-st}$ and $dv = \sin 2t \, dt$),

$$Y(s) = \int_0^\infty \sin(2t)e^{-st} dt$$

$$= -\frac{1}{2}\cos(2t)e^{-st}\Big|_{t=0}^\infty - \frac{s}{2}\int_0^\infty \cos(2t)e^{-st} dt$$

$$= \frac{1}{2} - \frac{s}{2}\int_0^\infty \cos(2t)e^{-st} dt.$$

To guarantee that $\cos(2t)e^{-st}$ has a finite limit as $t \to \infty$, it has been assumed that $\text{Re}(s) > 0$. Using integration by parts again, you find that

$$Y(s) = \frac{1}{2} - \frac{s^2}{4}Y(s).$$

Solving for Y, we get that $Y = 2/(s^2 + 4)$. Using the $\mathcal{L}(y)$ notation, we have that

$$\mathcal{L}(\sin 2t) = \frac{2}{s^2 + 4}. \quad \blacksquare$$

Example 2: If $y(t)$ is given in (6.6), find $Y(s)$.

Answer: Using the additive property of integrals,

$$Y(s) = \int_0^\infty y(t)e^{-st}dt$$

$$= \int_0^2 y(t)e^{-st}dt + \int_2^\infty y(t)e^{-st}dt.$$

Consequently, from (6.6),

$$Y(s) = \int_0^2 3e^{-st}dt - \int_2^\infty e^{-st}dt$$

$$= -\frac{3}{s}e^{-st}\Big|_{t=0}^2 + \frac{1}{s}e^{-st}\Big|_{t=2}^\infty$$

$$= -\frac{4}{s}e^{-2s} + \frac{3}{s}.$$

To guarantee that $\frac{1}{s}e^{-st}$ has a defined limit as $t \to \infty$, it has been assumed that $\operatorname{Re}(s) > 0$. $\quad\blacksquare$

In the above two examples, the condition on s so that $Y(s)$ is defined was stated explicitly. In the remainder of the chapter this will not be done, and it is assumed that the condition is obvious from the derivation.

Example 3 (version 1): If $y(t) = 3t - \sin 2t$, find $Y(s)$.

Answer: Using integration by parts, and the result from Example 1,

$$Y(s) = 3\int_0^\infty te^{-st}dt - \int_0^\infty \sin 2t e^{-st}dt \qquad (6.7)$$

$$= -\frac{3t}{s}e^{-st}\Big|_{t=0}^\infty + \frac{3}{s}\int_0^\infty e^{-st}dt - \frac{2}{s^2 + 4}$$

$$= \frac{3}{s^2} - \frac{2}{s^2 + 4}. \quad \blacksquare$$

Linear Operator

It states in (6.7) that $\mathcal{L}(3t - \sin 2t) = 3\mathcal{L}(t) - \mathcal{L}(\sin 2t)$. This is an illustration of an essential property of the Laplace transform. Namely, if c_1 and c_2 are constants, then

$$\mathcal{L}(c_1 y_1 + c_2 y_2) = c_1 \mathcal{L}(y_1) + c_2 \mathcal{L}(y_2). \tag{6.8}$$

Another way to write this is to let $y(t) = c_1 y_1(t) + c_2 y_2(t)$, in which case

$$Y(s) = c_1 Y_1(s) + c_2 Y_2(s), \tag{6.9}$$

where Y_1 and Y_2 are the Laplace transforms for y_1 and y_2, respectively. Because the Laplace transform has this property, it is said to be a **linear operator**. The usefulness of the linearity of the Laplace transform is why it is listed first in Table 6.1.

It is worth pointing out that you know several other linear operators. One is a matrix, because it satisfies $\mathbf{A}(c_1\mathbf{y}_1 + c_2\mathbf{y}_2) = c_1\mathbf{A}\mathbf{y}_1 + c_2\mathbf{A}\mathbf{y}_2$. A second is differentiation, as it satisfies $\frac{d}{dt}[c_1 y_1(t) + c_2 y_2(t)] = c_1\frac{d}{dt}y_1(t) + c_2\frac{d}{dt}y_2(t)$. You are probably wondering if it's possible for mathematicians, or even engineers, to write entire textbooks on linear operators. Well, a Google book search will answer this question.

Using a Table

Table 6.1, and specifically Properties 7-10 in the table, make it easier to find some of the more common Laplace transforms. You simply find the function $y(t)$ in the third column, and then its Laplace transform $Y(s)$ is in the second column. The next example illustrates how this is done.

Example 3 (version 2): If $y(t) = 3t - \sin 2t$, find $Y(s)$.

Answer: Using linearity, as expressed in (6.8),

$$Y(s) = \mathcal{L}(3t - \sin 2t) = 3\mathcal{L}(t) - \mathcal{L}(\sin 2t).$$

From Table 6.1, using Property 8 (with $n = 1$ and $a = 0$), and Property 9 (with $a = 0$ and $\omega = 2$),

$$Y(s) = \frac{3}{s^2} - \frac{2}{s^2 + 4}. \quad \blacksquare$$

It is possible to extend the usefulness of Table 6.1 by using some of the properties of a Laplace transform. Exercise 4 considers one of particular note.

Exercises

1. Find the Laplace transform of the following functions.

a) $y = -e^{5t}$ d) $y = e^{-2t} - e^{7t}$ g) $y = te^{-t}$

b) $y = 3 + 4t$ e) $y = 4t^2$ h) $y = 2\sin(3\pi t + 4)$

c) $y = 2t + 4e^{-t}$ f) $y = (t - 3)^2$ i) $y = e^{2t} + 4\cos(2t)$

2. Find the Laplace transform of the following functions.

a) $y(t) = \begin{cases} 0 & \text{if } 0 \le t \le 2, \\ 5 & \text{if } 2 < t \end{cases}$

d) $y(t) = \begin{cases} 3 & \text{if } 0 \le t \le 1, \\ e^{-t} & \text{if } 1 < t \end{cases}$

b) $y(t) = \begin{cases} t & \text{if } 0 \le t \le 2, \\ 2 & \text{if } 2 < t \end{cases}$

e) $y(t) = \begin{cases} 5 - t & \text{if } 0 \le t \le 3, \\ t - 1 & \text{if } 3 < t \end{cases}$

c) $y(t) = \begin{cases} -1 & \text{if } 0 \le t \le 1, \\ 1 & \text{if } 1 < t < 2, \\ 0 & \text{if } 2 \le t \end{cases}$

f) $y(t) = \begin{cases} 0 & \text{if } 0 \le t \le 12, \\ 2 & \text{if } 12 < t < 15, \\ 0 & \text{if } 15 \le t \end{cases}$

3. One way to avoid using integration by parts is to use the formulas
$\cos x = \frac{1}{2}\left(e^{ix} + e^{-ix}\right)$ and $\sin x = \frac{1}{2i}\left(e^{ix} - e^{-ix}\right)$ (see Section 3.4.1).
Use these to find the Laplace transform of $y(t)$.

a) $y(t) = \cos(3t)$ c) $y(t) = e^{-t}\cos(\pi t)$

b) $y(t) = 4\sin(7t)$ d) $y(t) = \cos(t)\sin(2t)$

4. The exercise explores the usefulness of the formula

$$\int_0^\infty ty(t)e^{-st}dt = -\frac{d}{ds}\int_0^\infty y(t)e^{-st}dt.$$

Use this, and Table 6.1, to find the Laplace transform of the following
functions:

a) $t\sin(3t)$ b) $6t\cos(7t)$ c) $t^2\cos(t)$ d) $te^{-2t}\sin(5t)$

6.2 ▪ Inverse Laplace Transform

As will be seen when we get around to solving differential equations, we
will use the Laplace transform to change the problem from solving for y
to solving for Y. It is actually fairly easy to do this. Once Y is known,
it is then necessary to determine y. This requires us to know how to find
the inverse Laplace transform.

Using the $\mathcal{L}(y)$ notation, the inverse Laplace transform is written as
$\mathcal{L}^{-1}(Y)$. As an example, earlier we found that

$$\mathcal{L}(\sin 2t) = \frac{2}{s^2 + 4}.$$

	$Y(s) = \mathcal{L}(y)$	$y(t) = \mathcal{L}^{-1}(Y)$
1.	$aY(s) + bV(s)$	$ay(t) + bv(t)$
2.	$V(s)Y(s)$	$\int_0^t v(t-r)y(r)dr$
3.	$sY(s)$	$y'(t) + y(0)$
4.	$\frac{1}{s}Y(s)$	$\int_0^t y(r)dr$
5.	$e^{-as}Y(s)$	$y(t-a)H(t-a)$ for $a > 0$
6.	$Y(s+a)$	$e^{-at}y(t)$
7.	$\frac{1}{s}e^{-as}$	$H(t-a)$ for $a > 0$
8.	$\frac{n!}{(s+a)^{n+1}}$	$t^n e^{-at}$ for $n = 0, 1, 2, 3, \ldots$
9.	$\frac{\omega}{(s+a)^2+\omega^2}$	$e^{-at}\sin(\omega t)$
10.	$\frac{s+a}{(s+a)^2+\omega^2}$	$e^{-at}\cos(\omega t)$
11.	$\frac{cs+d}{(s-s_1)(s-s_2)}$	$\left[c + (ac+d)t\right]e^{at}$ if $s_1 = s_2 = a$ $\frac{1}{a-b}\left[(ac+d)e^{at} - (bc+d)e^{bt}\right]$ if $\begin{array}{l}s_1 = a\\ s_2 = b\end{array}$ $e^{at}\left[c\cos(bt) + \frac{ac+d}{b}\sin(bt)\right]$ if $\begin{array}{l}s_1 = a+ib\\ s_2 = a-ib\end{array}$
12.	$\frac{p(s)}{(s-s_1)(s-s_2)\cdots(s-s_n)}$	see (6.16)
13.	e^{-as}	$\delta(t-a)$ for $a > 0$
14.	$\frac{1}{(s+b)^n}e^{-as}$	$\frac{1}{(n-1)!}(t-a)^{n-1}e^{-b(t-a)}H(t-a)$ for $\begin{array}{l}a > 0,\\ n = 1, 2, 3, \ldots\end{array}$
15.	$\frac{1}{s}e^{-as}Y(s)$	$H(t-a)\int_0^{t-a} y(r)dr$ for $a > 0$

Table 6.1. *Laplace and inverse Laplace transforms. The function $H(x)$ is defined in (6.13), and $\delta(t)$ is defined in Section 6.5.1. Also, recall that $0! = 1$, and if $t > 0$, then $t^0 = 1$.*

The inverse is therefore

$$\mathcal{L}^{-1}\left(\frac{2}{s^2+4}\right) = \sin 2t\,.$$

The caveat here is that if $Y = \mathcal{L}(y)$, it is not always true that $y = \mathcal{L}^{-1}(Y)$. It is true for the above example, and this is because the original function $y(t)$ is continuous. What happens when $y(t)$ has a jump discontinuity will be discussed later.

In Section 6.4, the first differential equation we will solve using a Laplace transform is $y' + 3y = e^{2t}$. We will find that $Y = \frac{1}{s+3}(2 - \frac{1}{2-s})$, and this will mean that to find y we will need to determine $\mathcal{L}^{-1}(Y)$. There is a general formula for the inverse Laplace transform, which involves a line integral in the complex plane. Although this can provide some entertaining mathematical challenges, most find the inverse transform by using tables. Table 6.1 is an example, and it is the one used in this text. Note that the first six entries are general properties for the transform. The first one listed is the linearity property, as given in (6.8). Writing it in terms of the inverse transform, we have that

$$\mathcal{L}^{-1}\big(c_1 Y_1 + c_2 Y_2\big) = c_1 \mathcal{L}^{-1}(Y_1) + c_2 \mathcal{L}^{-1}(Y_2).$$

This is used for most of the examples in this chapter.

As demonstrated in the next example, when using a table, finding an inverse transform can be very easy.

Example: If $Y(s) = \frac{3}{s^2} - \frac{7s}{s^2+25}$, find $y(t)$.

Answer: Using the linearity property,

$$\mathcal{L}^{-1}(Y) = \mathcal{L}^{-1}\left(\frac{3}{s^2} - \frac{7s}{s^2+25}\right)$$

$$= 3\mathcal{L}^{-1}\left(\frac{1}{s^2}\right) - 7\mathcal{L}^{-1}\left(\frac{s}{s^2+25}\right).$$

From Property 8 in Table 6.1, with $n = 1$ and $a = 0$,

$$\mathcal{L}^{-1}\left(\frac{1}{s^2}\right) = t.$$

Similarly, from Property 10, with $a = 0$, and $\omega = 5$,

$$\mathcal{L}^{-1}\left(\frac{s}{s^2+25}\right) = \cos(5t).$$

Therefore,

$$y(t) = 3t - 7\cos(5t). \quad \blacksquare$$

6.2.1 · Jump Discontinuities

At points t where the original function $y(t)$ has a jump discontinuity, then $\mathcal{L}^{-1}(Y)$ equals the average in the jump in y. The formula is, for $t > 0$,

$$\mathcal{L}^{-1}(Y) = \frac{1}{2}\left[y(t^+) + y(t^-)\right]. \tag{6.10}$$

To illustrate, earlier we found that if

$$y(t) = \begin{cases} 3 & \text{if } 0 \le t \le 2, \\ -1 & \text{if } 2 < t, \end{cases} \tag{6.11}$$

then

$$Y(s) = -\frac{4}{s}e^{-2s} + \frac{3}{s}.$$

Except for $t = 2$, $\mathcal{L}^{-1}(Y) = y$. At $t = 2$, the average in the jump in $y(t)$ is $\frac{1}{2}\left[y(2^+) + y(2^-)\right] = \frac{1}{2}(3 - 1) = 1$. Therefore, the inverse transform is

$$\mathcal{L}^{-1}(Y) = \begin{cases} 3 & \text{if } 0 \le t < 2, \\ 1 & \text{if } t = 2, \\ -1 & \text{if } 2 < t. \end{cases} \tag{6.12}$$

It is convenient to use what is called the **Heaviside step function** $H(x)$ when jumps occur. This is defined as

$$H(x) \equiv \begin{cases} 0 & \text{if } x < 0, \\ \frac{1}{2} & \text{if } x = 0, \\ 1 & \text{if } 0 < x, \end{cases} \tag{6.13}$$

and this is shown in Figure 6.1. Note that this has built into its definition the value at a jump that is needed for the inverse Laplace transform.

To rewrite (6.12) using $H(x)$, since $\mathcal{L}^{-1}(Y)$ involves a jump of -4 at $t = 2$, then $\mathcal{L}^{-1}(Y) = 3 - 4H(t - 2)$.

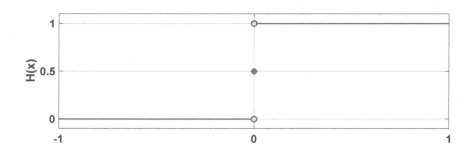

Figure 6.1. *Heaviside step function $H(x)$ as defined in (6.13).*

Example: If $Y = \frac{2}{s} + \frac{5}{s}e^{-3s} - \frac{6}{s}e^{-4s}$, find and then sketch y.

Answer: Using the linearity property,

$$\mathcal{L}^{-1}(Y) = \mathcal{L}^{-1}\left(\frac{2}{s} + \frac{5}{s}e^{-3s} - \frac{6}{s}e^{-4s}\right)$$

$$= 2\mathcal{L}^{-1}\left(\frac{1}{s}\right) + 5\mathcal{L}^{-1}\left(\frac{1}{s}e^{-3s}\right) - 6\mathcal{L}^{-1}\left(\frac{1}{s}e^{-4s}\right).$$

From Property 8 in Table 6.1, with $n = 0$ and $a = 0$,

$$\mathcal{L}^{-1}\left(\frac{1}{s}\right) = 1.$$

From Property 7, with $a = 3$ and $a = 4$,

$$\mathcal{L}^{-1}\left(\frac{1}{s}e^{-3s}\right) = H(t-3), \quad \text{and} \quad \mathcal{L}^{-1}\left(\frac{1}{s}e^{-4s}\right) = H(t-4).$$

Therefore,

$$y(t) = 2 + 5H(t-3) - 6H(t-4). \tag{6.14}$$

So, the solution starts out at $y = 2$, it has a jump of 5 at $t = 3$, so $y = 7$, and then it has another jump of -6 at $t = 4$, so $y = 1$. At the jumps, $y(3) = \frac{1}{2}(2+7) = \frac{9}{2}$, and $y(4) = \frac{1}{2}(7+1) = 4$. The plot of this function is given in Figure 6.2. ■

For those who are picky about doing things correctly, there is a mild case of notation abuse in the last example. Because the function $y(t)$ has a jump, and we only know its Laplace transform, it is not possible to determine the value of $y(t)$ at the jump. The function given in (6.14) is the answer that is consistent with the formula determined using the inverse Laplace transform. This situation will arise in this chapter any time the function $y(t)$ has a jump discontinuity.

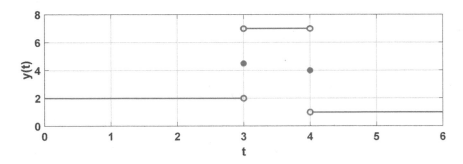

Figure 6.2. *The function $y(t)$ given in (6.14).*

6.2.2 ▪ Heaviside Expansion Theorem

There are numerous special cases for which formulas can be found for the inverse Laplace transform. One that deserves to be mentioned is the case of when $Y(s)$ can be written in the form

$$Y(s) = \frac{p(s)}{(s - s_1)(s - s_2) \cdots (s - s_n)}, \tag{6.15}$$

where $p(s)$ is a polynomial of degree less than n. The s_j's can be complex-valued but they must be distinct, which means that $s_j \neq s_k$ if $j \neq k$. In this case, using something called residue theory, it can be shown that the inverse transform $\mathcal{L}^{-1}(Y)$ is

$$y(t) = \sum_{j=1}^{n} \frac{p(s_j)}{q'(s_j)} e^{s_j t}, \tag{6.16}$$

where $q(s) = (s - s_1)(s - s_2) \cdots (s - s_n)$. The above result is often called the *Heaviside Expansion Theorem*.

Example: Find the inverse transform of

$$Y = \frac{2}{(s^2 + 1)(s^2 + 4)}.$$

Answer: To use the Heaviside Expansion Theorem, note that $q(s) = (s + i)(s - i)(s - 2i)(s + 2i)$. So, $s_1 = -i$, $s_2 = i$, $s_3 = 2i$, and $s_4 = -2i$. To compute $q'(s_j)$ it makes it a bit easier if you note that $q(s) = (s^2 + 1)(s^2 + 4) = s^4 + 5s^2 + 4$. So, $q'(s) = 4s^3 + 10s$, and this means that $q'(-i) = 4i - 10i = -6i$, $q'(i) = -6i$, $q'(2i) = -12i$, and $q'(-2i) = 12i$. With this, from (6.16) we get that

$$y(t) = \frac{2}{q'(s_1)} e^{s_1 t} + \frac{2}{q'(s_2)} e^{s_2 t} + \frac{2}{q'(s_3)} e^{s_3 t} + \frac{2}{q'(s_4)} e^{s_4 t}$$

$$= \frac{2}{-6i} e^{-it} + \frac{2}{6i} e^{it} + \frac{2}{-12i} e^{2it} + \frac{2}{12i} e^{-2it}$$

$$= \frac{1}{3i} \left(e^{it} - e^{-it} \right) - \frac{1}{6i} \left(e^{2it} - e^{-2it} \right).$$

Since $e^{i\theta} - e^{-i\theta} = 2i \sin \theta$, then

$$y(t) = \frac{2}{3} \sin t - \frac{1}{3} \sin 2t. \quad \blacksquare \tag{6.17}$$

Exercises

1. Sketch the function for $0 \leq t \leq T$, and then find its Laplace transform.

a) $y = H(t-6)$, $T = 10$ d) $y = 3H(t-2) - 4H(t-5)$, $T = 8$
b) $y = (t-1)H(t-1)$, $T = 3$ e) $y = 4H(3-t)$, $T = 5$
c) $y = [H(t-2)]^2$, $T = 4$ f) $y = 1/(2 + H(t-1))$, $T = 3$
g) $y = H(t) - H(t-1) + 3H(t-2) - H(t-3)$, $T = 5$
h) $y = H(t) + H(t-2) - H(4-t) - H(t-8)$, $T = 10$

2. Find the inverse Laplace transform of the following functions.

a) $Y = \frac{2}{s^2+9}$ i) $Y = \frac{2}{s^2+4} - \frac{3}{s^2+9}$

b) $Y = \frac{3}{(s+4)^2}$ j) $Y = \frac{5}{s^2} - \frac{3}{s-2}$

c) $Y = \frac{1}{s^2+3s-4}$ k) $Y = \frac{s+1}{(s+1)^2+9}e^{-3s}$

d) $Y = \frac{s+1}{s^2+2s+5}$ l) $Y = \left(\frac{1}{s^2} - \frac{1}{s^3}\right)e^{-2s}$

e) $Y = \frac{2s-3}{s^2-4}$ m) $Y = \frac{1}{s}\left(e^{-s} - e^{-2s} + e^{-3s}\right)$

f) $Y = \frac{2s-3}{s^2+2s+10}$ n) $Y = \frac{2}{s} - \frac{1}{s^2} + \frac{4}{s^3} - \frac{7}{s^4}$

g) $Y = \frac{s}{(s^2+9)(s^2+16)}$ o) $Y = \frac{5s+1}{s^2}e^{-5s}$

h) $Y = \frac{s}{(s^2-1)(s^2-2)}$ p) $Y = \frac{5s+1}{s^2+1}e^{-6s}$

3. Suppose that $y(t)$ is periodic with period $T > 0$. So, $y(t+T) = y(t)$ for all $t \geq 0$.

a) Show that
$$\int_T^\infty y(t)e^{-st}dt = e^{-sT}Y(s).$$

b) Writing $\int_0^\infty y(t)e^{-st}dt = \int_0^T y(t)e^{-st}dt + \int_T^\infty y(t)e^{-st}dt$, use the result from part (a) to show that
$$\mathcal{L}(y) = \frac{1}{1-e^{-sT}}\int_0^T y(t)e^{-st}dt.$$

4. The following functions are periodic with period T. Sketch the function for $0 \leq t \leq 3T$, and then use the result of Exercise 3(b) to find the Laplace transform. Also, provide an explanation for where the name of the wave comes from.

a) Square wave: $T = 2$, and $y(t) = H(t) - H(t-1)$, for $0 \leq t < 2$.
b) Sawtooth wave: $T = 1$, and $y(t) = t$, for $0 \leq t < 1$.
c) Triangle wave: $T = 2$, and $y(t) = tH(t) - 2(t-1)H(t-1)$, for $0 \leq t < 2$.
d) Bang-bang wave: $T = 2$, and $y(t) = H(t) - 2H(t-1)$, for $0 \leq t < 2$.

5. The floor function $y(t) = \lfloor t \rfloor$ is the greatest integer less than or equal to t. So, $\lfloor 5.3 \rfloor = 5$ and $\lfloor 7.0 \rfloor = 7$.

   a) Writing $\lfloor t \rfloor = t - g(t)$, what are: $g(0)$, $g(0.1)$, $g(0.8)$, and $g(1)$?

   b) Sketch $g(t)$ for $0 \le t < 5$. Use this to explain why $g(t)$ is periodic.

   c) Use the result from Exercise 3(b) to find $\mathcal{L}(\lfloor t \rfloor)$.

6. It is sometimes necessary to use a power series to determine an inverse transform. For example, to use the geometric series $(1 - z)^{-1} = 1 - z + z^2 + \cdots$ to write $(1 - e^{-s})^{-1} = 1 - e^{-s} + e^{-2s} + \cdots$. In this problem you are to use a Maclaurin series to find the inverse Laplace transform.

   a) $Y = \dfrac{1}{s(1-e^{-s})}$, use the geometric series for $(1 - z)^{-1}$

   b) $Y = \dfrac{1}{s\sqrt{1+e^{-s}}}$, use the series for $(1 + z)^{-1/2}$

   c) $Y = \dfrac{1}{s}\sqrt{1 + (1/s)}$, use the series for $\sqrt{1+z}$

6.3 ▪ Properties of the Laplace Transform

What follows is the derivation of Properties 2 and 3 in Table 6.1. They are important as they will be needed when solving differential equations.

6.3.1 ▪ Transformation of Derivatives

One of the hallmarks of the Laplace transform, as with most integral transforms, is that it converts differentiation into multiplication. To explain what this means, using integration by parts (with $u = e^{-st}$ and $dv = y'(t)dt$), we have the following:

$$\mathcal{L}(y'(t)) = \int_0^\infty y'(t)e^{-st}dt$$

$$= ye^{-st}\Big|_{t=0}^\infty + s\int_0^\infty ye^{-st}dt$$

$$= s\mathcal{L}(y) - y(0). \tag{6.18}$$

This holds assuming that $y'(t)$ is piecewise continuous, and $y(t)$ is continuous, for $t \ge 0$.

The above formula can be used to find the transform of higher derivatives. As an example, for the second derivative we have that

$$\mathcal{L}(y'') = s\mathcal{L}(y') - y'(0) = s\big[s\mathcal{L}(y) - y(0)\big] - y'(0)$$

$$= s^2\mathcal{L}(y) - y'(0) - sy(0). \tag{6.19}$$

The requirement here is that $y''(t)$ is piecewise continuous, and $y(t)$ and $y'(t)$ are continuous, for $t \ge 0$. Generalizing this to higher derivatives,

$$\mathcal{L}(y^{(n)}) = s^n\mathcal{L}(y) - y^{(n-1)}(0) - sy^{(n-2)}(0) - \cdots - s^{n-1}y(0),$$

with the corresponding generalization in the continuity requirements.

6.3.2 ▪ Convolution Theorem

A common integral that arises when solving differential equations is a convolution integral of the form

$$y(t) = \int_0^t g(t-\tau)v(\tau)d\tau. \tag{6.20}$$

Taking the Laplace transform of this equation we obtain

$$\mathcal{L}(y) = \int_0^\infty \int_0^t g(t-\tau)v(\tau)e^{-st}d\tau dt$$

$$= \int_0^\infty \int_\tau^\infty g(t-\tau)v(\tau)e^{-st}dt d\tau.$$

In the last line above, interchanging the order of integration used the fact that $0 < t < \infty$, $0 < \tau < t$ is equivalent to $0 < \tau < \infty$, $\tau < t < \infty$. Now, making the change of variables $t = r + \tau$ in the inner integral, we get that

$$\mathcal{L}(y) = \int_0^\infty \int_0^\infty g(r)v(\tau)e^{-s(r+t)}dr d\tau$$

$$= \int_0^\infty \left(v(\tau)e^{-s\tau} \int_0^\infty g(r)e^{-sr}dr \right) d\tau = V(s)G(s).$$

Using the inverse transform this can be written as

$$\mathcal{L}^{-1}(V(s)G(s)) = \int_0^t g(t-\tau)v(\tau)d\tau. \tag{6.21}$$

This is Property 2, in Table 6.1, and it is known as the convolution theorem.

Exercises

1. Find the Laplace transform in terms of $Y(s)$.

   a) $\mathcal{L}(y' - 4y)$, where $y(0) = 1$
   b) $\mathcal{L}(2y' + 7y)$, where $y(0) = -2$
   c) $\mathcal{L}(y'' + 5y)$, where $y(0) = 1$ and $y'(0) = -1$
   d) $\mathcal{L}(y'' + 3y' - 2y)$, where $y(0) = 1$ and $y'(0) = -3$
   e) $\mathcal{L}(4y'' + 2y')$, where $y(0) = -1$ and $y'(0) = 1$

2. Use the convolution theorem, as given in (6.21), to find the inverse transform. Note that how you select G and V will determine how difficult the resulting integral is to carry out.

   a) $\dfrac{1}{(s-1)(s^2+1)}$, taking $G(s) = \dfrac{1}{s-1}$ and $V(s) = \dfrac{1}{s^2+1}$

b) $\frac{s}{(s^2+1)^2}$, taking $V(s) = \frac{1}{s^2+1}$ and $G(s) = \frac{s}{s^2+1}$

c) $\frac{5}{(s+1)(s^2+4)}$

d) $\frac{1}{(s^2+1)(s^2-1)}$

e) $\frac{1}{s^3(s^2+1)}$

3. Explain why Property 4 in Table 6.1 is a special case of the convolution theorem.

6.4 ▪ Solving Differential Equations

The examples to follow illustrate how to use the Laplace transform to solve a linear initial value problem. As you will see, it is fairly easy to transform the equation and then solve for $Y(s)$. Most of the work is done trying to determine the inverse transform to find $y(t)$.

Example 1: Solve $y' + 3y = e^{2t}$, where $y(0) = 2$.

Answer: The first step is to take the Laplace transform of the differential equation, which gives

$$\mathcal{L}(y' + 3y) = \mathcal{L}(e^{2t}).$$

Using the linearity of the transform, and the derivative formula (6.18),

$$\begin{aligned}\mathcal{L}(y' + 3y) &= \mathcal{L}(y') + 3\mathcal{L}(y) \\ &= s\mathcal{L}(y) - y(0) + 3\mathcal{L}(y) \\ &= (s+3)Y(s) - 2.\end{aligned} \qquad (6.22)$$

Also,

$$\mathcal{L}(e^{2t}) = \int_0^\infty e^{2t}e^{-st}dt = \int_0^\infty e^{(2-s)t}dt = \frac{1}{s-2}.$$

The transformed problem is therefore $(s+3)Y - 2 = 1/(s-2)$, and from this we get that

$$Y = \frac{1}{s+3}\left(2 + \frac{1}{s-2}\right).$$

Consequently, using Table 6.1 (Properties 7 and 11),

$$y = \mathcal{L}^{-1}(Y) = 2\mathcal{L}^{-1}\left(\frac{1}{s+3}\right) + \mathcal{L}^{-1}\left(\frac{1}{(s+3)(s-2)}\right)$$

$$= 2e^{-3t} + \frac{1}{5}\left(e^{2t} - e^{-3t}\right) = \frac{9}{5}e^{-3t} + \frac{1}{5}e^{2t}. \quad \blacksquare$$

Example 2: Solve $y'' + y' - 2y = -\sin t$, where $y(0) = 1$ and $y'(0) = 1$.

Answer: Taking the Laplace transform of the differential equation

$$\mathcal{L}(y'' + y' - 2y) = \mathcal{L}(-\sin t).$$

Using the linearity of the transform, and the derivative formulas (6.18) and (6.19),

$$\mathcal{L}(y'' + y' - 2y) = \mathcal{L}(y'') + \mathcal{L}(y') - 2\mathcal{L}(y)$$
$$= s^2 Y - y'(0) - sy(0) + sY - y(0) - 2Y \quad (6.23)$$
$$= (s^2 + s - 2)Y - s - 2.$$

Since, using Property 9 in Table 6.1, $\mathcal{L}(\sin t) = 1/(s^2 + 1)$, then the transformed problem is

$$(s^2 + s - 2)Y - s - 2 = -\frac{1}{s^2 + 1}.$$

Solving for Y gives us

$$Y = \frac{1}{s - 1} - \frac{1}{(s^2 + 1)(s^2 + s - 2)}. \quad (6.24)$$

Taking the inverse transform, and using linearity,

$$y = \mathcal{L}^{-1}\left(\frac{1}{s - 1}\right) - \mathcal{L}^{-1}\left(\frac{1}{(s^2 + 1)(s^2 + s - 2)}\right).$$

Using Table 6.1, Property 8,

$$\mathcal{L}^{-1}\left(\frac{1}{s - 1}\right) = e^t.$$

For the other inverse transform, we will use partial fractions. The assumption is that

$$\frac{1}{(s^2 + 1)(s^2 + s - 2)} = \frac{As + B}{s^2 + 1} + \frac{Cs + D}{s^2 + s - 2}$$
$$= \frac{(A + C)s^3 + (A + B + D)s^2 + (-2A + B + C)s - 2B + D}{(s^2 + 1)(s^2 + s - 2)}.$$

Equating like powers of s in the numerators, we get that $A + C = 0$, $A + B + D = 0$, $-2A + B + C = 0$, and $-2B + D = 1$. Solving these equations one finds that $A = -1/10$, $B = -3/10$, $C = 1/10$, and $D = -2/5$. So, using Table 6.1, Properties 10 (for A), 9 (for B), and 11 (for C and D),

$$\mathcal{L}^{-1}\left(\frac{1}{(s^2+1)(s^2+s-2)}\right) = \mathcal{L}^{-1}\left(\frac{As+B}{s^2+1}\right) + \mathcal{L}^{-1}\left(\frac{Cs+D}{s^2+s-2}\right)$$

$$= A\cos t + B\sin t + \frac{1}{2}\Big[(C+D)e^t + (2C-D)e^{-2t}\Big].$$

$$(6.25)$$

Therefore, the solution is

$$y = \frac{1}{10}\cos t + \frac{3}{10}\sin t + \frac{1}{15}e^{-2t} + \frac{5}{6}e^t. \quad \blacksquare$$

Two comments need to be made about the above examples. First, both can be solved *much* easier using the method of undetermined coefficients. The Laplace transform was used to illustrate how it can be used to solve such problems. Second, the question invariability comes up as to what is the easiest way to determine the inverse transform. For example, you can use the Heaviside expansion theorem, the convolution theorem, or partial fractions to obtain (6.25). There is often no clear answer to which one to use, and it often depends on what you are the most comfortable with and what is applicable. As it turns out, except perhaps when taking a course in differential equations, very few people work out even slightly complicated inverse transforms by hand. Instead, they either buy a book of tables, such as Oberhettinger and Badii [1973], or, even more likely, they use a symbolic computing system like Maple or Mathematica.

6.4.1 ▪ The Transfer Function

In engineering, when solving a linear differential equation, it is common to introduce what is known as the transfer function $\overline{H}(s)$. To find $\overline{H}(s)$ you take the Laplace transform of the differential equation, assuming the initial conditions are all zero, and then solve for $Y(s)$. This yields $Y(s) = \overline{H}(s)F(s)$, where $F(s)$ is the Laplace transform of the forcing function. In this sense, $\overline{H}(s)$ is the transfer function from the input $F(s)$ to the output $Y(s)$. It should be pointed out that the transfer function is usually denoted as $H(s)$. In this text, $\overline{H}(s)$ is used to avoid confusing it with the Heaviside function.

Example 1: Find the transfer function for $y' + 3y = \sqrt{t}$.

Answer: Taking $y(0) = 0$, then from (6.22), $(s+3)Y = F$, where $F = \mathcal{L}(\sqrt{t})$. Consequently, $\overline{H}(s) = 1/(s+3)$. $\quad\blacksquare$

Example 2: Find the transfer function for $y'' + y' - 2y = \ln(1+t^2)$.

Answer: Taking $y(0) = 0$ and $y'(0) = 0$, then from (6.23), we have that $(s^2 + s - 2)Y = F$, where $F = \mathcal{L}(\ln(1+t^2))$. Consequently, $\overline{H}(s) = 1/(s^2 + s - 2)$. $\quad\blacksquare$

Once you know the transfer function, then a particular solution of the differential equation can be written down using the convolution theorem. Namely, using (6.21), a particular solution is

$$y_p(t) = \int_0^t h(t - \tau) f(\tau) d\tau, \qquad (6.26)$$

where $h(t) = \mathcal{L}^{-1}(\overline{H})$.

The above solution is useful as it can be used to solve the IVP when the initial conditions are not zero. This is because the solution can be written as $y(t) = y_p(t) + y_h(t)$, where $y_p(t)$ is given in (6.26) and $y_h(t)$ is the solution of the associated homogeneous differential equation that satisfies the nonzero initial conditions. This is similar to the approach used in Section 3.9.1. Moreover, it is not necessary to use the Laplace transform to find $y_h(t)$. An example of solving an IVP in this way is given next.

Example 3: Solve $y'' - 2y' - 3y = \sqrt{t}$, where $y(0) = 1$ and $y'(0) = -1$.

Step 1: Find y_p. The transfer function for $y'' - 2y' - 3y = \sqrt{t}$ is $\overline{H}(s) = 1/(s^2 - 2s - 3)$. Using Property 11 from Table 6.1, $h(t) = \mathcal{L}^{-1}(\overline{H}) = (e^{3t} - e^{-t})/4$. So, from (6.26),

$$y_p(t) = \frac{1}{4} \int_0^t \left[e^{3(t-\tau)} - e^{-t+\tau} \right] \sqrt{\tau} d\tau.$$

The integral can not be written in terms of elementary functions, and so this is the final answer.

Step 2: Find y_h. The IVP to solve is $y'' - 2y' - 3y = 0$, where $y(0) = 1$ and $y'(0) = -1$. Assuming that $y = e^{rt}$, and proceeding as in Section 3.5, one ends up finding that $y_h(t) = e^{-t}$.

Step 3: The solution is $y = y_p + y_h$. In other words,

$$y(t) = e^{-t} + \frac{1}{4} \int_0^t \left[e^{3(t-\tau)} - e^{-t+\tau} \right] \sqrt{\tau} d\tau. \quad \blacksquare$$

6.4.2 ▪ Comments and Limitations on Using the Laplace Transform

It is useful to know some of the limitations on using the Laplace transform to solve a differential equation. First, the differential equation must be linear. As the examples illustrate, the Laplace transform can be used irrespective of the order of the equation. It can also be used to solve partial differential equations, delay equations, and integral equations. However, in all cases, the equations are linear.

A second limitation is that the differential equation should have constant coefficients. For example, the Laplace transform will not be successful when trying to solve $y' + e^t y = 0$ or $y'' + (1 + t)^2 y' + 5y = 0$.

Occasionally you will come across an equation with non-constant coefficients that can be solved using a Laplace transform, and an example is Airy's equation $y'' + ty = 0$. You might try finding the Laplace transform of this equation to see why the coefficients are "just right" so that the method works.

Many of the formulas for the inverse transform have been stated without proof. This includes the Heaviside Expansion Theorem (6.16) and the formula at a jump discontinuity (6.10). If you are interested in learning about the more theoretical aspects of the subject, you might want to consult Davies [2002] or, if you are more adventurous, Widder [1941].

Exercises

1. Use the Laplace transform to find the solution of the IVP.

   a) $2y' + y = 1$, $\quad y(0) = 2$
   b) $3y' = -y + e^{-t}$, $\quad y(0) = \frac{1}{2}$
   c) $y'' + y' - 2y = 0$, $\quad y(0) = 0$, $y'(0) = -1$
   d) $y'' - 6y' + 9y = 0$, $\quad y(0) = 0$, $y'(0) = 2$
   e) $5y'' - y' = 0$, $\quad y(0) = -1$, $y'(0) = -1$
   f) $4y'' + y = 0$, $\quad y(0) = -1$, $y'(0) = -1$
   g) $y'' - 2y' + 2y = 0$, $\quad y(0) = -1$, $y'(0) = -1$
   h) $y'' + 2y' + 5y = 0$, $\quad y(0) = 0$, $y'(0) = -6$

2. Use the Laplace transform to find the solution of the IVP.

   a) $y'' + y' - 2y = 12t$, $y(0) = 0$, $y'(0) = 0$
   b) $y'' + 4y = 8t^2$, $y(0) = 0$, $y'(0) = 0$
   c) $y'' - y' = 2\sin t$, $y(0) = 0$, $y'(0) = 0$
   d) $y'' + 3y' = 3t + 1$, $y(0) = 0$, $y'(0) = 0$
   e) $y'' - 2y' + 5y = 5 - 4e^{-t}$, $y(0) = 0$, $y'(0) = 0$

3. For the following, find the transfer function $\overline{H}(s)$ and then write down the resulting particular solution. You do not need to evaluate the integral.

   a) $y' + 3y = \ln(1 + 3t)$
   b) $y'' + 9y = \sqrt{1 + t}$
   c) $2y'' + 3y' - 2y = 1/(1 + t)$
   d) $y'' + 2y' + 5y = \sin(1 + t^2)$

4. Proceeding as in Example 3, find the solution of the following IVPs.

   a) $y' + 3y = \ln(1 + 3t)$, where $y(0) = 1$
   b) $y'' + 9y = \sqrt{1 + t}$, where $y(0) = 1$ and $y'(0) = 0$
   c) $2y'' + 3y' - 2y = 1/(1 + t)$, where $y(0) = 2$ and $y'(0) = -3$
   d) $y'' + 2y' + 5y = \sin(1 + t^2)$, where $y(0) = 0$ and $y'(0) = 2$

6.5 ▪ Solving Equations with Non-Smooth Forcing

The next example considers how to solve a differential equation with a discontinuous forcing function. This is a situation that is not uncommon in applications.

Example: Solve $y'' + 3y' + 2y = f(t)$, where $y(0) = 1$, $y'(0) = -1$, and

$$f(t) = \begin{cases} 2 & \text{if } 0 \le t \le 3, \\ 0 & \text{if } 3 < t. \end{cases}$$

Answer: Taking the Laplace transform of the differential equation,

$$\mathcal{L}(y'' + 3y' + 2y) = \mathcal{L}(f). \tag{6.27}$$

Using the linearity of the transform, and the derivative formulas (6.18) and (6.19),

$$\mathcal{L}(y'' + 3y' + 2y) = \mathcal{L}(y'') + 3\mathcal{L}(y') + 2\mathcal{L}(y)$$
$$= s^2 Y - y'(0) - sy(0) + 3(sY - y(0)) + 2Y$$
$$= (s^2 + 3s + 2)Y - s - 2.$$

Also, $\mathcal{L}(f) = \int_0^3 2e^{-st} dt = 2(1 - e^{-3s})/s$. Consequently, from (6.27), we have that

$$(s+1)(s+2)Y = s + 2 + \frac{2}{s}\left(1 - e^{-3s}\right),$$

which means that

$$Y = \frac{1}{s+1} + \frac{2}{s(s+2)(s+1)}\left(1 - e^{-3s}\right). \tag{6.28}$$

To determine the inverse transform, using Property 8 from Table 6.1, $\mathcal{L}^{-1}(1/(s+1)) = e^{-t}$. Also, from Property 11,

$$\mathcal{L}^{-1}\left(\frac{1}{(s+2)(s+1)}\right) = e^{-t} - e^{-2t}.$$

Consequently, using Properties 5 and 15 (respectively),

$$\mathcal{L}^{-1}\left(\frac{2}{s(s+2)(s+1)}\left(1 - e^{-3s}\right)\right)$$
$$= \mathcal{L}^{-1}\left(\frac{2}{s(s+2)(s+1)}\right) - \mathcal{L}^{-1}\left(\frac{2}{s(s+2)(s+1)}e^{-3s}\right)$$
$$= 2\int_0^t (e^{-r} - e^{-2r})dr + 2H(t-3)\int_0^{t-3}(e^{-r} - e^{-2r})dr$$
$$= -2e^{-t} + e^{-2t} + 1 + H(t-3)(1 - 2e^{3-t} + e^{-2t+6}).$$

The resulting solution is therefore

$$y = 1 + e^{-2t} - e^{-t} - \left(1 + e^{-2(t-3)} - 2e^{-(t-3)}\right)H(t-3). \quad \blacksquare$$

A comment needs to be made about the mathematical correctness of the solution we just derived. Namely, $y(t)$ and $y'(t)$ are defined and continuous for $0 \leq t < \infty$, but $y''(t)$ is not continuous at $t = 3$ (it is, however, continuous everywhere else). This throws into question whether the differential equation $y'' + 3y' + 2y = f(t)$ is defined at $t = 3$. The way this needs to be interpreted is that the differential equation holds for $0 < t < 3$, and then again for $3 < t < \infty$. The discontinuity in the forcing function effectively resets the problem at $t = 3$. One approach to dealing with this is to break the problem into two IVPs, one for $0 < t < 3$, and another for $3 < t < \infty$. By using the Laplace transform we have been able to avoid having to do this. This is possible because the continuity requirements to use (6.19) are satisfied for this problem.

6.5.1 ▪ Impulse Forcing

The idea underlying impulse forcing is that the force is fairly intense but it occurs over a short time interval. Writing the interval as $t_0 - \varepsilon < t < t_0 + \varepsilon$, we are considering the situation of when the forcing has the form

$$f(t) = \begin{cases} 0 & \text{if} \quad 0 \leq t \leq t_0 - \varepsilon, \\ d(t) & \text{if} \quad t_0 - \varepsilon < t < t_0 + \varepsilon, \\ 0 & \text{if} \quad t_0 + \varepsilon \leq t. \end{cases} \qquad (6.29)$$

With this, the solution of $y' = f$, where $y(0) = 0$, is

$$y = \begin{cases} 0 & \text{if} \quad 0 \leq t \leq t_0 - \varepsilon, \\ \int_{t_0 - \varepsilon}^{t} d(r)dr & \text{if} \quad t_0 - \varepsilon < t < t_0 + \varepsilon, \\ D & \text{if} \quad t_0 + \varepsilon \leq t, \end{cases} \qquad (6.30)$$

where

$$D = \int_{t_0 - \varepsilon}^{t_0 + \varepsilon} d(r)dr.$$

We are assuming that the forcing interval is very short, but D is large enough to be meaningful. To put this in physical terms, it is as if we are hitting the system with a hammer.

There is a mathematical idealization for a concentrated force that makes solving the problem easier than trying to use a formulation as in (6.29). This is done by introducing what is known as the delta function.

Delta Function. *The delta function $\delta(t)$ is defined to have the following properties:*

1. Given any t_0,

$$\delta(t - t_0) = 0, \quad \text{when } t \neq t_0. \qquad (6.31)$$

2. *Given any continuous function $g(t)$, and assuming $a < t_0 < b$:*

$$\int_a^b \delta(t - t_0)g(t)dt = g(t_0),$$ (6.32)

and

$$\int_a^{t_0} \delta(t - t_0)g(t)dt = \int_{t_0}^b \delta(t - t_0)g(t)dt = \frac{1}{2}g(t_0).$$ (6.33)

As an example of how the delta function is used, instead of using (6.29), the forcing is assumed to have the form $f(t) = D\delta(t - t_0)$. This means we are assuming that there is *a delta forcing at t_0 with strength D*. With this, the differential equation becomes

$$y' = D\delta(t - t_0),$$

where $y(0) = 0$. The solution of this IVP is

$$y = \int_0^t D\delta(r - t_0)dr.$$

To evaluate this, first note that if $0 \leq t < t_0$, then from (6.31), $y(t) = 0$. If $t = t_0$, then from (6.33), $y(t_0) = D/2$. Lastly, when $t_0 < t$, then from (6.32), $y(t) = D$. Consequently, the solution is

$$y = \begin{cases} 0 & \text{if} \quad 0 \leq t < t_0, \\ \frac{1}{2}D & \text{if} \quad t = t_0, \\ D & \text{if} \quad t_0 < t. \end{cases}$$ (6.34)

Except for the very small time interval $t_0 - \varepsilon < t < t_0 + \varepsilon$, this solution is the same as the one in (6.30). Moreover, the above solution is consistent with what is obtained using the line integral formula for the inverse Laplace transform.

The rationale for the stated properties of the delta function can be explained by considering the case of when d is constant. The assumption is that the total force D, what is known as the impulse, remains fixed as the time interval decreases (see Figure 6.3). This requires that $d = D/(2\varepsilon)$. In other words, the magnitude of the force increases as the time interval decreases. Consequently, in the limit, the forcing is zero if $t \neq t_0$ and it is infinite at $t = t_0$. This explains (6.31), and it also explains why you will see the statement that $\delta(0) = \infty$. This limit can also be used to explain (6.32). Finally, it is being assumed that the impulse forcing is symmetric about t_0, as it is in the case of when d is constant, and this gives us (6.33).

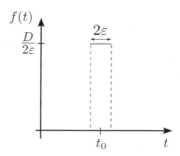

Figure 6.3. *A fixed impulse, applied over the time interval $t_0 - \varepsilon < t < t_0 + \varepsilon$, used to explain the stated properties of the delta function.*

Example 1: If $f(t) = \delta(t - a)$, where $a > 0$, find $\mathcal{L}(f)$.

Answer: Using (6.32),

$$\mathcal{L}\big(\delta(t - a)\big) = \int_0^\infty \delta(t - a)e^{-st}dt$$

$$= e^{-as}.$$

This is Property 13 in Table 6.1.   ■

Example 2: If $f(t) = 5\delta(t - 1) - 9\delta(t - 2) + \delta(t - 3)$, find $\mathcal{L}(f)$.

Answer: Using linearity and Property 13 in Table 6.1,

$$\mathcal{L}(f) = 5\mathcal{L}\big(\delta(t - 1)\big) - 9\mathcal{L}\big(\delta(t - 2)\big) + \mathcal{L}\big(\delta(t - 3)\big)$$

$$= 5e^{-s} - 9e^{-2s} + e^{-3s}.$$ ■

Example 3: Solve $y'' + y = 2\delta(t - 15)$, where $y(0) = 0$ and $y'(0) = 0$.

Answer: Taking the Laplace transform of the differential equation gives $\mathcal{L}(y'' + y) = \mathcal{L}(2\delta(t - 15))$. Using the linearity of the transform, and the derivative formula (6.19), we get that

$$s^2 Y - sy(0) - y'(0) + Y = 2e^{-15s} .$$

From the given initial conditions, and solving for Y,

$$Y = \frac{2}{s^2 + 1}e^{-15s} .$$

Since

$$\mathcal{L}^{-1}\left(\frac{2}{s^2 + 1}\right) = 2\sin t,$$

then using Property 5, from Table 6.1,

$$y = 2\sin(t - 15)H(t - 15).$$ ■

Example 4: Evaluate $\int_{-\infty}^{t} \delta(r)dr$, for $-\infty < t < \infty$.

Answer: This can be answered by considering three cases. First, if $t < 0$, then $\delta(r) = 0$ for $-\infty < r \leq t$, and we conclude the integral is zero. If $t > 0$, then from (6.32) with $g(t) = 1$, the integral is equal to one. Finally, when $t = 0$, from (6.33) we get the value of $1/2$. Therefore, we have that

$$H(t) = \int_{-\infty}^{t} \delta(r)dr.$$

In this sense we can write that

$$H'(t) = \delta(t). \quad \blacksquare$$

Mathematical Tidbits

As you likely noticed, $\delta(t)$ is not actually a function. The more accurate statement is that it is a *distribution*, or a *generalized function*. There are various ways to obtain a mathematically rigorous definition of $\delta(t)$, using limits or test functions. How limits are used was explained very briefly earlier. This will not be pursued any further, but the question does arise as to what is permitted when using the delta function. As demonstrated in Example 2, linear combinations of delta functions are allowed. It is also possible to both differentiate and integrate a delta function. What should be avoided is using a discontinuous $g(t)$ in (6.32), and Exercise 4 is an example why. Also, what is not allowed, generally, involves nonlinear operations. So, expressions such as $\delta(t-1)\delta(t-2)$, $\delta(t-1)/\delta(t-2)$, and $\sin(\delta(t-1))$ are not allowed. If you are interested in the various properties of the delta function, you might look at its Wikipedia page.

The nonstandard nature of the delta function amplifies a complication with the Laplace transform at $t = 0$ that needs to be mentioned. It is not uncommon in certain applications to use the forcing function $f(t) = \delta(t)$, which means that it is located at $t = 0$. This puts it at the lower point of integration for the Laplace transform. The resulting integral can be evaluated using (6.33), giving $\mathcal{L}(\delta(t)) = 1/2$. However, it is almost universally stated that $\mathcal{L}(\delta(t)) = 1$. One way to explain this involves continuity, in the sense that this is what you obtain from Property 13, in Table 6.1, when letting $a \to 0^+$. On the other hand, one gets $\mathcal{L}(\delta(t)) = 0$ when letting $a \to 0^-$. This has lead those determined to obtain $\mathcal{L}(\delta(t)) = 1$ to find some rather creative ways to redefine the Laplace transform. What this involves is not considered here, but if you are interested in learning more about this issue, you should consult Hoskins [2009].

Exercises

1. Use the Laplace transform to find the solution of the IVP.

   a) $y' + 4y = 3H(t - 1), \quad y(0) = 1$
   b) $2y' - y = 1 - H(t - 4), \quad y(0) = -1$
   c) $y' + y = 2\delta(t - 3), \quad y(0) = -1$
   d) $y' - 4y = 2H(t - 2) - \delta(t - 1), \quad y(0) = 0$
   e) $y'' - y' - 6y = 3H(t - 5), \quad y(0) = 0, \, y'(0) = 0$
   f) $y'' + 4y = 3H(t - 4) - 3H(t - 2), \quad y(0) = 0, \, y'(0) = 0$
   g) $y'' - 4y' = 3\delta(t - 1), \quad y(0) = 0, \, y'(0) = 0$
   h) $y'' + y = \delta(t - 3) - 2\delta(t - 2), \quad y(0) = 0, \, y'(0) = 0$

2. There are usually multiple ways to find an inverse transform, and this exercise illustrates this by reconsidering (6.28).

   a) Using partial fractions, the assumption is

   $$\frac{2}{s(s + 2)(s + 1)} = \frac{A}{s} + \frac{B}{s + 2} + \frac{C}{s + 1}.$$

   Find A, B, and C, and then determine the inverse transform.

   b) Find the inverse transform of the function in part (a) but use Property 12, with $n = 3$.

3. Show that the following identities hold for the delta function. Do this by showing that when the left and right sides of the equation are inserted into (6.31)-(6.33), that they produce the same result.

   a) $\delta(a(t - t_0)) = \frac{1}{a}\delta(t - t_0), \quad$ for $\quad a > 0$
   b) $\delta(t_0 - t) = \delta(t - t_0)$
   c) If g(t) is continuous, then $g(t)\delta(t - t_0) = g(t_0)\delta(t - t_0)$.

4. In quantum physics there are occasions when the coefficients of the differential equation contain delta functions. The point of this exercise is to demonstrate that care is needed in such situations.

   a) Consider the problem of solving

   $$y'(t) = \delta(t - t_0)y(t), \text{ for } t > 0,$$

   where $t_0 > 0$ and $y(0) = 1$. Using separation of variables, and Example 4, find the solution. Make sure to determine its value for $0 \le t < t_0$, for $t = t_0$, and for $t_0 < t$. For the record, this is the correct solution of this problem.

   b) By simply integrating the differential equation in part (a), and then using the initial condition, one gets that

   $$y(t) = 1 + \int_0^t y(r)\delta(r - t_0)dr.$$

Not thinking too hard about the situation, and using (6.31)-(6.33), explain how you might conclude that

$$y = \begin{cases} 1 & \text{if} \quad 0 \le t < t_0, \\ 2 & \text{if} \quad t = t_0, \\ 3 & \text{if} \quad t_0 < t. \end{cases}$$

This differs from the solution for part (a). Where is the error made in the derivation of the above solution?

6.6 ▪ Solving Linear Systems

The Laplace transform can be used to solve a linear system of differential equations, and this is often the approach taken for what are known as state space models in engineering. It is relatively easy to do this, and to explain why, suppose we want to solve

$$x' = ax + by + f(t), \tag{6.35}$$
$$y' = cx + dy + g(t), \tag{6.36}$$

where $x(0) = x_0$ and $y(0) = y_0$. Taking the Laplace transform of each equation, and using (6.18), we get

$$sX - x_0 = aX + bY + F, \tag{6.37}$$
$$sY - y_0 = cX + dY + G, \tag{6.38}$$

where X, Y, F, and G are the Laplace transforms of x, y, f, and g, respectively. What we have shown is that if the original differential equation is written as $\mathbf{x}' = \mathbf{A}\mathbf{x} + \mathbf{f}$, then the transformed equation is

$$s\mathbf{X} - \mathbf{x}_0 = \mathbf{A}\mathbf{X} + \mathbf{F}, \tag{6.39}$$

where $\mathbf{X} = \mathcal{L}(\mathbf{x})$, $\mathbf{F} = \mathcal{L}(\mathbf{f})$, and $\mathbf{x}_0 = \mathbf{x}(0)$. This is the form obtained in the general case of when there are n equations, and $\mathbf{A}$ is an $n \times n$ constant matrix.

The next step is to solve for X and Y, and then attempt to find the inverse transforms. How hard it is to find the inverse transforms depends on f and g.

Example 1: Using the Laplace transform, solve

$$x' = x - y,$$
$$y' = 4x - 2y,$$

where $x(0) = 1$ and $y(0) = -1$.

Answer: From (6.37) and (6.38) the transformed equations are

$$sX - 1 = X - Y,$$
$$sY + 1 = 4X - 2Y.$$

From the first equation, $Y = 1 + (1 - s)X$, and after substituting this into the second equation, and simplifying, one finds that

$$X = \frac{s + 3}{s^2 + s + 2}.$$

Since $s^2 + s + 2 = (s - s_1)(s - s_2)$, where $s_1 = (-1 + i\sqrt{7})/2$ and $s_2 = (-1 - i\sqrt{7})/2$, then from Property 11 of Table 6.1,

$$x = \mathcal{L}^{-1}(X) = e^{-t/2}\left(\cos(\omega t) + \frac{5}{2\omega}\sin(\omega t)\right),$$

where $\omega = \sqrt{7}/2$. To find y we can either find the inverse transform for Y, or we can use the first differential equation. The latter option is easiest, and so

$$y = x - x'$$

$$= e^{-t/2}\left(-\cos(\omega t) + \frac{11}{2\omega}\sin(\omega t)\right). \quad \blacksquare$$

Example 2: Using the Laplace transform, solve

$$x' = 3x - 6y + f(t),$$
$$y' = x - 4y + g(t),$$

where $x(0) = 0$ and $y(0) = 0$. Also, $f(t)$ and $g(t)$ are continuous functions.

Answer: From (6.37) and (6.38) the transformed equations are

$$sX = 3X - 6Y + F,$$
$$sY = X - 4Y + G.$$

From the second equation, $X = (s+4)Y - G$, and after substituting this into the first equation, and simplifying, one finds that

$$Y = \frac{s - 3}{s^2 + s - 6}G(s) + \frac{1}{s^2 + s - 6}F(s).$$

The convolution theorem is going to be used in finding the inverse transform, and in preparation for this note that, using Property 11 of Table 6.1,

$$\mathcal{L}^{-1}\left(\frac{1}{s^2 + s - 6}\right) = \mathcal{L}^{-1}\left(\frac{1}{(s - 2)(s + 3)}\right) = \frac{1}{5}\left(e^{2t} - e^{-3t}\right),$$

and

$$\mathcal{L}^{-1}\left(\frac{s-3}{s^2+s-6}\right) = \frac{1}{5}\left(6e^{-3t} - e^{2t}\right).$$

So, using the convolution theorem, which is Property 2 of Table 6.1,

$$\mathcal{L}^{-1}\left(\frac{1}{s^2+s-6}F(s)\right) = \int_0^t \frac{1}{5}\left(e^{2(t-r)} - e^{-3(t-r)}\right)f(r)dr,$$

and

$$\mathcal{L}^{-1}\left(\frac{s-3}{s^2+s-6}G(s)\right) = \int_0^t \frac{1}{5}\left(6e^{-3(t-r)} - e^{2(t-r)}\right)g(r)dr.$$

Therefore, the solution is

$$y(t) = \frac{1}{5}\int_0^t \left(e^{2(t-r)} - e^{-3(t-r)}\right)f(r)dr$$

$$+ \frac{1}{5}\int_0^t \left(6e^{-3(t-r)} - e^{2(t-r)}\right)g(r)dr.$$

To find x you can either find the inverse transform for X, or you can use the second differential equation (similar to what was done in the previous example). ■

6.6.1 ▪ Chapter 4 versus Chapter 6

In Chapter 4 we solved problems as in Example 1 using an eigenvalue approach. In contrast, using the Laplace transform avoids this and it solves the problem directly. Moreover, in Example 2, using the Laplace transform the inhomogeneous problem was solved with little fanfare. This was not done in Chapter 4 as it would have involved introducing either undetermined coefficients or variation of parameters. The apparent conclusion is that linear systems are more easily solved using the Laplace transform than the eigenvalue approach. This is true for systems with two equations and the reason is that it is relatively easy to solve for X and Y. However, for larger systems the advantage switches to the eigenvalue approach. The reason is that larger systems are almost always solved numerically (i.e., using a computer). The eigenvalue approach provides a representation of the solution (4.25), and it is relatively easy to compute the terms in that expression. In contrast, from (6.39),

$$\mathbf{X} = \left(s\mathbf{I} - \mathbf{A}\right)^{-1}(\mathbf{F} + \mathbf{x}_0).$$

This requires finding the inverse matrix and then trying to determine the inverse transform of the resulting formula for $\mathbf{X}$. There are ways this can be done, such as using a geometric series expansion for $(s\mathbf{I} - \mathbf{A})^{-1}$, but how this is carried out is beyond the purview of this textbook. Those interested might want to look at Friedland [2005] and Cohen [2007].

Exercises

1. Use the Laplace transform to find the solution of the IVP, with

$$\mathbf{x}(0) = \begin{pmatrix} 4 \\ -1 \end{pmatrix}.$$

a) $\mathbf{x}' = \begin{pmatrix} -1 & 6 \\ 1 & 0 \end{pmatrix} \mathbf{x}$ c) $\mathbf{x}' = \begin{pmatrix} 3 & 1 \\ 1 & 3 \end{pmatrix} \mathbf{x}$ e) $\mathbf{x}' = \begin{pmatrix} 2 & 0 \\ -1 & 2 \end{pmatrix} \mathbf{x}$

b) $\mathbf{x}' = \begin{pmatrix} 0 & \frac{1}{4} \\ 1 & 0 \end{pmatrix} \mathbf{x}$ d) $\mathbf{x}' = \begin{pmatrix} 2 & 1 \\ 6 & 3 \end{pmatrix} \mathbf{x},$ f) $\mathbf{x}' = \begin{pmatrix} 1 & 1 \\ -4 & 1 \end{pmatrix} \mathbf{x}$

2. This exercise uses the Laplace transform to solve

$$x' = ax + by,$$
$$y' = cx + dy,$$

where $x(0) = x_0$ and $y(0) = y_0$.

a) Taking the Laplace of the above equations, and then solving for X and Y, show that

$$X = \frac{1}{(s - r_1)(s - r_2)} \big((s - d)x_0 + by_0\big),$$

$$Y = \frac{1}{(s - r_1)(s - r_2)} \big(cx_0 + (s - a)y_0\big).$$

b) What values of a, b, c, and d result in r_1 and r_2 being real and $r_1 \neq r_2$? Assuming this is the case, use the inverse Laplace transform to find x and y.

c) What values of a, b, c, and d result in r_1 and r_2 being complex (with a nonzero imaginary part)? Assuming this is the case, use the inverse Laplace transform to find x and y.

d) What values of a, b, c, and d result in $r_1 = r_2$? Assuming this is the case, use the inverse Laplace transform to find x and y.

3. As defined in Section 6.4.1, the transfer function $\overline{\mathbf{H}}(s)$ is obtained from (6.39) by setting $\mathbf{x}_0 = \mathbf{0}$ and solving for $\mathbf{X}$. The result is

$$\overline{\mathbf{H}}(s) = (s\mathbf{I} - \mathbf{A})^{-1}.$$

Find the transfer function for the following systems.

a) $\mathbf{x}' = \begin{pmatrix} -1 & 6 \\ 1 & 0 \end{pmatrix} \mathbf{x}$

c) $\mathbf{x}' = \begin{pmatrix} 2 & 0 \\ -1 & 2 \end{pmatrix} \mathbf{x}$

b) $\mathbf{x}' = \begin{pmatrix} 0 & \frac{1}{4} \\ 1 & 0 \end{pmatrix} \mathbf{x}$

d) $\mathbf{x}' = \begin{pmatrix} 1 & -4 \\ 1 & 1 \end{pmatrix} \mathbf{x}$

Chapter 7

Partial Differential Equations

A partial differential equation is simply a differential equation with more than one independent variable. It is typical that the independent variables are time (t) and space (x). If $u(x,t)$ is the dependent variable, then examples of partial differential equations (PDEs) are

$$\text{Advection Equation:} \quad u_t + au_x = 0$$

$$\text{Diffusion Equation:} \quad u_t = Du_{xx}$$

$$\text{Wave Equation:} \quad u_{tt} = c^2 u_{xx}.$$

Each of these PDEs is linear and homogeneous. Also, the advection equation is first order, while the other two are second order.

Subscripts are used in the above PDEs to indicate partial differentiation. There are two other ways this can be done that are very common. First, there is the form used in calculus, and examples are

$$\frac{\partial u}{\partial t}, \quad \frac{\partial u}{\partial x}, \quad \frac{\partial^2 u}{\partial t^2}, \quad \frac{\partial^2 u}{\partial t \partial x}, \quad \frac{\partial^2 u}{\partial x^2}.$$

A more contemporary notation is to abbreviate the above expressions, and write

$$\partial_t u, \quad \partial_x u, \quad \partial_t^2 u, \quad \partial_t \partial_x u, \quad \partial_x^2 u.$$

All three forms will be used in this chapter.

In this chapter, at the start, the method of separation of variables is used to solve PDEs. Later, in Section 7.7, it will be shown how separation of variables leads to another approach, called the Galerkin method. It is also possible to use the Laplace transform to solve many of the problems considered in this chapter, although that will not be pursued here.

Introduction to Differential Equations, M. H. Holmes, 2020

7.1 ▪ Balance Laws

The PDEs listed above are the mathematical consequence of a balance law, much like the ODEs obtained for simple harmonic motion in Section 3.10, and the various modeling examples in Section 2.3. For example, the wave equation describes the vertical displacement $u(x, t)$ of an elastic string. The PDE is a force balance equation coming from Newton's second law $F = ma$. In this case, the acceleration is $a = u_{tt}$, and F is the vertical component of the restoring force in the string due to its being stretched.

In contrast, the diffusion equation can be used to determine the density, or concentration, of objects moving along the x-axis due to Brownian motion. The balance law in this case is the requirement that the total number of objects is constant, which means that if one region experiences an increase, then this is balanced by a decrease in other regions. In older textbooks this equation is usually identified as the heat equation. However, it has far more applicability than heat propagation, and since about 1950 it is more often referred to as the diffusion equation in the research literature.

Explaining the physical and mathematical assumptions underlying the derivation of PDEs is outside the purview of this textbook. If you are interested in this you should consult Holmes [2019].

7.2 ▪ Boundary Value Problems

The PDEs listed above involve the spatial variable x. Consequently, it is worth first considering how to solve an ODE involving x. A typical example is to find the function $u(x)$ that satisfies

$$u'' - 4u = 0, \quad \text{for } 0 < x < 2, \tag{7.1}$$

where

$$u(0) = 1, \tag{7.2}$$

and

$$u(2) = -3. \tag{7.3}$$

This is called a **boundary value problem** (BVP), and it consists of a differential equation and **two boundary conditions**, one at each end of the spatial interval. Because this involves a linear differential equation with constant coefficients, the methods developed in Chapter 3 can be used to solve it. So, assuming that $u = e^{rx}$, and then substituting this into the differential equation (7.1), you obtain the characteristic equation $r^2 = 4$. The two solutions are $r_1 = -2$ and $r_2 = 2$, which means that the general solution of (7.1) is

$$u = c_1 e^{-2x} + c_2 e^{2x}.$$

To satisfy the boundary condition at $x = 0$ we need $c_1 + c_2 = 1$ and to satisfy the boundary condition at $x = 2$ we need $c_1 e^{-4} + c_2 e^4 = -3$. Solving these two equations yields

$$c_1 = \frac{e^4 + 3}{e^4 - e^{-4}} \quad \text{and} \quad c_2 = -\frac{e^{-4} + 3}{e^4 - e^{-4}}.$$

The other methods derived in Chapter 3 are easily modified to solve BVPs. As will be demonstrated in Example 1, the method of undetermined coefficients can be used to solve a BVP. However, a complication can arise as it is possible for the boundary conditions to be incompatible with the differential equation. If this happens then the BVP has no solution, and Example 2 is a demonstration of when this can happen.

Example 1: Solve $u'' - 3u' + 2u = 4x$, where $u(0) = 3$ and $u(4) = 0$.

Step 1: The associated homogeneous equation is $u'' - 3u' + 2u = 0$. Assuming $u = e^{rx}$, one gets the characteristic equation $r^2 - 3r + 2 = 0$. The roots are $r = 1$ and $r = 2$, and so $u_h = c_1 e^x + c_2 e^{2x}$.

Step 2: To find a particular solution, we assume that $u = Ax + B$. From the differential equation, we get that

$$2Ax - 3A + 2B = 4x.$$

Equating the respective coefficients, $2A = 4$ and $-3A + 2B = 0$. Solving these two equation yields $A = 2$ and $B = 3$.

Step 3: The general solution is

$$u = 2x + 3 + c_1 e^x + c_2 e^{2x}.$$

Step 4: For $u(0) = 3$ we need $c_1 + c_2 = 0$, and for $u(4) = 0$ we need $11 + c_1 e^4 + c_2 e^8 = 0$. Consequently, $c_1 = -c_2 = 11/(e^4(e^4 - 1))$, and the resulting solution is

$$u = 2x + 3 + \frac{11}{e^4(e^4 - 1)}\left(e^x - e^{2x}\right). \quad \blacksquare$$

Example 2: Show that $u'' + u = 0$, where $u(0) = 1$ and $u(\pi) = -3$, has no solution.

Ans: Assuming $u = e^{rx}$ gives $r^2 = -1$, from which we get the general solution $u = c_1 \cos x + c_2 \sin x$. To satisfy $u(0) = 1$ we need $c_1 = 1$ and to satisfy $u(\pi) = -3$ we need $c_1 = 3$. This is not possible, and so the BVP has no solution. $\blacksquare$

7.2.1 ▪ Eigenvalue Problems

We are going to have to consider a particular type of BVP when we solve a PDE. An example is the problem of solving

$$u'' - \lambda u = 0, \quad \text{for } 0 < x < 1, \tag{7.4}$$

where

$$u(0) = 0, \tag{7.5}$$

and

$$u(1) = 0. \tag{7.6}$$

The function $u = 0$ is a solution, but what we want to know is whether there are nonzero solutions. To be specific, is it possible to find values of the constant λ so there are solutions that are not identically zero? This is the same question asked when solving the eigenvalue problem $\mathbf{Aa} = \lambda\mathbf{a}$. In other words, finding $u(x)$ and λ is an **eigenvalue problem**. In this context, the u's are called **eigenfunctions**, and the λ's are the **eigenvalues**. A distinctive difference from the matrix eigenvalue problem is that there can be an infinite number of eigenvalues for an eigenvalue BVP.

Finding λ and u is not hard. As usual, assuming that $u = e^{rx}$, then the characteristic equation coming from (7.4) is $r^2 - \lambda = 0$. This means that $r = \pm\sqrt{\lambda}$. Assuming λ is a real number then we have the following three cases:

$\lambda > 0$: In this case, the general solution is $u = ae^{\sqrt{\lambda}x} + be^{-\sqrt{\lambda}x}$. To satisfy $u(0) = 0$ we need $a + b = 0$, and for $u(1) = 0$ we need $ae^{\sqrt{\lambda}} + be^{-\sqrt{\lambda}} = 0$. So, $b = -a$, and this means that $a(e^{\sqrt{\lambda}} - e^{-\sqrt{\lambda}}) = 0$. Since $e^{\sqrt{\lambda}} \neq e^{-\sqrt{\lambda}}$ when $\lambda > 0$, the conclusion is that $a = 0$, and this means we just get the zero solution.

$\lambda = 0$: The general solution of (7.4) is $u = a + bx$. To satisfy $u(0) = 0$ we need $a = 0$, and for $u(1) = 0$ we need $a + b = 0$. So, $a = b = 0$ and this means we just get the zero solution.

$\lambda < 0$: Setting $\lambda = -k^2$, where $k > 0$, then $r = \pm ik$. This means that the general solution of (7.4) is

$$u(x) = a\cos(kx) + b\sin(kx).$$

To satisfy $u(0) = 0$ we need $a = 0$. To satisfy $u(1) = 0$ we need $b\sin(k) = 0$. To obtain a not identically zero solution for $u(x)$ we take k so that $\sin(k) = 0$. This holds if any one of the following values are used:

$$k = \pi, 2\pi, 3\pi, \ldots.$$

The conclusion is that the eigenfunctions are

$$u_n(x) = b_n \sin(n\pi x), \tag{7.7}$$

where b_n is an arbitrary nonzero constant, and the associated eigenvalues are

$$\lambda_n = -(n\pi)^2, \tag{7.8}$$

for $n = 1, 2, 3, \ldots$.

Skipping the Two Real Roots Case

An observation can be made that will simplify solving an eigenvalue problem. In the above example, when there were *two* real-valued solutions for r, we ended up with the zero solution. This always happens. So, this case will often be skipped and the stated reason will be that it corresponds to two real roots. For example, if the characteristic equation is $r^2 = -\lambda$, then to skip the two real roots case it will be assumed that $\lambda \geq 0$. Similarly, if the characteristic equation is $r^2 + \lambda r + 4 = 0$, then $r = \frac{1}{2}(-\lambda \pm \sqrt{\lambda^2 - 16})$, and so skipping the two real roots case means that it is assumed that $\lambda^2 \leq 16$.

Rayleigh Quotient

It is possible to show that the eigenvalues for the above BVP must be negative, without having to first derive the formula for them. This can be done using what is called the *Rayleigh quotient*, and this is explained in Exercise 4. In fact, the steps in this exercise can be modified to also prove that the eigenvalues must be real-valued, which is an assumption we made in solving the eigenvalue problem.

The Rayleigh quotient is more than a theoretical tool as it plays an important role when studying mechanical vibrations as well as when finding quantum energy levels. It is also used extensively in scientific computing when solving eigenvalue problems.

Exercises

1. Solve the given BVP.

    a) $u'' - 4u = 0$, for $0 < x < 2$; $u(0) = 0$ and $u(2) = 1$.
    b) $u'' + u = 0$, for $0 < x < 1$; $u(0) = 0$ and $u(1) = -1$.
    c) $u'' + u' + u = 0$, for $0 < x < 1$; $u(0) = 0$ and $u(1) = 1$.
    d) $u'' - u = 5$, for $0 < x < 2$; $u(0) = 0$ and $u(2) = 0$.
    e) $u'' + u' = x$, for $0 < x < 1$; $u(0) = 0$ and $u(1) = 0$.

2. Show that the given BVP has no solution.

a) $u'' + 9u = 0$, for $0 < x < \pi$; $u(0) = 2$ and $u(\pi) = 1$.

b) $4u'' + u = 0$, for $0 < x < \pi$; $u(0) = -1$ and $u'(\pi) = 4$.

c) $4u'' + \pi^2 u = 0$, for $0 < x < 1$; $u'(0) = 0$ and $u(1) = -3$.

3. Find the eigenvalues and eigenfunctions of the given BVP. You can use the "skip the two real roots" simplification, just make sure to state the resulting assumption on λ.

a) $u'' = \lambda u$, for $0 < x < 1$; $u(0) = 0$ and $u'(1) = 0$.

b) $u'' = \lambda u$, for $0 < x < 4$; $u'(0) = 0$ and $u'(4) = 0$.

c) $u'' + \lambda u' + u = 0$, for $0 < x < 4$; $u(0) = 0$ and $u(4) = 0$.

d) $u'' + u' = \lambda u$, for $0 < x < 1$; $u(0) = 0$ and $u(1) = 0$.

e) $u'' + \lambda u = 0$, for $0 < x < 1$; $u(0) = u(1)$ and $u'(0) = u'(1)$. These are called periodic boundary conditions.

4. This exercise explores the usefulness of what is known as the Rayleigh quotient for the eigenvalue problem (7.4)-(7.6).

a) If you multiply (7.4) by u, and then integrate over the interval, you get

$$\int_0^1 (uu'' - \lambda u^2) dx = 0.$$

From this show that

$$\lambda \int_0^1 u^2 dx = - \int_0^1 (u')^2 dx.$$

The Rayleigh quotient for this problem is obtained when you solve the above equation for λ.

b) Use part (a) to explain why, given an eigenfunction $u(x)$, that the associated eigenvalue must be negative.

c) The fundamental eigenfunction corresponds to the case of $n = 1$ in (7.7). Taking $b_1 = 1$, sketch $u_1(x)$ for $0 \le x \le 1$. On the same axes, also sketch $w(x) = 4x(1 - x)$.

d) Part (c) shows that $w(x)$ can be used as an approximation of $u_1(x)$. Use w in the Rayleigh quotient to obtain an approximation for λ_1.

7.3 ▪ Separation of Variables

The solution method will be introduced by using it to solve a problem involving the diffusion equation. This requires a correctly formulated problem, and the one considered is to find the function $u(x,t)$ that satisfies

$$D\frac{\partial^2 u}{\partial x^2} = \frac{\partial u}{\partial t}, \quad \text{for} \quad \left\{ \begin{array}{l} 0 < x < L, \\ 0 < t. \end{array} \right. \tag{7.9}$$

In this equation, the positive constant D is the called the *diffusion coefficient*. To complete the formulation we will prescribe the values of u at the two endpoints, where $x = 0$ and $x = L$, and at the beginning, when $t = 0$. Specifically, for boundary conditions it is assumed that

$$u(0, t) = 0, \tag{7.10}$$

and

$$u(L, t) = 0. \tag{7.11}$$

For the initial condition, it is assumed that

$$u(x, 0) = g(x), \quad \text{for } 0 < x < L, \tag{7.12}$$

where $g(x)$ is a given function.

When using the method of separation of variables, you first find all possible nonzero solutions of the PDE that satisfy the boundary conditions. It is important to note that $u = 0$ is a possible solution of (7.9) that also satisfies (7.10) and (7.11). What we want are the nonzero ones.

The fact that $u = 0$ is a solution of the PDE, and the boundary conditions, is required for the method of separation of variables to work. The reason is that this will enable us to use the principle of superposition. So, if the left boundary condition is changed to, say, $u(0, t) = 1$, or the PDE is changed to, say, $Du_{xx} = u_t + x$, then separation of variables will not work. What is necessary in these cases is to first transform the problem into one where $u = 0$ is a solution of the PDE and boundary conditions. How this is done is considered in Sections 7.6 and 7.7.

7.3.1 ▪ Separation of Variables Assumption

The assumption is simply that

$$u(x, t) = F(x)G(t). \tag{7.13}$$

Substituting this into the PDE (7.9) gives $DF''(x)G(t) = F(x)G'(t)$. Separating variables yields

$$D\frac{F''(x)}{F(x)} = \frac{G'(t)}{G(t)}. \tag{7.14}$$

Now comes the key observation. The only way a function of x can equal a function of t, since x and t are independent, is that the function of x is a constant, the function of t is a constant, and the constants are equal. In other words, there is a constant λ so that

$$D\frac{F''(x)}{F(x)} = \lambda,$$

and

$$\frac{G'(t)}{G(t)} = \lambda.$$

These can be rewritten as

$$DF''(x) = \lambda F(x) \,. \tag{7.15}$$

and

$$G'(t) = \lambda G(t) \,. \tag{7.16}$$

The λ appearing here is called, not surprisingly, the **separation constant**.

7.3.2 ▪ Finding $F(x)$ and λ

The separation of variables assumption must be applied to the boundary conditions. So, to have $u(0,t) = 0$, we need $F(0)G(t) = 0$. For this to happen, and u not be identically zero, we require that $F(0) = 0$. Similarly, we need $F(L) = 0$. Consequently, all-together, the function $F(x)$ must satisfy

$$DF''(x) = \lambda F(x) \,, \quad \text{for } 0 < x < L, \tag{7.17}$$

where

$$F(0) = 0 \quad \text{and} \quad F(L) = 0, \tag{7.18}$$

The solution of this BVP depends on whether λ is zero or not. So, we have two cases to consider.

$\lambda = 0$: In this case (7.17) is $F'' = 0$, and so $F(x) = a + bx$. To satisfy $F(0) = 0$ we need $a = 0$, and for $F(L) = 0$ we need $b = 0$. So, we just get the zero solution in this case.

$\lambda \neq 0$: Assuming $F(x) = e^{rx}$, then (7.17) reduces to $Dr^2 = \lambda$. We will skip the two real roots case, which means we only consider $\lambda < 0$. Setting $\lambda = -k^2$, where $k > 0$, then $Dr^2 = -k^2$. This means that $r = \pm ik/\sqrt{D}$. The resulting general solution of (7.17) is

$$F(x) = a \cos(kx/\sqrt{D}) + b \sin(kx/\sqrt{D}).$$

To satisfy $F(0) = 0$ we need $a = 0$. To satisfy $F(L) = 0$ we need $b \sin(kL/\sqrt{D}) = 0$. To obtain a function $F(x)$ that is not identically zero, we take k so that $\sin(kL/\sqrt{D}) = 0$. This holds if any one of the following values are used:

$$kL/\sqrt{D} = \pi, 2\pi, 3\pi, \ldots,$$

or equivalently

$$k = \frac{\pi\sqrt{D}}{L}, \frac{3\pi\sqrt{D}}{L}, \frac{3\pi\sqrt{D}}{L}, \ldots. \tag{7.19}$$

The conclusion is that the not identically zero solutions of (7.17) and (7.18) are

$$F_n(x) = b_n \sin\left(\frac{n\pi x}{L}\right), \tag{7.20}$$

and

$$\lambda_n = -D\left(\frac{n\pi}{L}\right)^2, \tag{7.21}$$

for $n = 1, 2, 3, \ldots$. Also, b_n is an arbitrary constant.

7.3.3 ▪ Finding $G(t)$

For $\lambda = \lambda_n$, the general solution of (7.16) is

$$G_n(t) = a_n e^{\lambda_n t}, \tag{7.22}$$

where a_n is an arbitrary constant. The function $G_n(t)$ is not required to satisfy the initial condition (7.12); that condition will be satisfied once we determine the general solution.

7.3.4 ▪ The General Solution

We have shown that for any given n, the function $u_n(x, t) = F_n(x)G_n(t)$ is a solution of the PDE that satisfies the boundary conditions. Because the PDE and boundary conditions are homogeneous, and the problem is linear, the principle of superposition can be used (see page 5). Therefore, the resulting general solution, that satisfies the PDE and boundary conditions, is

$$u(x, t) = \sum_{n=1}^{\infty} u_n(x, t),$$

or equivalently

$$u(x, t) = \sum_{n=1}^{\infty} b_n e^{\lambda_n t} \sin\left(\frac{n\pi x}{L}\right), \tag{7.23}$$

where b_n is an arbitrary constant, and λ_n is given in (7.21). In writing this down, the constant a_n in (7.22) has been absorbed into the b_n.

7.3.5 ▪ Satisfying the Initial Condition

It remains to satisfy the initial condition, which is $u(x, 0) = g(x)$. According to our solution in (7.23), we need

$$\sum_{n=1}^{\infty} b_n \sin\left(\frac{n\pi x}{L}\right) = g(x). \tag{7.24}$$

This is the equation that is used to determine the b_n's. However, the left-hand-side is an example of what is known as a Fourier series. More specifically, it is an example of a Fourier sine series. There are some significant mathematical questions that arise here, one of which is whether the series converges. This, and some related questions, are addressed in the next section. For the moment, we simply state the conclusion. If $g(x)$ is continuous, except perhaps for a few jump discontinuities, then

$$b_n = \frac{2}{L} \int_0^L g(x) \sin\left(\frac{n\pi x}{L}\right) dx. \tag{7.25}$$

7.3.6 ▪ Examples

Example 1: Suppose that $D = 1$, $L = 2$, and $g(x) = 3\sin(\pi x)$. In this case, from (7.21), $\lambda_n = -(n\pi/2)^2$, and the resulting general solution (7.23) is

$$u(x,t) = \sum_{n=1}^{\infty} b_n e^{-n^2 \pi^2 t/4} \sin\left(\frac{n\pi x}{2}\right).$$

To satisfy the initial condition, it helps to notice that $g(x)$ is one of the sine functions in the series. To make this more evident, the

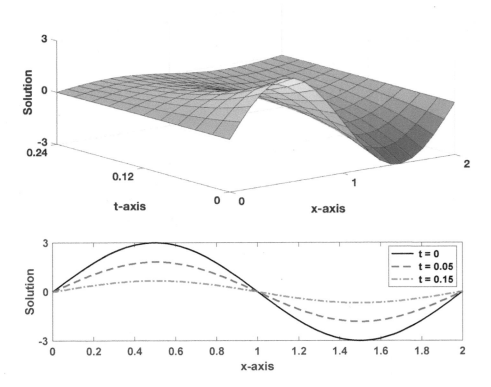

Figure 7.1. *Solution of the diffusion equation in Example 1. Shown is the solution surface as well as the solution profiles at specific time values.*

requirement that $u(x,0) = g(x)$ means that we need

$$\sum_{n=1}^{\infty} b_n \sin\left(\frac{n\pi x}{2}\right) = 3\sin(\pi x),$$

or equivalently

$$b_1 \sin\left(\frac{\pi x}{2}\right) + b_2 \sin(\pi x) + b_3 \sin\left(\frac{3\pi x}{2}\right) + b_4 \sin(2\pi x) + \cdots = 3\sin(\pi x).$$

To satisfy this equation, take $b_2 = 3$ and set all the other b_n's to zero. Therefore, the solution is

$$u(x,t) = 3e^{-\pi^2 t}\sin(\pi x). \tag{7.26}$$

This solution is shown in Figure 7.1, both as time slices and as the solution surface for $0 \le t \le 0.24$.   ■

Example 2: Suppose that in the previous example,

$$g(x) = 3\sin\left(\frac{\pi x}{2}\right) - 4\sin\left(\frac{3\pi x}{2}\right) + 5\sin(2\pi x).$$

This is an example of when $g(x)$ involves the sum of three of the sine functions in the series. The requirement is that

$$\sum_{n=1}^{\infty} b_n \sin\left(\frac{n\pi x}{2}\right) = 3\sin\left(\frac{\pi x}{2}\right) - 4\sin\left(\frac{3\pi x}{2}\right) + 5\sin(2\pi x).$$

To satisfy this we take $b_1 = 3$, $b_3 = -4$, $b_4 = 5$, and all the other b_n's are zero. The resulting solution is

$$u(x,t) = 3e^{-\pi^2 t/4}\sin\left(\frac{\pi x}{2}\right) - 4e^{-9\pi^2 t/4}\sin\left(\frac{3\pi x}{2}\right)$$
$$+ 5e^{-4\pi^2 t}\sin(2\pi x).   ■$$

Example 3: Suppose that $D = 1$, $L = 1$, and

$$g(x) = \begin{cases} 1 & \text{if } \frac{1}{3} \le x \le \frac{2}{3}, \\ 0 & \text{otherwise.} \end{cases} \tag{7.27}$$

In this case, it is necessary to use (7.25) to find the b_n's. Carrying out the integration

$$b_n = 2\int_{1/3}^{2/3} \sin(n\pi x)dx$$
$$= \frac{2}{n\pi}\Big(\cos(n\pi/3) - \cos(2n\pi/3)\Big).$$

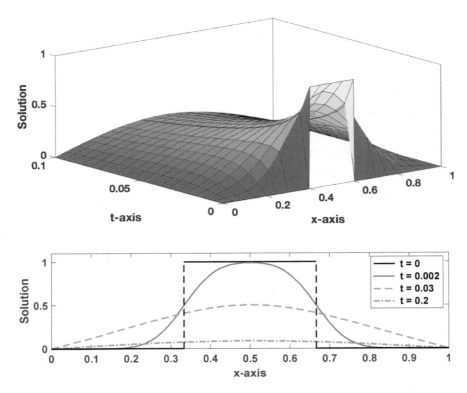

Figure 7.2. *Solution of the diffusion equation in Example 3. Shown is the solution surface as well as the solution profiles at specific time values.*

As for the solution, since $\lambda_n = -(n\pi)^2$, then

$$u(x,t) = \sum_{n=1}^{\infty} b_n e^{-n^2\pi^2 t} \sin(n\pi x). \tag{7.28}$$

This solution is shown in Figure 7.2 for $0 \le t \le 0.1$. ∎

Exercises

1. You are to find the solution of the diffusion problem for the following initial conditions. Assume that $L = 1$ and $D = 3$. Note that you should be able to answer this question without using integration.

   a) $g(x) = -4\sin(5\pi x)$.

   b) $g(x) = 6\sin(11\pi x)$.

   c) $g(x) = \sin(\pi x) + 8\sin(4\pi x) - 10\sin(7\pi x)$.

   d) $g(x) = -\sin(3\pi x) + 7\sin(8\pi x) + 2\sin(15\pi x)$.

   e) $g(x) = 4\sin(2\pi x)\cos(\pi x)$.

2. You are to find the solution of the diffusion problem for the following initial conditions. Assume that $L = 2$ and $D = 4$.

a) $g(x) = 1$

b) $g(x) = 2 + x$

c) $g(x) = \cos(\pi x)$

d) $g(x) = \begin{cases} -1 & \text{if } 0 \le x \le 1 \\ 0 & \text{otherwise} \end{cases}$

e) $g(x) = \begin{cases} 1 & \text{if } 0 \le x \le \frac{1}{3} \\ 2 & \text{otherwise} \end{cases}$

3. Find the solution of

$$9\frac{\partial^2 u}{\partial x^2} = \frac{\partial u}{\partial t}, \quad \text{for } \begin{cases} 0 < x < 3, \\ 0 < t, \end{cases}$$

where $u(0, t) = 0$, $u(3, t) = 0$, and $u(x, 0) = -5x$.

4. Find the solution of

$$10\,\partial_x^2 u = \partial_t u, \quad \text{for } \begin{cases} 0 < x < 2, \\ 0 < t, \end{cases}$$

where $u(0, t) = 0$, $u(2, t) = 0$, and $u(x, 0) = \begin{cases} 1 & \text{if } \frac{1}{2} \le x \le \frac{3}{2} \\ 0 & \text{otherwise.} \end{cases}$

5. Find the general solution of the following.

a) $u_{xx} = u_t$, for $0 < x < 1$, with the boundary conditions $u(0, t) = 0$ and $u_x(1, t) = 0$.

b) $4u_{xx} = u_t$, for $0 < x < 1$, with the boundary conditions $u_x(0, t) = 0$ and $u(1, t) = 0$.

c) $(1 + t)\partial_x^2 u = \partial_t u$, for $0 < x < 1$, with the boundary conditions $u(0, t) = 0$ and $u(1, t) = 0$.

d) $u_{xx} = u_t + e^{-t}u$, for $0 < x < 1$, with the boundary conditions $u(0, t) = 0$ and $u(1, t) = 0$.

6. Find the solution of the problem for the given initial condition.

a) Exercise 5(a), with $u(x, 0) = 3\sin\left(\frac{\pi x}{2}\right) - 7\sin\left(\frac{9\pi x}{2}\right)$.

b) Exercise 5(b), with $u(x, 0) = -5\cos\left(\frac{3\pi x}{2}\right) - 2\cos\left(\frac{11\pi x}{2}\right)$.

c) Exercise 5(c), with $u(x, 0) = 14\sin(10\pi x) + 30\sin(18\pi x)$.

d) Exercise 5(d), with $u(x, 0) = -24\sin(3\pi x) - 12\sin(15\pi x)$.

7. Find the resulting ODEs obtained using separation of variables on the given PDE.

a) $(1 + x)u_{xx} + tu = 7u_t$, assuming $u = F(x)G(t)$

b) $r^2 u_{rr} + ru_r + u_{\theta\theta} = 0$, assuming $u = R(r)\Theta(\theta)$

c) $\partial_x(e^x \partial_x u) = (1 + x^2)\partial_t u$, assuming $u = F(x)G(t)$

d) $u_{zz} + 3zu_z = u_{yy} + 9u$, assuming $u = Z(z)Y(y)$

e) $u_x^2 + u_t^2 = e^{-t}u^2$, assuming $u = F(x)G(t)$

7.4 ▪ Sine and Cosine Series

To satisfy the initial condition for the diffusion problem considered in the previous section, we were required to find the b_n's so that

$$g(x) = \sum_{n=1}^{\infty} b_n \sin\left(\frac{n\pi x}{L}\right), \quad \text{for } 0 < x < L. \tag{7.29}$$

This is an example of a Fourier sine series. Finding the b_n's is not hard. However, this requires knowing what restrictions must be placed on $g(x)$, and so, this is where we begin.

One of the requirements is that $g(x)$ is **piecewise continuous** for $0 \le x \le L$. This means that $g(x)$ is continuous on the interval except, possibly, for a finite number of jump discontinuities. What a **jump discontinuity** means is that $g(x)$ is not continuous at the point, but the limits of $g(x)$ from the left, $g(x^-)$, and from the right, $g(x^+)$, are defined and finite. This is the requirement when $0 < x < L$. For $x = 0$, then $g(0^+)$ must be defined and finite, but it is not required to equal $g(0)$. Similarly, for $x = L$, $g(L^-)$ must be defined and finite, but it is not required to equal $g(L)$. An example of a function with two jumps is given in (7.27). Also, all of the functions in Exercise 2 in the previous section are piecewise continuous.

A consequence of the assumption that $g(x)$ is piecewise continuous is that the integral in (7.25) is well-defined.

7.4.1 ▪ Finding the b_n's

The working hypothesis is that the sine series converges, and we can integrate it term-by-term. The reason for this assumption is that the key for finding the coefficients is the integration formula: if m and n are positive integers, then

$$\int_0^L \sin\left(\frac{n\pi x}{L}\right) \sin\left(\frac{m\pi x}{L}\right) dx = \begin{cases} \dfrac{L}{2} & \text{if } m = n, \\[2mm] 0 & \text{if } m \ne n. \end{cases} \tag{7.30}$$

The derivation of this formula is often done in calculus, and it involves using the identity $\sin ax \sin bx = \frac{1}{2}\left[\cos(a-b)x - \cos(a+b)x\right]$.

To illustrate how (7.30) is used, suppose we want to find the value for, say, b_7. Multiplying (7.29) by $\sin(7\pi x/L)$, and then integrating yields

$$\int_0^L g(x) \sin\left(\frac{7\pi x}{L}\right) dx = \sum_{n=1}^{\infty} b_n \int_0^L \sin\left(\frac{7\pi x}{L}\right) \sin\left(\frac{n\pi x}{L}\right) dx.$$

According to (7.30), all of the integrals on the right are zero except when $n = 7$. Consequently,

$$\int_0^L g(x) \sin\left(\frac{7\pi x}{L}\right) dx = \frac{L}{2} b_7,$$

or equivalently

$$b_7 = \frac{2}{L} \int_0^L g(x) \sin\left(\frac{7\pi x}{L}\right) dx.$$

A similar result is obtained for the other b_n's, and the resulting formula is

$$b_n = \frac{2}{L} \int_0^L g(x) \sin\left(\frac{n\pi x}{L}\right) dx. \tag{7.31}$$

7.4.2 ▪ Convergence Theorem

Proving a sine series converges requires more than just using the ratio test, which is the way you prove a power series converges. The proof is beyond the scope of this textbook, but the result is important for our using a sine series when solving PDEs.

Sine Series Convergence Theorem. *Assume that $g(x)$ and $g'(x)$ are piecewise continuous for $0 \le x \le L$, and the b_n's are given in (7.31).*

For $0 < x < L$: If $g(x)$ is continuous at x, then

$$g(x) = \sum_{n=1}^{\infty} b_n \sin\left(\frac{n\pi x}{L}\right), \tag{7.32}$$

and if $g(x)$ has a jump discontinuity at x, then

$$\frac{1}{2}\left[g(x^+) + g(x^-)\right] = \sum_{n=1}^{\infty} b_n \sin\left(\frac{n\pi x}{L}\right). \tag{7.33}$$

At $x = 0$ or $x = L$: The sine series is zero when $x = 0$ or $x = L$.

In words, the theorem states that the sine series equals the function $g(x)$ at points in the interval where $g(x)$ is continuous, and it equals the average in the jump of $g(x)$ at a jump discontinuity. At the endpoints, no matter what the value of $g(0)$ or $g(L)$, the series sums to zero.

7.4.3 ▪ Examples

Finding a sine series is rather uneventful as it is simply a matter of evaluating the given formulas. The only concern is how hard it is to evaluate the integrals to find the coefficients. So, in the examples below, a more practical question is also considered. Namely, how many terms of the series do you have to add together to obtain an accurate approximation of the function $g(x)$? As will be seen, the answer depends on whether the function is continuous, and whether it has the right values at the endpoints.

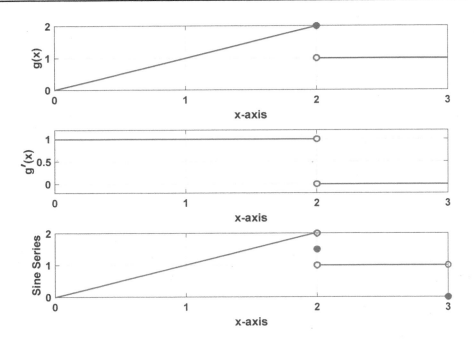

Figure 7.3. *The functions $g(x)$, $g'(x)$, and the function that the sine series sums to for Example 1.*

Example 1: Taking $L = 3$, suppose

$$g(x) = \begin{cases} x & \text{if } 0 \le x \le 2, \\ 1 & \text{if } 2 < x \le 3. \end{cases}$$

Sketch $g(x)$ and $g'(x)$ for $0 \le x \le 3$, and use this to explain why they are piecewise continuous. Also, sketch the function that the sine series for $g(x)$ converges to for $0 \le x \le 3$.

Answer: The functions $g(x)$ and $g'(x)$ are shown in Figure 7.3. Although $g(x)$ is not continuous at $x = 2$, and $g'(x)$ is not defined there, the left and right limits of both functions are defined and finite at that point. Therefore, both functions are piecewise continuous for $0 \le x \le 3$. As for the sine series, for $0 < x < 3$, it equals $g(x)$ except at the discontinuity, where it sums to the average in the jump. So, at $x = 2$, it converges to $\frac{1}{2}[g(2^+) + g(2^-)] = \frac{1}{2}(1 + 2) = \frac{3}{2}$. Finally, at $x = 0$, and at $x = 3$, the series sums to zero. The sketch of the resulting function is given in Figure 7.3. ■

Example 2: Taking $L = 5$, suppose $g(x) = \sqrt{x}$. Are $g(x)$ and $g'(x)$ piecewise continuous for $0 \le x \le 5$?

Answer: The function $g(x)$ is continuous for $0 \le x \le 5$ (and it is, therefore, piecewise continuous). Its derivative $g'(x) = 1/(2\sqrt{x})$ is continuous for $0 < x \le 5$, but $g'(0^+) = \infty$. Because this limit is not finite, $g'(x)$ is not piecewise continuous for $0 \le x \le 5$. ■

Example 3: For $0 \le x \le 1$, find the sine series of

$$g(x) = \begin{cases} 3x & \text{if } 0 \le x \le \frac{1}{3}, \\ \frac{3}{2}(1-x) & \text{if } \frac{1}{3} < x \le 1. \end{cases}$$

Answer: Using (7.31), and integrating by parts,

$$b_n = 6 \int_0^{1/3} x \sin(n\pi x)dx + 3 \int_{1/3}^1 (1-x)\sin(n\pi x)dx$$

$$= \frac{9}{\pi^2 n^2}\sin(n\pi/3).$$

Because $g(x)$ is continuous, and $g(0) = g(1) = 0$, we have that

$$g(x) = \sum_{n=1}^{\infty} \frac{9}{\pi^2 n^2}\sin(n\pi/3)\sin(n\pi x), \quad \text{for } 0 \le x \le 1. \qquad (7.34)$$

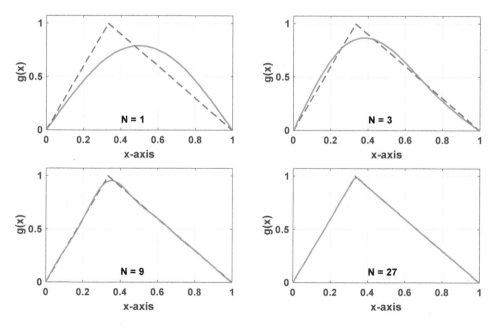

Figure 7.4. *Comparison between the function $g(x)$ in Example 3, shown with the dashed blue curve, and the sine series approximation in (7.35), shown using a solid red curve.*

When computing the value of the sine series it is necessary to pick an N, and then use the approximation

$$g(x) \approx \sum_{n=1}^{N} \frac{9}{2\pi^2 n^2} \sin(n\pi/3) \sin(n\pi x). \tag{7.35}$$

The accuracy of this is shown in Figure 7.4. It is evident that for smaller values of N the approximation is not very good, but it is not bad for $N = 27$. ■

Example 4: For $0 \leq x \leq 1$, find the sine series of

$$g(x) = \begin{cases} 1 & \text{if } 0 \leq x \leq \frac{1}{4}, \\ 0 & \text{otherwise.} \end{cases}$$

Also, sketch the function the sine series converges to for $0 \leq x \leq 1$. *Answer:* Using (7.31),

$$b_n = 2 \int_0^{1/4} \sin(n\pi x)dx = \frac{2}{n\pi}\Big[1 - \cos(n\pi/4)\Big].$$

From this we have that, except for $x = 0$ and $x = 1/4$,

$$g(x) = \sum_{n=1}^{\infty} \frac{2}{n\pi}\Big[1 - \cos(n\pi/4)\Big] \sin(n\pi x). \tag{7.36}$$

At $x = 0$ the series is zero, and at $x = 1/4$ the series sums to $1/2$, which is the average in the jump of $g(x)$ at this point. The resulting function is shown in Figure 7.5.

The resulting approximation is, given N,

$$g(x) \approx \sum_{n=1}^{N} \frac{2}{n\pi}\Big[1 - \cos(n\pi/4)\Big] \sin(n\pi x). \tag{7.37}$$

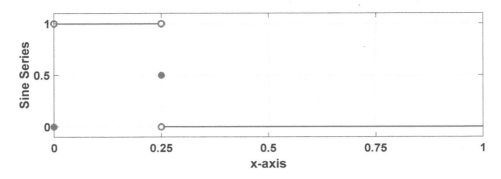

Figure 7.5. *The function the sine series in Example 4 converges to for $0 \leq x \leq 1$.*

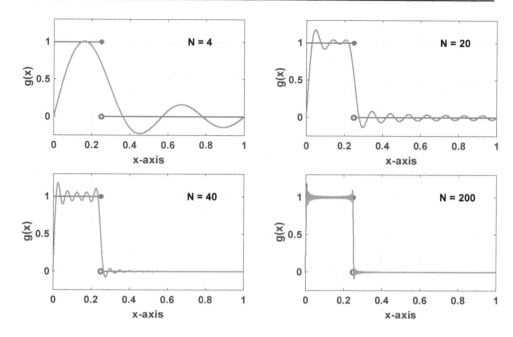

Figure 7.6. *Comparison between the function $g(x)$ for Example 4, shown with the blue curve, and the sine series approximation in (7.37), shown using the red curve.*

The accuracy of this is shown in Figure 7.6. Because of the jump in the function, the sine series requires a larger value of N than needed in Example 3 to provide an accurate approximation. However, even with a larger N, the series has difficulty in the immediate vicinity of the jump. It has the same problem near $x = 0$ since the series is zero at $x = 0$ but $g(0) = 1$. The larger oscillations near the jump points are associated with what is called **Gibbs phenomenon**. As can be seen in the figure, the region where these oscillations occur can be reduced by taking larger values of N. However, the maximum overshoot and undershoot on either side of the jump do not go to zero. Instead, for $0 < x < L$, they approach a value that is equal to about 9% of the jump in the function. Because jump discontinuities arise so often in applications, there has been considerable research into how to remove the over and under shoots in the Fourier series solution. One of the more well known methods involves filtering them out, and an example is Fejér summation. More about this can be found in Jerri [1998]. ■

7.4.4 ▪ Cosine Series

Using separation of variables, it is not uncommon to end up with a cosine series rather than a sine series. In this case, the initial condition requires finding the a_n's that satisfy

$$g(x) = \frac{1}{2}a_0 + \sum_{n=1}^{\infty} a_n \cos\left(\frac{n\pi x}{L}\right), \quad \text{for } 0 < x < L. \tag{7.38}$$

The convergence theorem for this is very similar to the one for the sine series. First, the needed integration formula is, if m and n are integers,

$$\int_0^L \cos\left(\frac{n\pi x}{L}\right) \cos\left(\frac{m\pi x}{L}\right) dx = \begin{cases} L & \text{if } m = n = 0, \\ \dfrac{L}{2} & \text{if } m = n \neq 0, \\ 0 & \text{if } m \neq n. \end{cases} \tag{7.39}$$

The derivation of this formula is a straightforward calculation using the identity $\cos ax \cos bx = \left(\cos(a-b)x + \cos(a+b)x\right)/2$. This formula is used in the same way the one for the sine series was used. Namely, if you want to determine, say, a_4, you multiply (7.38) by $\cos(4\pi x/L)$ and then integrate over the interval $0 \leq x \leq L$. The resulting formula, for general n, is

$$a_n = \frac{2}{L} \int_0^L g(x) \cos\left(\frac{n\pi x}{L}\right) dx. \tag{7.40}$$

This brings us to the next result.

Cosine Series Convergence Theorem. *Assume that $g(x)$ and $g'(x)$ are piecewise continuous for $0 \leq x \leq L$, and the a_n's are given in (7.40). If $g(x)$ is continuous at x, then*

$$g(x) = \frac{1}{2}a_0 + \sum_{n=1}^{\infty} a_n \cos\left(\frac{n\pi x}{L}\right). \tag{7.41}$$

If $g(x)$ has a jump discontinuity at x, and $0 < x < L$, then

$$\frac{1}{2}\left[g(x^+) + g(x^-)\right] = \frac{1}{2}a_0 + \sum_{n=1}^{\infty} a_n \cos\left(\frac{n\pi x}{L}\right). \tag{7.42}$$

At $x = 0$, the series sums to $g(0^+)$, and at $x = L$, the series sums to $g(L^-)$.

In words, the theorem states that the cosine series equals the function $g(x)$ at points in the interval where $g(x)$ is continuous, and it equals the average in the jump of $g(x)$ at a jump discontinuity. At the endpoints, it sums to the respective limit of $g(x)$ at the endpoint.

Example 5: For $0 \le x \le 1$, find the cosine series of

$$g(x) = \begin{cases} x + 1 & \text{if } 0 \le x \le \frac{1}{2}, \\ 2 & \text{if } \frac{1}{2} < x \le 1. \end{cases}$$

Answer: Using (7.40), if $n \ne 0$,

$$
\begin{aligned}
a_n &= 2 \int_0^1 g(x) \cos(n\pi x) dx \\
&= 2 \int_0^{1/2} (x + 1) \cos(n\pi x) dx + 2 \int_{1/2}^1 2 \cos(n\pi x) dx \\
&= \frac{2}{n^2 \pi^2} \left(\cos\left(\frac{n\pi}{2}\right) - 1 \right) - \frac{1}{n\pi} \sin\left(\frac{n\pi}{2}\right),
\end{aligned}
$$

and when $n = 0$, $a_0 = 13/4$. From this we have that, except for $x = 1/2$,

$$g(x) = \frac{13}{8} + \sum_{n=1}^{\infty} \left[\frac{2}{n^2 \pi^2} \left(\cos\left(\frac{n\pi}{2}\right) - 1 \right) - \frac{1}{n\pi} \sin\left(\frac{n\pi}{2}\right) \right] \cos(n\pi x).$$

$$(7.43)$$

At $x = 1/2$ the series sums to the average in the jump in $g(x)$, and so it equals $7/4$. The resulting function is shown in Figure 7.7.

The resulting approximation is, given N,

$$g(x) \approx \frac{13}{8} + \sum_{n=1}^{N} \left[\frac{2}{n^2 \pi^2} \left(\cos\left(\frac{n\pi}{2}\right) - 1 \right) - \frac{1}{n\pi} \sin\left(\frac{n\pi}{2}\right) \right] \cos(n\pi x).$$

$$(7.44)$$

The accuracy of this is shown in Figure 7.8. As happened with the sine series, in the immediate vicinity of the jump the series oscillates. However, unlike Example 4, there are no oscillations at the endpoints. ■

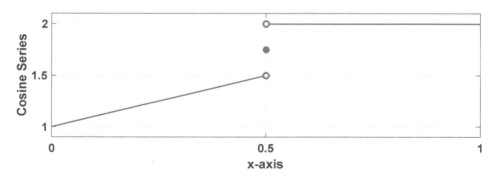

Figure 7.7. *The function the cosine series in Example 5 converges to for $0 \le x \le 1$.*

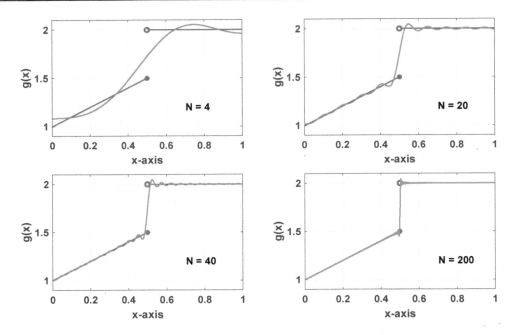

Figure 7.8. *Comparison between the function $g(x)$ for Example 5, shown with the blue curve, and the cosine series approximation in (7.44), shown using the red curve.*

7.4.5 ▪ Differentiability

In using a sine or cosine series when solving a PDE, it is implicitly assumed you can differentiate the series term-by-term. What this means is that it is assumed that

$$\frac{d}{dx}\sum_{n=1}^{\infty}p_n(x) = \sum_{n=1}^{\infty}\frac{d}{dx}p_n(x).$$

With this in mind, in Example 4, if you try this with (7.36), you get

$$g'(x) = \sum_{n=1}^{\infty}2\bigl(1 - \cos(n\pi/4)\bigr)\cos(n\pi x). \qquad (7.45)$$

As you should recall, if an infinite series $\sum a_n$ converges, then it must be true that $a_n \to 0$ as $n \to \infty$. The above series for $g'(x)$ does not satisfy this condition, and therefore it does not converge. In other words, you can not differentiate (7.36) term-by-term. In contrast, for Example 3 you can differentiate the series term-by-term. The theorem that explains this states that if $g(x)$ is continuous, and $g'(x)$ is piecewise continuous, for $0 \le x \le L$, then you can differentiate the cosine series term-by-term, but to do this for a sine series you need an additional assumption [Tolstov and Silverman, 1976]. An easy to use version of the needed assumption is that $g(0) = g(L) = 0$. This holds for Example 3, and that is why term-by-term differentiation can be done with that sine series. For both the cosine and sine series, if $g(x)$ is not continuous, then term-by-term differentiation is not possible without additional assumptions. Those interested in pursuing this issue a bit further should look at Exercise 11.

The situation for term-by-term integration is better. Specifically, if $g(x)$ satisfies the requirements of the convergence theorem, its sine, and cosine, series can be integrated term-by-term.

The next question is whether the potential non-differentiability of a sine series means that we can not use it to solve the diffusion equation. To explain why this is not a problem, consider the solution (7.43), which is

$$u(x,t) = \sum_{n=1}^{\infty} b_n e^{-n^2\pi^2 t}\sin(n\pi x).$$

As long as $t > 0$, the coefficients of this series are exponentially decreasing functions of n^2. This, along with the fact that the series for $g(x)$ converges, guarantee that you can differentiate the series term-by-term without reservation, as long as $t > 0$.

7.4.6 • Infinite Dimensional

For vectors in $\mathbb{R}^3$, the dot product is used to determine orthogonality. As you should recall, $\mathbf{x}$ and $\mathbf{y}$ are orthogonal if $\mathbf{x} \cdot \mathbf{y} = 0$. Also, any vector in $\mathbb{R}^3$ can be written in terms of the three coordinate vectors $\mathbf{i}$, $\mathbf{j}$, and $\mathbf{k}$. This means that it is possible to write $\mathbf{x}$ as a linear combination of these vectors: $\mathbf{x} = x\mathbf{i} + y\mathbf{j} + z\mathbf{k}$. In this sense, $\mathbf{i}$, $\mathbf{j}$, and $\mathbf{k}$ are a basis for $\mathbb{R}^3$. In fact, since $\mathbf{i}$, $\mathbf{j}$, and $\mathbf{k}$ are orthogonal to each other, they form what is called an *orthogonal basis*. Because there are three vectors in the basis, $\mathbb{R}^3$ is three dimensional.

Now, the Sine Series Convergence Theorem states when a function $g(x)$ can be written as a linear combination of the sine functions $\sin(\pi x/L)$, $\sin(2\pi x/L)$, $\sin(3\pi x/L)$, $\cdots$. There is also a dot product, or what is usually called an *inner product*, for the sine functions, and it involves the integral appearing in the integration formula in (7.30). According to this integration rule, the sine functions are orthogonal to each other. This means that $\sin(\pi x/L)$, $\sin(2\pi x/L)$, $\sin(3\pi x/L)$, $\cdots$ is an orthogonal basis. Because this basis contains an infinite number of elements, the space we are considering is infinite dimensional. This viewpoint gives rise to what is called a Hilbert space, and these play a fundamental role in many areas in science and engineering. For an introduction to Hilbert spaces and partial differential equations, you might consult Gustafson [1999].

Exercises

1. Sketch the graph of $f(x)$ for $0 \leq x \leq 1$. Also, determine whether $f(x)$ is continuous, piecewise continuous, or neither for $0 \leq x \leq 1$.

a) $f(x) = \begin{cases} 1 & \text{if } 0 \leq x \leq \frac{1}{2} \\ 2x & \text{if } \frac{1}{2} < x \leq \frac{3}{4} \\ \frac{3}{2} & \text{if } \frac{3}{4} < x \leq 1 \end{cases}$ c) $f(x) = \begin{cases} 0 & \text{if } x = 0 \\ \ln x & \text{if } 0 < x < 1 \\ 1 & \text{if } x = 1 \end{cases}$

b) $f(x) = \begin{cases} 1 & \text{if } x = \frac{1}{4}, \frac{1}{2}, \frac{3}{4}, 1 \\ 2 & \text{otherwise} \end{cases}$ d) $f(x) = \begin{cases} 0 & \text{if } 0 \leq x \leq \frac{1}{2} \\ \frac{1}{2x-1} & \text{if } \frac{1}{2} < x \leq 1 \end{cases}$

2. Assuming that $L = 2$, explain why $g(x)$ does not satisfy the conditions stated in the Sine Series Convergence Theorem.

a) $g(x) = x^{1/3}$ b) $g(x) = \tan x$ c) $g(x) = \frac{1}{x^2+4x-1}$

3. In the following, $g(x)$ and $g'(x)$ are piecewise continuous. Assuming that $L = 2$, sketch the function to which the sine series converges, for $0 \leq x \leq 2$.

a) $g(x) = x$

b) $g(x) = e^x$

c) $g(x) = \cos(\pi x)$

d) $g(x) = \begin{cases} 1 & \text{if } 0 \leq x \leq \frac{1}{2} \\ -3 & \text{if } \frac{1}{2} < x \leq 2 \end{cases}$

e) $g(x) = \begin{cases} 2 - x & \text{if } 0 \leq x \leq 1 \\ 0 & \text{if } 1 < x \leq 2 \end{cases}$

f) $g(x) = \begin{cases} 3 & \text{if } x = 0, \frac{1}{2}, 1, 2 \\ x & \text{otherwise} \end{cases}$

g) $g(x) = \begin{cases} -1 & \text{if } x = 0, \frac{1}{3}, 2 \\ e^x & \text{otherwise} \end{cases}$

h) $g(x) = \begin{cases} 1 & \text{if } 0 \leq x \leq \frac{1}{3} \\ 0 & \text{if } \frac{1}{3} < x \leq \frac{4}{3} \\ 3 & \text{if } \frac{4}{3} < x \leq 2 \end{cases}$

4. Find the sine series for the functions in Exercise 3.

5. For the functions in Exercise 3, sketch the function to which the cosine series converges, for $0 \leq x \leq 2$.

6. Find the cosine series for the functions in Exercise 3.

7. For any given x from the interval $0 \leq x \leq 1$, use the comparison test to show that the series in (7.34) converges absolutely.

8. In this exercise let $g(x) = x^2$, for $0 \leq x \leq 1$.

   a) Find the cosine series for $g(x)$.

   b) For any given x from the interval $0 \leq x \leq 1$, use the comparison test to show that the series in part (a) converges absolutely.

c) Using your result from part (a), show that

$$\sum_{n=1}^{\infty} \frac{(-1)^{n+1}}{n^2} = \frac{\pi^2}{12}.$$

9. In this exercise let $g(x) = x$, for $0 \leq x \leq 1$.

a) Find the sine series for $g(x)$.

b) Using your result from part (a), show that

$$\frac{\pi}{4} = 1 - \frac{1}{3} + \frac{1}{5} - \frac{1}{7} + \cdots.$$

10. Find a function $g(x)$ that is continuous for $0 \leq x \leq 1$, except for a jump discontinuity at $x = 1/2$, and which equals its sine series for $0 \leq x \leq 1$.

11. This exercise deals with the restriction on term-by-term differentiability of the sine series. This requires you to have read Section 6.5.1. If the observation made in this exercise interests you, you might want to look at Stakgold [2000].

a) Write the function $g(x)$ in Example 4 in terms of the Heaviside function $H(x)$.

b) Using Example 4, from Section 6.5.1, what is $g'(x)$?

c) Using your result from part (b), what is the sine series for $g'(x)$? How does this differ from the result in (7.45)?

7.5 ▪ Wave Equation

The problem involves finding the function $u(x,t)$ that satisfies

$$c^2 \frac{\partial^2 u}{\partial x^2} = \frac{\partial^2 u}{\partial t^2}, \quad \text{for} \quad \begin{cases} 0 < x < L, \\ 0 < t, \end{cases} \tag{7.46}$$

where c is a positive constant. This PDE is known as the wave equation. It applies, for example, to the vertical displacement $u(x,t)$ of an elastic string. This provides an interesting interpretation of the terms in the sine series solution, and this is discussed in Section 7.5.2.

To complete the problem, the boundary conditions are

$$u(0,t) = 0, \tag{7.47}$$

and

$$u(L,t) = 0. \tag{7.48}$$

For the initial conditions, it is assumed that

$$u(x,0) = g(x), \quad \text{for } 0 < x < L, \tag{7.49}$$

and
$$u_t(x, 0) = h(x), \quad \text{for } 0 < x < L, \tag{7.50}$$

where $g(x)$ and $h(x)$ are given functions. To avoid the complication with differentiability, as described in Section 7.4.5, it is assumed that $g(x)$ and $h(x)$ are smooth functions that satisfy the boundary conditions, and $g''(0) = g''(L) = 0$.

As with the diffusion problem, separation of variables will be used to find the general solution of the PDE and boundary conditions. After that, the initial conditions will be satisfied. Also, you should notice, as with the diffusion problem, the PDE and boundary conditions are homogeneous. This is required for separation of variables to work.

Separation of Variables Assumption

Assuming
$$u(x, t) = F(x)G(t), \tag{7.51}$$

and then substituting this into the PDE gives us

$$c^2 \frac{F''(x)}{F(x)} = \frac{G''(t)}{G(t)}. \tag{7.52}$$

Since the left-hand-side is only a function of x, and the right-hand-side is only a function of t, we can conclude that there is a constant λ so that

$$c^2 F''(x) = \lambda F(x), \tag{7.53}$$

and
$$G''(t) = \lambda G(t). \tag{7.54}$$

Finding $F(x)$ and λ

The separation of variables assumption must be used on the boundary conditions. So, to have $u(0, t) = 0$, we need $F(0)G(t) = 0$. For this to happen, and u not be identically zero, we require that $F(0) = 0$. Similarly, we need $F(L) = 0$. Consequently, all-together, the function $F(x)$ must satisfy

$$c^2 F''(x) = \lambda F(x), \tag{7.55}$$

where
$$F(0) = 0 \quad \text{and} \quad F(L) = 0, \tag{7.56}$$

The only difference between the above BVP, and the one for the diffusion equation, is that we now have the coefficient c^2 instead of D. Consequently, from (7.20) and (7.21), the nonzero solutions of (7.55) and (7.56) are

$$F_n(x) = \bar{b}_n \sin\left(\frac{n\pi x}{L}\right), \tag{7.57}$$

and

$$\lambda_n = -c^2 \left(\frac{n\pi}{L}\right)^2,$$ (7.58)

for $n = 1, 2, 3, \ldots$. Also, $\bar{b}_n$ is an arbitrary constant.

Finding $G(t)$

Now that we know λ, (7.54) takes the form

$$G''(t) = -c^2 \left(\frac{n\pi}{L}\right)^2 G(t)$$

Assuming that $G(t) = e^{rt}$, we get that $r^2 = -(cn\pi/L)^2$. So, $r = \pm icn\pi/L$, and from this we get the general solution

$$G_n(t) = a_n \cos(\omega_n t) + b_n \sin(\omega_n t),$$ (7.59)

where

$$\omega_n = \frac{cn\pi}{L},$$ (7.60)

and a_n and b_n are arbitrary constants.

The General Solution

We have shown that for any given n, the function $u_n(x, t) = F_n(x)G_n(t)$ is a solution of the PDE that satisfies the boundary conditions. The resulting general solution, that satisfies the PDE and boundary conditions, is, therefore,

$$u(x, t) = \sum_{n=1}^{\infty} u_n(x, t),$$

or equivalently

$$u(x, t) = \sum_{n=1}^{\infty} \left[a_n \cos(\omega_n t) + b_n \sin(\omega_n t)\right] \sin\left(\frac{n\pi x}{L}\right),$$ (7.61)

where a_n and b_n are arbitrary constants, and ω_n is given in (7.60). In writing this down, the constant $\bar{b}_n$ in (7.57) has been absorbed into the a_n and b_n.

Satisfying the Initial Conditions

$u(x, 0) = g(x)$: We need

$$\sum_{n=1}^{\infty} a_n \sin\left(\frac{n\pi x}{L}\right) = g(x).$$ (7.62)

From (7.31), this means that

$$a_n = \frac{2}{L} \int_0^L g(x) \sin\left(\frac{n\pi x}{L}\right) dx.$$ (7.63)

$u_t(x, 0) = h(x)$: From (7.61), it is required that

$$\sum_{n=1}^{\infty} \omega_n b_n \sin\left(\frac{n\pi x}{L}\right) = h(x). \tag{7.64}$$

Letting $B_n = \omega_n b_n$, then the above equation takes the form

$$\sum_{n=1}^{\infty} B_n \sin\left(\frac{n\pi x}{L}\right) = h(x). \tag{7.65}$$

This is the same problem we had in Section 7.3.5, except that the coefficient is being denoted as B_n instead of b_n. So, from (7.25),

$$B_n = \frac{2}{L} \int_0^L h(x) \sin\left(\frac{n\pi x}{L}\right) dx.$$

Since $b_n = B_n/\omega_n$, the conclusion is that

$$b_n = \frac{2}{cn\pi} \int_0^L h(x) \sin\left(\frac{n\pi x}{L}\right) dx. \tag{7.66}$$

7.5.1 ▪ Examples

Example 1: Suppose that $c = 1$, $L = 2$, $g(x) = 3\sin(\pi x)$, and $h(x) = 0$. In this case, from (7.60), $\omega_n = n\pi/2$. The resulting general solution (7.61) is

$$u(x, t) = \sum_{n=1}^{\infty} \left[a_n \cos\left(\frac{n\pi}{2}t\right) + b_n \sin\left(\frac{n\pi}{2}t\right) \right] \sin\left(\frac{n\pi x}{2}\right).$$

To satisfy the initial condition, since $h(x) = 0$ then, from (7.66), the b_n's are all zero. As for the a_n's, note that $g(x)$ is one of the sine functions in the series. Namely, it is the one when $n = 2$. This enables us to avoid the integral in (7.63). To satisfy (7.62) we simply take $a_2 = 3$, and all the other b_n's are zero. Therefore, the solution is

$$u(x, t) = 3\cos(\pi t)\sin(\pi x). \tag{7.67}$$

This solution is shown in Figure 7.9, both as time slices and as the solution surface for $0 \leq t \leq 3T$, where $T = 2$ is the period of oscillation. ■

Example 2: Suppose that in the previous example, the initial conditions are $g(x) = 0$ and

$$h(x) = 3\sin\left(\frac{\pi x}{2}\right) - 4\sin\left(\frac{3\pi x}{2}\right) + 5\sin(2\pi x).$$

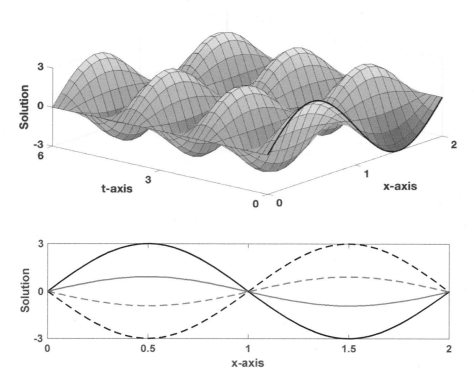

Figure 7.9. *Solution of the wave equation in Example 1. Shown is the solution surface as well as the solution profiles at specific time values.*

This consists of the sum of three of the sine functions in (7.65): $n = 1$, $n = 3$, and $n = 4$. To satisfy (7.65) we take $B_1 = 3$, $B_3 = -4$, $B_4 = 5$, and all the other B_n's are zero. With this, $b_1 = 3/\omega_1 = 6/\pi$, $b_3 = -4/\omega_3 = -8/(3\pi)$, $b_4 = 5/\omega_4 = 5/(2\pi)$. Also, since $g(x) = 0$, then from (7.63), all the a_n's are zero. The resulting solution is

$$u(x,t) = \frac{6}{\pi} \sin\left(\frac{\pi t}{2}\right) \sin\left(\frac{\pi x}{2}\right) - \frac{8}{3\pi} \sin\left(\frac{3\pi t}{2}\right) \sin\left(\frac{3\pi x}{2}\right)$$
$$+ \frac{5}{2\pi} \sin(2\pi t) \sin(2\pi x). \quad \blacksquare$$

7.5.2 ▪ Natural Modes and Standing Waves

The curves shown in the lower plot in Figure 7.9 resemble what you see for time lapse photographs of a vibrating string. There is a reason for this, which is that the wave equation can be used to model the vibrational motion of an elastic string. To pursue this a bit further, we found that the solution of the wave equation problem consists of the superposition of functions of the form

$$u_n(x,t) = \left[a_n \cos(\omega_n t) + b_n \sin(\omega_n t)\right] \sin\left(\frac{n\pi x}{L}\right), \qquad (7.68)$$

where

$$\omega_n = \frac{cn\pi}{L}.$$ (7.69)

The expression in the square brackets is a periodic function of t, with period $2\pi/\omega_n$. In this context, $\sin(n\pi x/L)$ is called a natural mode for the problem, having natural frequency ω_n. The resulting solution in (7.68) corresponds to what is called a standing wave. So, the curves shown in the lower plot in Figure 7.9 are plots of a standing wave in the case of when $n = 2$. It is also possible to have traveling wave solutions, similar to waves on a lake or ocean. If you want to learn about traveling waves, you might look at Strauss [2007] or Holmes [2019].

Exercises

1. You are to find the solution of the wave equation problem for the following initial conditions. Assume that $L = 1$ and $c = 4$. Note that you should be able to answer this question without using integration.

    a) $g(x) = \sin(3\pi x)$, and $h(x) = 0$
    b) $g(x) = 0$, and $h(x) = -2\sin(8\pi x)$
    c) $g(x) = -\sin(\pi x) + 4\sin(3\pi x)$, and $h(x) = -3\sin(5\pi x)$
    d) $g(x) = 5\sin(7\pi x)$, and $h(x) = 2\sin(8\pi x) + 3\sin(12\pi x)$
    e) $g(x) = 2\sin(2\pi x)\cos(\pi x)$, and $h(x) = -2\sin(8\pi x)$
    f) $g(x) = 3\cos(2\pi x - \frac{\pi}{2})$, and $h(x) = -3\cos(7\pi x)\sin(2\pi x)$

2. Find the general solution of the following.

    a) $u_{xx} = u_{tt}$, for $0 < x < 1$, with the boundary conditions $u(0, t) = 0$ and $u_x(1, t) = 0$.
    b) $4u_{xx} = u_{tt}$, for $0 < x < 1$, with the boundary conditions $u_x(0, t) = 0$ and $u(1, t) = 0$.
    c) $u_{xx} = 4u_{tt}$, for $0 < x < 1$, with the boundary conditions $u(0, t) = u(1, t)$ and $u_x(0, t) = u_x(1, t)$.
    d) $u_{xx} = u_{tt} + u_t$, for $0 < x < 1$, with the boundary conditions $u(0, t) = 0$ and $u(1, t) = 0$. This is an example of what is called a damped wave equation.

3. Solve

$$4\frac{\partial^2 u}{\partial x^2} = \frac{\partial^2 u}{\partial t^2}, \quad \text{for} \quad \begin{cases} 0 < x < 1, \\ 0 < t, \end{cases}$$

where $u(0, t) = 0$, $u(1, t) = 0$, $u(x, 0) = 0$, and $u_t(x, 0) = x(1 - x)$.

7.6 ▪ Inhomogeneous Boundary Conditions

Solving the diffusion and wave equations using separation of variables required the boundary conditions to be homogeneous. We now consider how to find the solution when the boundary conditions are inhomogeneous, and have the form

$$u(0, t) = \alpha, \tag{7.70}$$

and

$$u(L, t) = \beta, \tag{7.71}$$

where α and β are constants. The method used to find the solution is to write it as

$$u(x, t) = w(x) + v(x, t),$$

where we pick $w(x)$ so it satisfies the given boundary conditions. In other words, so that $w(0) = \alpha$ and $w(L) = \beta$. Pretty much any smooth function can be used, but it makes things easier if w comes from the steady state equation. What this entails is explained below.

7.6.1 ▪ Steady State Solution

The steady state problem is the one that comes from the PDE and boundary conditions when assuming the solution is independent of t. Assuming we are solving the diffusion equation (7.9), then we are looking for the function $w(x)$ that satisfies

$$\frac{d^2 w}{dx^2} = 0, \quad \text{for } 0 < x < L,$$

where, from (7.70) and (7.71), $w(0) = \alpha$ and $w(L) = \beta$. The resulting solution is

$$w(x) = \alpha + \frac{\beta - \alpha}{L} x.$$

7.6.2 ▪ Transformed Problem

Now that we know the steady state solution, we write the solution of the original diffusion problem as

$$u(x, t) = \alpha + \frac{\beta - \alpha}{L} x + v(x, t). \tag{7.72}$$

Since $u_{xx} = v_{xx}$ and $u_t = v_t$, then from the diffusion equation (7.9) we have that

$$D \frac{\partial^2 v}{\partial x^2} = \frac{\partial v}{\partial t}, \quad \text{for } \begin{cases} 0 < x < L, \\ 0 < t. \end{cases} \tag{7.73}$$

At $x = 0$, from (7.72), $v(0, t) = u(0, t) - \alpha = 0$. This also happens at the other endpoint. So, the boundary conditions are

$$v(0, t) = 0, \tag{7.74}$$

and

$$v(L, t) = 0. \tag{7.75}$$

Finally, if the initial condition is $u(x,0) = g(x)$, then the resulting initial condition for v is

$$v(x,0) = g(x) - \alpha - \frac{\beta - \alpha}{L}x, \quad \text{for } 0 < x < L. \tag{7.76}$$

The above problem for $v(x,t)$ has the same form as the one for $u(x,t)$, as given in (7.9)-(7.12), except for a slightly different looking initial condition. Consequently, we can use the solution as given in (7.23) and (7.25) if we make the appropriate adjustments. In particular,

$$v(x,t) = \sum_{n=1}^{\infty} b_n e^{\lambda_n t} \sin\left(\frac{n\pi x}{L}\right),$$

where

$$b_n = \frac{2}{L} \int_0^L \left(g(x) - \alpha - \frac{\beta - \alpha}{L}x\right) \sin\left(\frac{n\pi x}{L}\right) dx, \tag{7.77}$$

and

$$\lambda_n = -D\left(\frac{n\pi}{L}\right)^2.$$

7.6.3 · Summary

We have shown that the solution of

$$D\frac{\partial^2 u}{\partial x^2} = \frac{\partial u}{\partial t}, \quad \text{for } \begin{cases} 0 < x < L, \\ 0 < t, \end{cases}$$

where $u(0,t) = \alpha$, $u(L,t) = \beta$, and $u(x,0) = g(x)$, is

$$u(x,t) = \alpha + \frac{\beta - \alpha}{L}x + \sum_{n=1}^{\infty} b_n e^{\lambda_n t} \sin\left(\frac{n\pi x}{L}\right), \tag{7.78}$$

where b_n is given in (7.77).

Example: Find the solution of

$$4\partial_x^2 u = \partial_t u, \quad \text{for } \begin{cases} 0 < x < 5, \\ 0 < t, \end{cases}$$

where $u(0,t) = 3$, $u(5,t) = 2$, and $u(x,0) = 0$.

Answer: In this problem $D = 4$, $L = 5$, $\alpha = 3$, and $\beta = 2$. So, from (7.77),

$$b_n = \frac{2}{5} \int_0^5 \left(-3 + \frac{x}{5}\right) \sin\left(\frac{n\pi x}{5}\right) dx = -\frac{2}{n\pi}\left[3 - 2(-1)^n\right].$$

Therefore, from (7.78), the solution of the diffusion problem is

$$u(x,t) = 3 - \frac{x}{5} - \sum_{n=1}^{\infty} \frac{2}{n\pi}\left[3 - 2(-1)^n\right]e^{\lambda_n t} \sin\left(\frac{n\pi x}{5}\right),$$

where $\lambda_n = -4\left(\frac{n\pi}{5}\right)^2$. ■

7.6.4 · Wave Equation

The method works, without change, on the wave equation. The only complication is, as it usually is with the wave equation, differentiability. To explain, if the boundary conditions are $u(0,t) = \alpha$ and $u(L,t) = \beta$, and the initial conditions are $u(x,0) = g(x)$ and $u_t(x,0) = h(x)$, then it is required that

$$g(0) = \alpha, \qquad h(0) = 0, \qquad g''(0) = 0,$$

and

$$g(L) = \beta, \qquad h(L) = 0, \qquad g''(L) = 0.$$

These are called *compatibility conditions*. If they are satisfied, and $g''(x)$ and $h'(x)$ are continuous, then the solution has the differentiability requited to satisfy the wave equation.

Exercises

1. You are to find the solution of the diffusion equation $4u_{xx} = u_t$ for the given boundary and initial conditions. Assume that $L = 1$.

   a) $u(0,t) = 1$, $u(1,t) = -1$, and $u(x,0) = 0$.

   b) $u(0,t) = 2$, $u(1,t) = -5$, and $u(x,0) = 2$.

   c) $u(0,t) = -4$, $u(1,t) = 1$, and $u(x,0) = x$.

2. Find the steady state solution of the following problems.

   a) $u_{xx} = u_t$, for $0 < x < 2$, with the boundary conditions $u(0,t) = 1$ and $u_x(2,t) = -1$.

   b) $4u_{xx} = u_t$, for $0 < x < 4$, with the boundary conditions $u_x(0,t) = 2$ and $u(4,t) = 1$.

   c) $(1+t)u_{xx} = u_t$, for $0 < x < 1$, with the boundary conditions $u(0,t) = -1$ and $u(1,t) = 2$.

   d) $u_{xx} = u_t + u$, for $0 < x < 3$, with the boundary conditions $u(0,t) = 1$ and $u(3,t) = 2$.

   e) $u_{xx} - u_x = u_t$, for $0 < x < 2$, with the boundary conditions $u(0,t) = -1$ and $u(2,t) = 1$.

3. Solve
   $$\frac{\partial^2 u}{\partial x^2} = \frac{\partial u}{\partial t}, \quad \text{for } \begin{cases} 0 < x < 2, \\ 0 < t, \end{cases}$$
   where $u(0,t) = 1$, $u_x(2,t) = -1$, and $u(x,0) = 0$.

4. Solve
   $$(1+t)\partial_x^2 u = \partial_t u, \quad \text{for } \begin{cases} 0 < x < 1, \\ 0 < t, \end{cases}$$
   where $u(0,t) = -1$, $u(1,t) = 2$, and $u(x,0) = 0$.

5. Solve

$$9\frac{\partial^2 u}{\partial x^2} = \frac{\partial^2 u}{\partial t^2}, \quad \text{for} \quad \left\{ \begin{array}{l} 0 < x < 1, \\ 0 < t, \end{array} \right.$$

where $u(0,t) = 1$, $u(1,t) = -1$, $u(x,0) = 1 - 2x - 7\sin(3\pi x)$, and $u_t(x,0) = 0$.

7.7 ▪ Inhomogeneous PDEs

It is common in applications to have a PDE that is not homogeneous. To explain how to solve such a problem, suppose the PDE is

$$D\frac{\partial^2 u}{\partial x^2} = \frac{\partial u}{\partial t} + p(x,t), \quad \text{for} \quad \left\{ \begin{array}{l} 0 < x < L, \\ 0 < t, \end{array} \right. \tag{7.79}$$

where $p(x,t)$ is a given smooth function of x and t. It is assumed the boundary conditions are homogeneous, and so,

$$u(0,t) = 0, \tag{7.80}$$

and

$$u(L,t) = 0. \tag{7.81}$$

Sine Series Expansions

The general solution when $p \equiv 0$, which is given in (7.23), consists of the superposition of functions containing $\sin(n\pi x/L)$. The solution for nonzero p can also be expanded in this way. Specifically, we can write

$$u(x,t) = \sum_{n=1}^{\infty} w_n(t) \sin\left(\frac{n\pi x}{L}\right), \quad \text{for } 0 \leq x \leq L, \tag{7.82}$$

where the $w_n(t)$'s are determined from the PDE. The expansion in (7.82) is guaranteed from the Sine Convergence Theorem (page 189) because u is a smooth function and it satisfies the homogeneous boundary conditions (7.80) and (7.81).

We will also expand the forcing function p is a sine series, and write

$$p(x,t) = \sum_{n=1}^{\infty} p_n(t) \sin\left(\frac{n\pi x}{L}\right), \quad \text{for } 0 < x < L, \tag{7.83}$$

where

$$p_n(t) = \frac{2}{L} \int_0^L p(x,t) \sin\left(\frac{n\pi x}{L}\right) dx. \tag{7.84}$$

Because $p(x,t)$ is known, the $p_n(t)$'s are known. Note that it is not assumed that $p = 0$ at the endpoints, which is why the interval in (7.83) is $0 < x < L$ and not $0 \leq x \leq L$.

Solving the PDE

Assuming the series for u can be differentiated term-by-term, we get that

$$u_{xx} = -\sum_{n=1}^{\infty} \left(\frac{n\pi}{L}\right)^2 w_n(t) \sin\left(\frac{n\pi x}{L}\right) \quad \text{and} \quad u_t = \sum_{n=1}^{\infty} w_n'(t) \sin\left(\frac{n\pi x}{L}\right).$$

Introducing these into (7.79), as well as using (7.83), we have that

$$\sum_{n=1}^{\infty} \left[D\left(\frac{n\pi}{L}\right)^2 w_n(t) + w_n'(t) + p_n(t) \right] \sin\left(\frac{n\pi x}{L}\right) = 0. \tag{7.85}$$

For this to hold, the term in the square bracket must be zero. The proof of this uses the integration formula (7.30), in exactly the same way it was used to find the coefficients of the sine series. The conclusion is that

$$D\left(\frac{n\pi}{L}\right)^2 w_n(t) + w_n'(t) + p_n(t) = 0,$$

or equivalently,

$$w_n' + \kappa_n w_n = -p_n, \tag{7.86}$$

where

$$\kappa_n = D\left(\frac{n\pi}{L}\right)^2.$$

This is a first-order linear differential equation for w_n, which can be solved using an integrating factor. The integrating factor in this case is, from (2.18), $\mu = e^{\kappa_n t}$. So, from (2.21), we get the general solution of (7.86) is

$$w_n(t) = e^{-\kappa_n t}\left[-\int_0^t p_n(s) e^{\kappa_n s} ds + w_n(0) \right]. \tag{7.87}$$

Satisfying the Initial Condition

To solve the problem it remains to satisfy the initial condition

$$u(x, 0) = g(x), \quad \text{for } 0 < x < L. \tag{7.88}$$

From (7.25), and since $b_n = w_n(0)$, it is required that

$$w_n(0) = \frac{2}{L} \int_0^L g(x) \sin\left(\frac{n\pi x}{L}\right) dx.$$

7.7.1 ▪ Summary

To summarize our findings, the solution of the inhomogeneous diffusion problem (7.79)-(7.81), which satisfies the initial condition (7.88), is

$$u(x, t) = \sum_{n=1}^{\infty} w_n(t) \sin\left(\frac{n\pi x}{L}\right), \tag{7.89}$$

where

$$w_n(t) = e^{-\kappa_n t}\left[- \int_0^t p_n(s)e^{\kappa_n s}ds + w_n(0)\right], \tag{7.90}$$

$$p_n(t) = \frac{2}{L}\int_0^L p(x,t)\sin\left(\frac{n\pi x}{L}\right)dx, \tag{7.91}$$

$$w_n(0) = \frac{2}{L}\int_0^L g(x)\sin\left(\frac{n\pi x}{L}\right)dx,$$

and $\kappa_n = D(n\pi/L)^2$.

Example

Suppose the problem to solve is

$$4\frac{\partial^2 u}{\partial x^2} = \frac{\partial u}{\partial t} + 3\sin(2t)\sin(\pi x), \quad \text{for } \begin{cases} 0 < x < 1, \\ 0 < t, \end{cases} \tag{7.92}$$

where

$$u(0,t) = 0, \tag{7.93}$$
$$u(1,t) = 0, \tag{7.94}$$

and

$$u(x,0) = 0, \quad \text{for } 0 < x < 1. \tag{7.95}$$

In this problem, $D = 4$ and $L = 1$. The first step is to find the p_n's. From (7.91), we want

$$3\sin(2t)\sin(\pi x) = \sum_{n=1}^{\infty} p_n(t)\sin(n\pi x).$$

So, $p_1(t) = 3\sin 2t$ and all the other p_n's are zero. Also, since $g(x) = 0$ then $w_n(0) = 0$, for all n This leaves the integral in (7.90), and so

$$\int_0^t p_1(s)e^{\kappa_1 s}ds = \int_0^t 3\sin(2s)e^{\kappa_1 s}ds$$
$$= 3\frac{2 + \kappa_1 e^{\kappa_1 t}\sin(2t) - 2e^{\kappa_1 t}\cos(2t)}{\kappa_1^2 + 4}.$$

Since $\kappa_1 = 4\pi^2$, then

$$w_1(t) = \frac{3}{2(1 + 4\pi^4)}\left[\cos(2t) - 2\pi^2\sin(2t) - e^{-4\pi^2 t}\right].$$

Therefore, the solution of the diffusion problem is

$$u(x,t) = \frac{3}{2(1 + 4\pi^4)}\left[\cos(2t) - 2\pi^2\sin(2t) - e^{-4\pi^2 t}\right]\sin(\pi x). \quad \blacksquare$$

7.7.2 ▪ A Very Useful Observation

As you might have noticed, the problem was solved without using separation of variables. Instead we assumed that the solution can be expanded in a sine series, as expressed in (7.82). For this to work it is essential that the functions $\sin(n\pi x/L)$ satisfy the boundary conditions, which they do for this problem. By using this sine series expansion, the problem reduces to solving a relatively simple ODE for the coefficients of the series. This approach can be used on other PDEs and examples of how this is done are given in Exercises 3 and 4. In fact, this idea is the basis for what is called the *Galerkin method* for computing the solution of a PDE.

Exercises

1. You are to find the solution of the diffusion equation (7.79), where $u(0, t) = 0$, $u(1, t) = 0$, $u(x, 0) = 0$, and $p(x, t)$ is given below. Assume that $D = 4$ and $L = 1$.

   a) $p(x, t) = -4 \cos(t) \sin(5\pi x)$.
   b) $p(x, t) = e^{-2t} \sin(3\pi x)$.
   c) $p(x, t) = 1$.

2. There is a simpler way to solve an inhomogeneous PDE when the forcing function does not dependent on t. In this problem assume that $p(x, t) = x^2$.

   a) Find the steady state solution of (7.79), that satisfies (7.80) and (7.81).
   b) Letting $u(x, t) = w(x) + v(x, t)$, where $w(x)$ is the steady state solution you found in part (a), find the PDE and boundary conditions satisfied by $v(x, t)$. Also, if $u(x, 0) = g(x)$, then what is the resulting initial condition for $v(x, t)$?
   c) Assuming $g(x) = 0$, find $v(x, t)$, and from this determine the solution of the original diffusion problem.

3. This exercise considers how to use a sine series to solve

$$\frac{\partial^2 u}{\partial x^2} = \frac{\partial u}{\partial t} + 5u, \quad \text{for} \quad \begin{cases} 0 < x < 2, \\ 0 < t, \end{cases}$$

   where $u(0, t) = 0$, $u(2, t) = 0$, and $u(x, 0) = x$. This is going to be done using the assumption in (7.82), which for this problem is

$$u(x, t) = \sum_{n=1}^{\infty} w_n(t) \sin\left(\frac{n\pi x}{2}\right), \quad \text{for } 0 \le x \le 2.$$

   a) Assuming $u(x, t)$ is smooth, explain why the Sine Series Convergence Theorem guarantees that the above series converges to $u(x, t)$.

b) Substitute the series into the PDE and rewrite the result so it resembles (7.85). From this determine the differential equation $w_n(t)$ satisfies.

c) Find the general solution for $w_n(t)$, and from this write down the general solution for $u(x, t)$.

d) Use the general solution to satisfy the initial condition, and from this determine the solution of the problem.

4. Solve

$$(1 + t)\frac{\partial^2 u}{\partial x^2} = \frac{\partial u}{\partial t}, \quad \text{for} \quad \begin{cases} 0 < x < 3, \\ 0 < t, \end{cases}$$

where $u(0, t) = 0$, $u(3, t) = 0$, and $u(x, 0) = 1$. Find the solution using the procedure outlined in Exercise 3 (with the appropriate modifications).

7.8 ▪ Laplace's Equation

We are going to consider how to solve the equation

$$\nabla^2 u = 0, \tag{7.96}$$

where ∇^2 is called the **Laplacian**, or the **Laplacian operator**. The formula for ∇^2 depends on the coordinate system you are using. In the case of Cartesian coordinates,

$$\nabla^2 = \frac{\partial^2}{\partial x^2} + \frac{\partial^2}{\partial y^2},$$

in which case (7.96) is simply

$$u_{xx} + u_{yy} = 0. \tag{7.97}$$

Later we will consider polar coordinates, and the respective formula for ∇^2 will be given at that time.

It should not be a surprise that (7.96) is known as **Laplace's equation**. It plays a fundamental role in applied mathematics. If you look through a junior or senior level textbook in complex variables, fluid dynamics, electromagnetism, heat transfer, etc, it will appear often. As an example, heat conduction is governed by the diffusion equation $u_t = D\nabla^2 u$. So, if you want to determine the steady-state temperature distribution, then you must solve (7.96).

Our goal is to find the function $u(x, y)$ that satisfies Laplace's equation for (x, y) in a region, as illustrated in Figure 7.10, along with a boundary condition $u = f$ on the boundary of the region. To keep things simple we will only consider simple shapes, and that means rectangular and circular. In both cases, the method of separation of variables is used to find the solution.

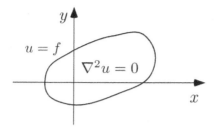

Figure 7.10. *The solution $u(x,y)$ is to satisfy Laplace's equation in a given region in the x,y-plane, and also satisfy $u = f$ on the boundary of the region.*

The symbol ∇^2 appearing in Laplace's equation comes from vector calculus. Namely, using the gradient ∇ and the dot product, one writes

$$\nabla^2 = \nabla \cdot \nabla.$$

In Cartesian coordinates the gradient is $\nabla = \left(\frac{\partial}{\partial x}, \frac{\partial}{\partial y}\right)$, and from this you get that $\nabla^2 = \frac{\partial^2}{\partial x^2} + \frac{\partial^2}{\partial y^2}$. This can also be used to derive the formula for ∇^2 is other coordinate systems, such as polar coordinates.

7.8.1 ▪ Rectangular Domain

The problem to solve is

$$u_{xx} + u_{yy} = 0, \quad \text{for} \quad \begin{cases} 0 < x < a, \\ 0 < y < b, \end{cases} \tag{7.98}$$

where the boundary conditions are shown in Figure 7.11. So, $u = 0$ when $x = 0$, when $x = a$, and when $y = 0$. Along the top, where $y = b$, $u = f(x)$.

The steps used in carrying out the separation of variables method are very similar to what was done earlier. We will first find the general solution of the PDE that satisfies the homogeneous boundary conditions.

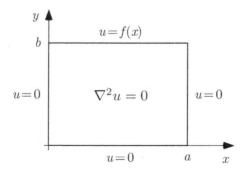

Figure 7.11. *Rectangular domain used when solving Laplace's equation and the corresponding boundary conditions.*

We will then use that solution to satisfy the inhomogeneous boundary condition (which is on the upper side of the rectangle).

Separation of Variables Assumption

Assuming

$$u(x, y) = X(x)Y(y), \tag{7.99}$$

and then substituting this into Laplace's equation gives us

$$\frac{X''(x)}{X(x)} = -\frac{Y''(y)}{Y(y)}. \tag{7.100}$$

Since the left-hand-side is only a function of x, and the right-hand-side is only a function of y, we can conclude that there is a constant λ so that

$$X''(x) = \lambda X(x), \tag{7.101}$$

and

$$Y''(y) = -\lambda Y(y). \tag{7.102}$$

As explained earlier, the separated solution (7.99) is required to satisfy the homogeneous boundary conditions shown in Figure 7.11.

Finding $X(x)$ and λ

The equation to solve is

$$X''(x) = \lambda X(x). \tag{7.103}$$

Since $u = 0$ when $x = 0$ and $x = a$, then it is required that

$$X(0) = 0 \quad \text{and} \quad X(a) = 0. \tag{7.104}$$

This is essentially the same problem we had when solving the diffusion and wave equations, and the general solution is

$$X_n(x) = c_n \sin\left(\frac{n\pi x}{a}\right), \tag{7.105}$$

and

$$\lambda_n = -\left(\frac{n\pi}{a}\right)^2, \tag{7.106}$$

for $n = 1, 2, 3, \ldots$. Also, c_n is an arbitrary constant.

Finding $Y(y)$

From (7.102), we now need to solve

$$Y''(y) = -\lambda_n Y(y),$$

where $Y(0) = 0$. The general solution of this ODE is

$$Y_n = A_n e^{n\pi y/a} + B_n e^{-n\pi y/a}.$$

To have $Y_n(0) = 0$ we need $B_n = -A_n$. Consequently,

$$Y_n = A_n\left(e^{n\pi y/a} - e^{-n\pi y/a}\right)$$
$$= 2A_n\sinh(n\pi y/a). \tag{7.107}$$

The General Solution

The resulting general solution, that satisfies the PDE and homogeneous boundary conditions, is, therefore,

$$u(x, y) = \sum_{n=1}^{\infty} X_n(x)Y_n(y),$$

or equivalently

$$u(x, y) = \sum_{n=1}^{\infty} c_n\sinh\left(\frac{n\pi y}{a}\right)\sin\left(\frac{n\pi x}{a}\right), \tag{7.108}$$

where the c_n's are arbitrary constants. In writing this down, the constant $2A_n$ in (7.107) has been absorbed into the c_n in (7.105).

Satisfying the Inhomogeneous Boundary Condition

To have $u(x, b) = f(x)$, we need

$$\sum_{n=1}^{\infty} c_n\sinh\left(\frac{n\pi b}{a}\right)\sin\left(\frac{n\pi x}{a}\right) = f(x). \tag{7.109}$$

This can be written as

$$\sum_{n=1}^{\infty} b_n\sin\left(\frac{n\pi x}{a}\right) = f(x),$$

where $b_n = c_n\sinh(n\pi b/a)$. According to the Sine Convergence Theorem (page 189), the b_n's that satisfy the above equation are

$$b_n = \frac{2}{a}\int_0^a f(x)\sin\left(\frac{n\pi x}{a}\right)dx.$$

From this we conclude that

$$c_n = \frac{2}{a \sinh(n\pi b/a)} \int_0^a f(x) \sin\left(\frac{n\pi x}{a}\right) dx. \qquad (7.110)$$

With this value for c_n, $u(x, y)$ given in (7.108) is the solution of the problem.

Example 1: Find the solution of

$$u_{xx} + u_{yy} = 0, \quad \text{for} \quad \left\{ \begin{array}{l} 0 < x < 1, \\ 0 < y < 1, \end{array} \right.$$

where $u(x, 1) = 8 \sin(5\pi x)$ and $u = 0$ on the other three sides of the square (see Figure 7.11).

Answer: In this problem $a = b = 1$, and $f(x) = 8 \sin(5\pi x)$. From (7.109), we need

$$8 \sin(5\pi x) = \sum_{n=1}^{\infty} c_n \sinh(n\pi) \sin(n\pi x).$$

So, $c_5 \sinh(5\pi) = 8$, and the other c_n's are zero. Therefore, the solution is

$$u(x, y) = 8 \frac{\sinh(5\pi y)}{\sinh(5\pi)} \sin(5\pi x).$$

The resulting solution is shown in Figure 7.12.   ■

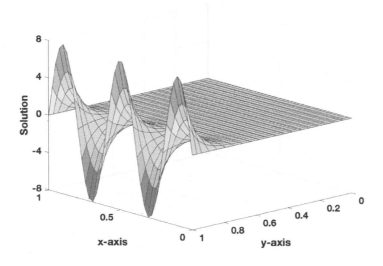

Figure 7.12. *Solution of Laplace's equation derived in Example 1.*

7.8.2 · Circular Domain

We now solve Laplace's equation when the domain is the circular region $x^2 + y^2 < a^2$, as illustrated in Figure 7.13. It makes it easier in this case to use polar coordinates and take $x = r\cos\theta$, $y = r\sin\theta$. Using the standard change of coordinate formulas, one finds that

$$\nabla^2 = \frac{\partial^2}{\partial r^2} + \frac{1}{r}\frac{\partial}{\partial r} + \frac{1}{r^2}\frac{\partial^2}{\partial\theta^2}.$$

Therefore, the problem we are solving is

$$u_{rr} + \frac{1}{r}u_r + \frac{1}{r^2}u_{\theta\theta} = 0, \quad \text{for} \quad \begin{cases} 0 \le r < a, \\ 0 \le \theta < 2\pi, \end{cases} \tag{7.111}$$

where the boundary condition is

$$u\big|_{r=a} = f(\theta). \tag{7.112}$$

As will be seen below, this problem is easily solved using separation of variables.

Using polar coordinates makes solving the problem easier, but it requires some comment. First, (7.111) is singular when $r = 0$. This always happens when using polar coordinates. To prevent the singular nature of the equation from interfering with us solving the problem, it is assumed that the solution is bounded. The second comment is that the positive x-axis corresponds to $\theta = 0$ and to $\theta = 2\pi$. The solution u and its derivative u_θ must be continuous in the circular domain, and this means we must require that

$$u\big|_{\theta=0} = u\big|_{\theta=2\pi} \quad \text{and} \quad u_\theta\big|_{\theta=0} = u_\theta\big|_{\theta=2\pi}. \tag{7.113}$$

In the vernacular of the subject, these are called *periodic boundary conditions*. Also, note that these boundary conditions are homogeneous because $u = 0$ satisfies both of them. Finally, if (7.113) hold then u_r is also continuous in the domain.

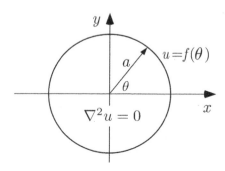

Figure 7.13. *Circular domain and corresponding boundary condition.*

Separation of Variables Assumption

Assuming
$$u = R(r)\Theta(\theta), \tag{7.114}$$
and then substituting this into Laplace's equation (7.111) gives us
$$r^2 \frac{R''(r)}{R(r)} + r\frac{R'(r)}{R(r)} = -\frac{\Theta''(\theta)}{\Theta(\theta)}. \tag{7.115}$$

Since the left-hand-side is only a function of r, and the right-hand-side is only a function of θ, we can conclude that there is a constant λ so that
$$r^2 R''(r) + rR'(r) = \lambda R(r), \tag{7.116}$$
and
$$\Theta''(\theta) = -\lambda\Theta(\theta). \tag{7.117}$$

From (7.113) we also must have that
$$\Theta(0) = \Theta(2\pi) \quad \text{and} \quad \Theta'(0) = \Theta'(2\pi). \tag{7.118}$$

Finding $\Theta(\theta)$ and λ

As usual, the first problem to solve is the one involving the homogeneous boundary conditions, which means solving (7.117) and (7.118).

$\lambda = 0$: In this case (7.117) is $\Theta'' = 0$, and so $\Theta = A + B\theta$, where A and B are constants. To satisfy (7.118) it must be that $B = 0$, and so the solution is $\Theta_0 = A_0$.

$\lambda \neq 0$: Assuming $\Theta = e^{r\theta}$, we get the characteristic equation $r^2 = -\lambda$. Skipping the two real roots case we take $\lambda > 0$, giving us the general solution
$$\Theta = A\cos(\theta\sqrt{\lambda}) + B\sin(\theta\sqrt{\lambda}).$$
To satisfy (7.118) one finds that $\cos(2\pi\sqrt{\lambda}) = 1$. This means that $2\pi\sqrt{\lambda} = 2\pi, 4\pi, 6\pi, \ldots$. In other words,
$$\lambda_n = n^2, \text{ for } n = 1, 2, 3, \ldots, \tag{7.119}$$
and
$$\Theta_n = A_n \cos(n\theta) + B_n \sin(n\theta). \tag{7.120}$$

Finding $R(r)$

$\lambda = 0$: In this case (7.116) is $r^2 R'' + rR' = 0$. This is an Euler equation, and how to solve it was explained in Section 3.11. One finds that $R = \overline{A} + \overline{B}\ln r$, where $\overline{A}$ and $\overline{B}$ are constants. To have a bounded solution we require $\overline{B} = 0$, and this means the solution is $R_0 = \overline{A}_0$.

$\lambda = n^2$: Now (7.116) is

$$r^2 R'' + rR' = n^2 R.$$

This is also an Euler equation, and the general solution is $R_n = \overline{A}_n r^n + \overline{B}_n r^{-n}$. Because the solution is bounded we require $\overline{B}_n = 0$.

The General Solution

The general solution of Laplace's equation that is bounded and satisfies (7.113) is

$$u = \sum_{n=0}^{\infty} R_n(r)\Theta_n(\theta),$$

or equivalently

$$u = \frac{1}{2}a_0 + \sum_{n=1}^{\infty} r^n \big[a_n \cos(n\theta) + b_n \sin(n\theta)\big]. \qquad (7.121)$$

The coefficients in this formula are written in a form similar to what was used earlier for a sine and cosine series. So, for example, we have written $R_0\Theta_0 = \overline{A}_0 A_0 = \frac{1}{2}a_0$.

Satisfying the Boundary Condition

To have $u = f(\theta)$ when $r = a$, we need

$$\frac{1}{2}a_0 + \sum_{n=1}^{\infty} a^n \big[a_n \cos(n\theta) + b_n \sin(n\theta)\big] = f(\theta). \qquad (7.122)$$

The a_n's and b_n's are determined in the same way as for a sine and cosine series. For example, to determine a_7 you multiply the above equation by $\cos(7\theta)$, integrate for $0 \leq \theta \leq 2\pi$, and use orthogonality conditions such as given in (7.30) and (7.39). The resulting formulas obtained in this way are

$$a_n = \frac{1}{\pi a^n} \int_0^{2\pi} f(\theta) \cos(n\theta)d\theta,$$

and

$$b_n = \frac{1}{\pi a^n} \int_0^{2\pi} f(\theta) \sin(n\theta)d\theta.$$

Example 2: Find the solution of

$$\nabla^2 u = 0, \quad \text{for } x^2 + y^2 < 1,$$

where $u = 3\sin(4\theta)$ for $x^2 + y^2 = 1$.

Answer: In this problem $a = 1$ and $f(\theta) = 3\sin(4\theta)$. From (7.122), we need

$$3\sin(4\theta) = \frac{1}{2}a_0 + \sum_{n=1}^{\infty} \left[(a_n \cos(n\theta) + b_n \sin(n\theta) \right].$$

So, $b_4 = 3$, and the other coefficients are zero. Therefore, the solution is

$$u = 3r^4 \sin(4\theta).$$

The resulting solution is shown in Figure 7.14.   ■

Exercises

1. You are to find the solution of the problem shown in Figure 7.11. Assume that $a = 1$ and $b = 2$. Note that you should be able to answer this question without using integration.

   a) $f(x) = 5\sin(2\pi x)$
   b) $f(x) = -3\sin(12\pi x)$
   c) $f(x) = \sin(\pi x) - 7\sin(8\pi x)$
   d) $f(x) = -3\sin(4\pi x) - \sin(7\pi x) + 6\sin(20\pi x)$

2. You are to find the solution of the problem shown in Figure 7.13. Assume that $a = 2$. Note that you should be able to answer this question without using integration.

   a) $f(\theta) = 4\cos(3\theta)$

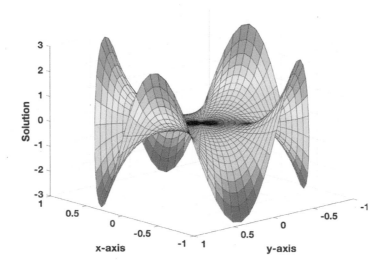

Figure 7.14. *Solution of Laplace's equation derived in Example 2.*

b) $f(\theta) = 1 - 3\sin(15\theta)$

c) $f(\theta) = \sin(\theta) + 3\cos(5\theta)$

d) $f(\theta) = 4 - 2\sin(5\theta) - 4\sin(9\theta) + 8\cos(14\theta)$

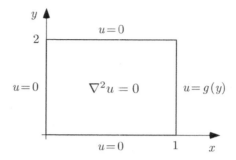

Figure 7.15. *Problem solved in Exercise 3.*

3. The problem concerns solving the problem shown in Figure 7.15.

a) Write down the differential equation and boundary conditions for this problem.

b) Find the general solution. This should satisfy Laplace's equation as well as the homogeneous boundary conditions.

c) Use the inhomogeneous boundary condition to find the formula for the coefficient in your general solution.

d) If $g(y) = 7\sin(3\pi y)$, then what is the solution?

e) If $g(y) = -2\sin(2\pi y) + 8\sin(7\pi y)$, then what is the solution?

4. The problem concerns solving the problem in the quarter circle shown in Figure 7.16.

a) In polar coordinates, write down the differential equation and boundary conditions for this problem.

b) Find the general solution. This should satisfy Laplace's equation as well as the homogeneous boundary conditions. It should not be

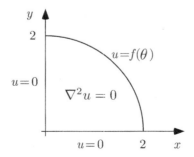

Figure 7.16. *Problem solved in Exercise 4.*

required to satisfy the conditions in (7.113), as those only apply when you have a domain with $0 \leq \theta \leq 2\pi$.

c) If $f(\theta) = -3\sin(4\theta)$, then what is the solution?

d) If $f(\theta) = 9\sin(2\theta) - 5\sin(14\theta)$, then what is the solution?

5. Setting $\lambda = -\kappa^2$, where $\kappa > 0$, what is the general solution of (7.117)? Show that to satisfy the boundary conditions (7.118) that the solution is identically zero.

6. Suppose that instead of using $0 \leq \theta < 2\pi$, one were to use $-\pi \leq \theta < \pi$. How are the periodic boundary conditions (7.113) changed?

Appendix A

Matrix Algebra: Summary

The following is a brief summary of the rules of matrix and vector algebra in two dimensions.

A.1 • Addition: $\mathbf{x} + \mathbf{y}$ and $\mathbf{A} + \mathbf{B}$

General:

$$\begin{pmatrix} x \\ y \end{pmatrix} + \begin{pmatrix} u \\ v \end{pmatrix} = \begin{pmatrix} x+u \\ y+v \end{pmatrix} \qquad \begin{pmatrix} a & b \\ c & d \end{pmatrix} + \begin{pmatrix} e & f \\ g & h \end{pmatrix} = \begin{pmatrix} a+e & b+f \\ c+g & d+h \end{pmatrix}$$

Examples:

$$\begin{pmatrix} 1 \\ 2 \end{pmatrix} + \begin{pmatrix} -3 \\ 4 \end{pmatrix} = \begin{pmatrix} -2 \\ 6 \end{pmatrix} \qquad \begin{pmatrix} 1 & -2 \\ -3 & 4 \end{pmatrix} + \begin{pmatrix} 1 & 0 \\ -7 & 3 \end{pmatrix} = \begin{pmatrix} 2 & -2 \\ 1 & 7 \end{pmatrix}$$

A.2 • Scalar Multiplication: $\alpha \mathbf{x}$ and $\alpha \mathbf{A}$

Scalar means a number (real or complex).

General:

$$\alpha \begin{pmatrix} x \\ y \end{pmatrix} = \begin{pmatrix} x \\ y \end{pmatrix} \alpha = \begin{pmatrix} \alpha a \\ \alpha b \end{pmatrix} \qquad \alpha \begin{pmatrix} a & b \\ c & d \end{pmatrix} = \begin{pmatrix} a & b \\ c & d \end{pmatrix} \alpha = \begin{pmatrix} \alpha a & \alpha b \\ \alpha c & \alpha d \end{pmatrix}$$

Examples:

$$4 \begin{pmatrix} 1 \\ -3 \end{pmatrix} = \begin{pmatrix} 4 \\ -12 \end{pmatrix} \qquad -4 \begin{pmatrix} 1 & 0 \\ -2 & 3 \end{pmatrix} = \begin{pmatrix} -4 & 0 \\ 8 & -12 \end{pmatrix}$$

$$\begin{pmatrix} 4 \\ -8 \end{pmatrix} = 4 \begin{pmatrix} 1 \\ -2 \end{pmatrix} \qquad \begin{pmatrix} 6 & 0 \\ 3 & -12 \end{pmatrix} = 3 \begin{pmatrix} 2 & 0 \\ 1 & -4 \end{pmatrix}$$

A.3 ▪ Equality: $\mathbf{x} = \mathbf{y}$ and $\mathbf{A} = \mathbf{B}$

General:

$$\begin{pmatrix} x \\ y \end{pmatrix} = \begin{pmatrix} u \\ v \end{pmatrix} \quad \text{means that } x = u,\ y = v$$

$$\begin{pmatrix} a & b \\ c & d \end{pmatrix} = \begin{pmatrix} e & f \\ g & h \end{pmatrix} \quad \text{means that } a = e,\ b = f,\ c = g,\ d = h$$

Examples: note that $\mathbf{I}$ is defined on page 85

$$\begin{pmatrix} a \\ b \end{pmatrix} = \mathbf{0} \quad \text{means that } a = 0,\ b = 0$$

$$\begin{pmatrix} a & b \\ c & d \end{pmatrix} = \mathbf{I} \quad \text{means that } a = 1,\ b = 0,\ c = 0,\ d = 1$$

A.4 ▪ Matrix-Vector Multiplication: $\mathbf{Ax}$ and $\alpha\mathbf{Ax} + \mathbf{y}$

General:

$$\begin{pmatrix} a & b \\ c & d \end{pmatrix}\begin{pmatrix} x \\ y \end{pmatrix} = \begin{pmatrix} ax + by \\ cx + dy \end{pmatrix}$$

Examples:

$$\begin{pmatrix} 1 & -2 \\ -3 & 4 \end{pmatrix}\begin{pmatrix} 1 \\ 2 \end{pmatrix} = \begin{pmatrix} -3 \\ 3 \end{pmatrix}$$

$$3\begin{pmatrix} 1 & -1 \\ 0 & 2 \end{pmatrix}\begin{pmatrix} -1 \\ 1 \end{pmatrix} - \begin{pmatrix} 1 \\ 5 \end{pmatrix} = 3\begin{pmatrix} -2 \\ 2 \end{pmatrix} - \begin{pmatrix} 1 \\ 5 \end{pmatrix} = \begin{pmatrix} -7 \\ 1 \end{pmatrix}$$

A.5 ▪ Differentiation: $\mathbf{x}'$ and $(\mathbf{a}f(t))'$

General:

$$\frac{d}{dt}\begin{pmatrix} x(t) \\ y(t) \end{pmatrix} = \begin{pmatrix} x'(t) \\ y'(t) \end{pmatrix}$$

$$\frac{d}{dt}\left[\begin{pmatrix} a \\ b \end{pmatrix} f(t)\right] = \begin{pmatrix} a \\ b \end{pmatrix} f'(t)$$

Examples:

$$\frac{d}{dt}\begin{pmatrix} t + t^3 \\ \sin t \end{pmatrix} = \begin{pmatrix} 1 + 3t^2 \\ \cos t \end{pmatrix}$$

$$\frac{d}{dt}\left[\begin{pmatrix} 1 \\ -2 \end{pmatrix} e^{5t}\right] = \begin{pmatrix} 1 \\ -2 \end{pmatrix} 5e^{5t} = 5\begin{pmatrix} 1 \\ -2 \end{pmatrix} e^{5t}$$

Appendix B

Answers

Chapter 1
Section 1.2, pg 4

2a) $r = -2$

2b) $r = 1/3$

2c) none

2d) $r = 0, -4$

2e) $r = -3, 1/2$

2f) $r = 2$

2g) none

2h) $r = 0$

2i) none

2j) none

3a) $r = -2, c = 1$

3b) $r = -1, c = -1$

3c) $r = 1/3, c = 3$

3d) $r = 1, c = -1$

3e) $r = -2/5, c = -7$

3f) $r = -4, c = 3$

Chapter 2
Section 2.1, pg 12

1a) $y = (9t + c)^{-1/3}$ and $y = 0$

1b) $y = \pm(2e^{-t} + c)^{-1/2}$ and $y = 0$

1c) $y = -1/(\cos t + c)$ and $y = 0$

1d) $y = 3 \pm \sqrt{t^2/2 + c}$

1e) $y = -\ln(\frac{1}{2}t^2 + 2t + c)$

1f) $y = -\frac{1}{3}\ln[3\ln(t+1) + c]$

1g) $y = -\frac{1}{4}\ln(2e^{2t} + c)$

1h) $y = -\frac{1}{\ln 2}\ln[t\ln(2) + c]$

1i) $y = \frac{1}{3}[-1\pm(6t+c)^{-1/2}]$, $y = -\frac{1}{3}$

1j) $y = -2 - 1/(t + c)$ and $y = -2$

1k) $y = 3 - 2/(t + c)$ and $y = 3$

1l) $y = \tan(t/3 + c)$

1m) $y = \ln[\tan(t^2/2 + c)]$

1n) $y = \ln(ce^t - 1)$

1o) $y = \pm\sqrt{ce^{t^2} - 1}$

2a) $y(t) = 5\frac{1}{\sqrt{150\,t+1}}$

2c) $y(t) = 4 + 7t$

2d) $y(t) = (1 + \ln(4 + e^t) - \ln(5))^{-1}$

2e) $y(t) = \ln\left(1/2\,\frac{t^2 e + 2}{e}\right)$

2f) $y(t) = -2 + \sqrt{4 + 2t}$

2g) $y(t) = 2\arctan(1 + t)$

2h) $y(t) = 5\left(1 + 4e^{5t}\right)^{-1}$

2i) $y(t) = \frac{1}{2}\ln\left(e^{-2t} + e^2 - 1\right) + t$

2j) $y(t) = \ln\left(t/2 + 1/2\sqrt{t^2 + 4}\right)$

3a) $q(r) = -\frac{1}{\sqrt{14\,r+1}}$

3c) $h(\tau) = -2 + 4e^{\tau/3}$

3d) $h(x) = 6\left(2 + e^{3x}\right)^{-1}$

3e) $z(r) = 6\left(1 + 6\ln\left((1 + e^r)/2\right)\right)^{-1}$

3f) $w(\tau) = 1/2\ln\left(1/8\,\tau^4 + 1\right)$

3g) $r(\theta) = 2\left(\theta + 1\right)^2$

3h) $r(\theta) = -1 + \sqrt{2\theta^2 + 1}$

4a) $y - \ln(1 + y) = t + 1 - \ln 2$

4b) $15t = y^5 + 5y + 6$

4c) $y + \ln(1 + y) = t + 5 + \ln(6)$

4c) $y - e^{-y} = t + 2 - e^{-2}$

Section 2.2, pg 18

1a) $y(t) = c\,e^{-3t}$

1b) $y(t) = -t/2 - 1/4 + e^{2t}c$

1c) $y(t) = -2t - 14 + e^{t/4}c$

1d) $y(t) = e^t - 1 + e^{-t}c$

1e) $y(t) = \frac{20t - \cos(4t) + c}{12t + 8}$

1f) $y(t) = \frac{t+c}{t+2}$

1g) $y = -\frac{1}{3} + e^{3t}\int_0^t \sqrt{s}\,e^{-3s}ds + ce^{3t}$

1h) $y = e^{-t/2}\left(\frac{1}{2}\int_0^t \frac{s\,e^{s/2}}{1+s}ds + c\right)$

2a) $y(t) = -4 + 3\,e^t$

2b) $y(t) = 3/4\,t - 3/16 + 3/16\,e^{-4t}$

2c) $y(t) = 2\,e^{-t/5}$

2d) $y(t) = -1/3\,e^{-t} + 2 - 2/3\,e^{t/2}$

2e) $y(t) = \frac{-t+10}{5+t}$

2f) $y = -(2/3)e^{-t^2/6}\int_0^t e^{s^2/6}ds$

3a) $q(z) = 2 - 3\,e^{-2z}$

3b) $p(x) = -x/4 + 1/16 - 1/16\,e^{-4x}$

3c) $w(\tau) = 1/3\,e^{2\tau} - 1/3\,e^{\tau/2}$

3d) $z(\tau) = -\tau/4 - \frac{5}{16} + \frac{5\,e^{4\tau}}{16}$

3e) $h(x) = \frac{-x+14}{x+7}$

3f) $h(z) = \frac{3z-1}{5z+1}$

4a) $y_p = -3, y_h = ce^{2t}$

4b) $y_p = 3\,te^{-t}, y_h = ce^{-t}$

4c) $y_p = -3 + 1/13\,e^{2t}, y_h = ce^{t/7}$

4d) $y_h = ce^{-t^2}$

6b) $w(t) = \frac{1}{\sqrt{5-4\,e^{-2t}}}$

Section 2.3, pg 28

1c) $\frac{\ln(2)}{\ln(4/3)}$ days

2d) either 40 or 39 BC

3c) $50\ln(10)$ min

4c) $5(1 - e^{-6})$ g

5b) $10^4(1 - e^{-1})$ kg

6c) $\frac{324000}{11}\left[1 - \left(\frac{25}{27}\right)^{11}\right]$ lbs

7a) $v = -20 + 120e^{-t/2}$ m/s

7c) $40(5 - \ln 6)$ m

8a) $v = -(176/c)(1 - e^{-2ct/11})$ fps

8d) $792 + 968e^{-20/11}$ ft

8e) -22 fps

9e) $m/c - cL/A$

11a) $P = \frac{N}{4}\left(4 + z - \sqrt{8z + z^2}\right), z = e^{-rt}$

12a) $P = 250\frac{9 - e^{-2t}}{3 - e^{-2t}}$

13d) $5\frac{\ln(64/39)}{\ln 2}$ min

14c) $k = (4^{1/4} - 2^{1/4})/5$

15b) $120\frac{\ln(42/37)}{\ln(4/3)}$ min

15c) $120\frac{\ln(93/74)}{\ln(4/3)}$ min

Section 2.4, pg 38
us=unstable; as=asymptotically stable

1a) as

1b) us

1c) as

1d) us

2a) $y = 1$, us; $y = -2$, as

2b) $y = \pm 1$, us; $y = 0$, as

2c) $y = \pm 2$, as; $y = 0$, us

2d) $y = -\ln 2$, as

2e) $y = -2$, as; $y = 2$, us

2f) $y = 0$, as; $y = \ln 3$, us

9c) 750

Chapter 3
Section 3.5, pg 50

1a) $-7, 1$

1b) $-2, 2$

1c) $\frac{1}{2}e^2\sqrt{3}, \frac{1}{2}e^2$

1d) $1 + 2e^2\sqrt{3}, 1 + 2e^2$

1e) $\frac{1}{2}(\sqrt{3} - 1)e^2, \frac{1}{2}(\sqrt{3} + 1)e^2$

1f) $-e^{12}, 0$

3a) $y(t) = c_1\,e^{-2t} + c_2\,e^t$

3b) $y(t) = c_1\,e^{-2t} + c_2\,e^{t/2}$

3c) $y(t) = c_1 + c_2\,e^{-3t}$

3d) $y(t) = c_1\,e^{-t/2} + c_2\,e^{t/2}$

3e) $y = c_1 + c_2t$

3f) $y(t) = c_1\,e^{3t} + c_2\,e^{3t}t$

3g) $y(t) = c_1\,e^{-t/2} + c_2\,e^{-t/2}t$

3h) $y = c_1\sin(t/2) + c_2\cos(t/2)$

3i) $y(t) = c_1\,e^t\sin(t) + c_2\,e^t\cos(t)$

3j) $y = e^{-t}(c_1\sin(2t) + c_2\cos(2t))$

4a) $y(t) = -1/3\,e^{2t} + 1/3\,e^{-t}$

4b) $y(t) = -4/5\,e^{t/2} - 1/5\,e^{-2t}$

4c) $y(t) = -4/3 + 1/3\,e^{-3t}$

4d) $y(t) = 4 - 5\,e^{t/5}$

4e) $y = 3\exp(-(1/3)\sqrt{3}t)$

4f) $y = 5\exp(-(1/2)t)$

4g) $y(t) = -e^{-t} - e^{-t}t$

4h) $y(t) = -1/3\,\sin(3t) - \cos(3t)$

4i) $y = -e^{-t}\sin(2t) - e^{-t}\cos(2t)$

4j) $y = 2\,e^{t/2}\cos(t/3)$

6a) $(1+t)^3$

6b) $\cos(t^2 + 6t)$

6c) $t + 2$

Section 3.8, pg 58

1a) $y(t) = e^{3t}c_2 + e^{-2t}c_1 - e^t$

1b) $y = c_1 e^{-2t} + c_2 e^{-t} + \frac{-\pi^2 \sin(\pi t) - 3\pi\cos(\pi t) + 2\sin(\pi t)}{\pi^4 + 5\pi^2 + 4}$

1c) $y(t) = e^{-5t}c_2 + e^t c_1 - 2/5\,t^2 - \frac{16t}{25} - \frac{84}{125}$

1d) $y(t) = 5\,e^{t/5}c_1 - \frac{3\sin(2t)}{202} - \frac{15\cos(2t)}{101} - \frac{15}{101} + 1/6\,e^{-t} + c_2$

1e) $y(t) = e^{2t}c_2 + e^{-t/3}c_1 - 1/2\,t^3 + \frac{15t^2}{4} - \frac{89t}{4} + \frac{535}{8}$

1f) $y(t) = e^{-t/4}c_2 + c_1\,e^{t/2} + \frac{4\cos(2t)}{221} - \frac{33\sin(2t)}{221} - 4$

1g) $y(t) = \sin(2t)\,c_2 + \cos(2t)\,c_1 + 1/25\,(5t-2)\,e^t$

1h) $y(t) = c_2 e^{-t} + c_1 e^{6t} + +1/9\,(3t-1)\cos(3t) + 1/15\,(-5t-2)\sin(3t)$

1i) $y(t) = \sin(2t)\,e^t c_2 + \cos(2t)\,e^t c_1 + t^2 + 4/5\,t + \frac{18}{25}$

1j) $y(t) = e^{-t}\sin(3t)\,c_2 + e^{-t}\cos(3t)\,c_1 + 1/10 + 3/13\,e^t$

1k) $y(t) = 1/3\,e^{3t}c_1 - 1/9\,t^2 - 1/9\,t^3 - 1/12\,t^4 + \frac{52t}{27} + c_2$

1l) $y(t) = e^{-t}c_2 + e^{2/3t}c_1 - 1/2\,e^{-2t}e^{3t} + 3/8\,e^{-2t}$

1m) $y(t) = e^{4t}\sin(t)\,c_2 + e^{4t}\cos(t)\,c_1 - 1/2\,e^{4t}t\cos(t)$

1n) $y(t) = e^{6t}c_2 + e^{-t}c_1 - \frac{15\cos(t+7)}{74} + \frac{21\sin(t+7)}{74}$

1o) $y(t) = -e^{-2t}c_1 - \frac{3\sin(2t)}{40} + 1/4 + 1/40\,\cos(2t) + e^{-t}c_2$

1p) $y(t) = -4\,e^{-t/4}c_1 - \frac{2\sin(2t)}{65} - \frac{\cos(2t)}{260} + c_2$

2a) $y(t) = e^t - 1/4\,e^{-2t} - 3/2\,t - 3/4$

2b) $y(t) = -1/8 + \frac{9\cos(2t)}{8} + 1/4\,t^2$

2c) $y(t) = -1/2\,e^t - 1/2\,\sin(t) + 1/2\,\cos(t) + 1$

2d) $y(t) = -\frac{2\,e^{-3t}}{27} + 1/3\,t^2 - 2/9\,t + \frac{29}{27}$

2e) $y(t) = \frac{19\,e^{-2t}}{16} + 11/4\,e^{-2t}t - 3/16\,e^{2t}$

2f) $y(t) = 1/2\,e^{-t/2} + 3/4\,e^{t/2} - 1 + 1/4\,(-t-1)\,e^{-t/2}$

2g) $y(t) = -1/9\,\sin(3t) + 1/3\,\cos(3t)\,t$

2h) $y(t) = -1/2\,e^{-t}\sin(2t) - 5/4\,e^{-t}\cos(2t) + 1/4\,e^{-t}$

2i) $y(t) = \frac{51\,e^{t/2}\sin(t/2)}{13} + \frac{21\,e^{t/2}\cos(t/2)}{13} - \frac{12\sin(3t)}{13} - \frac{34\cos(3t)}{13}$

4a) $y(t) = -2/5\,e^t + e^{6t}c$

4b) $y(t) = e^{-2/3t}c + \frac{-3\pi\cos(\pi t) + 2\sin(\pi t)}{9\pi^2 + 4}$

4c) $y(t) = 2/3\,t - 2/9 + e^{-3t}c$

4d) $y(t) = -3t - 15 - 1/6\,e^{-t} + e^{t/5}c$

4e) $y(t) = -\frac{1}{10}\,t\cos(2t) - 1/25\,\cos(2t) - 1/5\,t\sin(2t) - \frac{3\sin(2t)}{100} + e^{4t}c$

4f) $y(t) = -1/7\,e^{-t}t - 1/49\,e^{-t} - 1/3 + e^{6t}c$

4g) $y(t) = -1/10\,e^{-t}\cos(t) + 3/10\,\sin(t)\,e^{-t} + e^{-2/3t}c$

4h) $y(t) = -1/4\,\cos(2t+5) + 1/4\,\sin(2t+5) + e^{2t}c$

Section 3.9, pg 63

1a) $y = -2\,e^{-2t} + 2\,e^{t/2} - 5\,e^{-2t}t$

1b) $y = 3 + (-3\cos(t) + 3\sin(t))\,e^t$

1c) $y = -e^{-2t}\int_0^t \ln(1+s)\,e^{2s}\,ds + e^t\int_0^t \ln(1+s)\,e^{-s}\,ds$

1d) $y = t/3 + 2/15\,t^{5/2} + e^{-3t}\int_0^t -1/3\,(s^{3/2}+1)\,e^{3s}\,ds$

1e) $y = -2 \ln(t+1) + e^{t/5} \int_0^t 2 \frac{e^{-s/5}}{1+s} \, ds$

1f) $-\frac{1}{4} e^{-t/2} \int_0^t \sin(s^2+1) e^{s/2} \, ds + \frac{1}{4} e^{t/2} \int_0^t \sin(s^2+1) e^{-s/2} \, ds$

3a) $2t(-t + e^t - 1)$

3b) $1/2 (t-1) e^{2t} + 1/2 + t/2$

3c) $4t^{5/2}$

4b) $1/2 \sin(t) \sqrt{t}$

Section 3.10, pg 73

2b) $u = \frac{1}{4} \cos(8t - \pi)$

2e) 1

3b) $u = \frac{2}{3} \sqrt{3} \cos\left(2\sqrt{3}t - \frac{5\pi}{6}\right)$

3f) $\sqrt{3}\pi/18$

4b) $u = \frac{1}{20} \sqrt{2} \cos\left(10t - \frac{7\pi}{4}\right)$

4e) $5(2 + \sqrt{2}); 3\pi/40$

7b) $u = -\frac{1}{90} \sqrt{15} e^{-2t} \sin(2\sqrt{15}t)$

7d) $e^{-\tau}/24, \tau = z(\frac{3\pi}{2} - \operatorname{Arctan}(z)),$
$z = 1/\sqrt{15}$

8d) $u = \sqrt{2} e^{-3t} \cos(t - \pi/4)$

12b) $u(t) = 3/4 \sin(16t) t$

13b) $u(t) = \frac{5 \sin(3t)t}{12}$

Section 3.11, pg 77

1a) $y(x) = c_1 x^2 + c_2 x^2 \ln(x)$

1b) $y(x) = c_1 x^3 \sin(\ln(x)) + c_2 x^3 \cos(\ln(x))$

1c) $y(x) = \frac{c_1}{\sqrt{x}} + c_2 \sqrt[3]{x}$

1d) $y(x) = c_1 \sqrt{x} \sin\left(1/2 \sqrt{3} \ln(x)\right) + c_2 \sqrt{x} \cos\left(1/2 \sqrt{3} \ln(x)\right)$

1e) $y(x) = c_1 x^2 \sin(3 \ln(x)) + c_2 x^2 \cos(3 \ln(x))$

1f) $y(x) = \frac{c_1}{x} + \frac{c_2}{x^{2/5}}$

1g) $y(x) = c_2 \ln(x) + c_1$

1h) $y(x) = c_2 x^3 + c_1$

1i) $y(x) = \frac{c_1}{x^n} + c_2 x^{n+2}$

2a) $y(x) = -x^2 e + x e^x$

2b) $y(x) = -1/4 x^4 - x + 1/4 + x^2$

2c) $y(x) = -2x + x \ln(x) + \ln(x) + 2$

2d) $y(x) = 1/4 x^2 - 3/2 \ln(x) + 3/4$

2e) $y(x) = 1/2 (x-1)^{-1} + x/2 - 1/2$

Chapter 4

Section 4.3, pg 91

2a) $3, -2$ 2b) $5, -1$ 3a) $2 \pm 2i$ 3b) $-1 \pm 2i$

Section 4.5, pg 98

1a) $\begin{bmatrix} c_1 e^{-3t} + c_2 e^{2t} \\ -1/3 c_1 e^{-3t} + 1/2 c_2 e^{2t} \end{bmatrix}$

1b) $\begin{bmatrix} c_1 e^{-t/2} + c_2 e^{t/2} \\ -2 c_1 e^{-t/2} + 2 c_2 e^{t/2} \end{bmatrix}$

1c) $\begin{bmatrix} c_1 + c_2 e^{5t} \\ -2 c_1 + 3 c_2 e^{5t} \end{bmatrix}$

1d) $\begin{bmatrix} -c_2 e^{2t} \\ c_1 e^{2t} + c_2 e^{2t} t \end{bmatrix}$

1e) $\begin{bmatrix} c_1 e^{-2t} \\ c_2 e^{-2t} \end{bmatrix}$

1f) $\begin{bmatrix} c_1 \sin(3t) + c_2 \cos(3t) \\ -1/3 c_1 \cos(3t) + 1/3 c_2 \sin(3t) \end{bmatrix}$

$$\text{1g)} \begin{bmatrix} c\_1 \, \sin{(t/2)} + c\_2 \, \cos{(t/2)} \\ c\_1 \, (-1/5 \, \sin{(t/2)} + 1/10 \, \cos{(t/2)}) \\ +c\_2 \, (-1/5 \, \cos{(t/2)} - 1/10 \, \sin{(t/2)}) \end{bmatrix}$$

$$\text{1h)} \begin{bmatrix} c\_1 \, e^{t/2} \sin{(t)} + c\_2 \, e^{t/2} \cos{(t)} \\ c\_1 \, (-2 \, e^{t/2} \sin{(t)} + 4 \, e^{t/2} \cos{(t)}) \\ +c\_2 \, (-2 \, e^{t/2} \cos{(t)} - 4 \, e^{t/2} \sin{(t)}) \end{bmatrix}$$

$$\text{1i)} \begin{bmatrix} c\_1 \, e^{2t} \sin{(\sqrt{2}t)} + c\_2 \, e^{2t} \cos{(\sqrt{2}t)} \\ c\_1 \, (1/3 \, e^{2t} \sin{(\sqrt{2}t)} + 1/3 \, e^{2t} \sqrt{2} \cos{(\sqrt{2}t)}) \\ +c\_2 \, (1/3 \, e^{2t} \cos{(\sqrt{2}t)} - 1/3 \, e^{2t} \sqrt{2} \sin{(\sqrt{2}t)}) \end{bmatrix}$$

2 $a) \left\{ c\_1 = 2/5, c\_2 = \frac{18}{5} \right\}, b) \left\{ c\_1 = 7/4, c\_2 = 9/4 \right\},$
$c) \left\{ c\_1 = \frac{13}{5}, c\_2 = 7/5 \right\}, d) \left\{ c\_1 = -1, c\_2 = -4 \right\}, e) \left\{ c\_1 = 4, c\_2 = -1 \right\},$
$f) \left\{ c\_1 = 3, c\_2 = 4 \right\}, g) \left\{ c\_1 = -2, c\_2 = 4 \right\}, h) \left\{ c\_1 = 7/4, c\_2 = 4 \right\},$
$i) \left\{ c\_1 = -7/2 \, \sqrt{2}, c\_2 = 4 \right\}$

$$\text{4a)} \begin{bmatrix} c\_1 \, e^{-t} + c\_2 \, e^{2t} \\ -2 \, c\_1 \, e^{-t} + c\_2 \, e^{2t} - c\_3 \, e^{-t} \\ c\_1 \, e^{-t} + c\_2 \, e^{2t} + c\_3 \, e^{-t} \end{bmatrix}$$

$$\text{4b)} \begin{bmatrix} c\_1 \, e^{t} + 3 \, c\_2 \, e^{2t} + 2 \, c\_3 \, e^{t}t \\ c\_2 \, e^{2t} \\ c\_2 \, e^{2t} + c\_3 \, e^{t} \end{bmatrix}$$

$$\text{4c)} \begin{bmatrix} 2 \, c\_1 \, e^{t} - c\_2 \, e^{-2t} \\ 3 \, c\_1 \, e^{t} \\ 7 \, c\_1 \, e^{t} + 4 \, c\_2 \, e^{-2t} + c\_3 \, e^{-t} \end{bmatrix}$$

$$\text{4d)} \begin{bmatrix} c\_1 \, e^{-t} \\ 2 \, c\_2 \, e^{\sqrt{5}t} + 2 \, c\_3 \, e^{-\sqrt{5}t} \\ -c\_3 \, (\sqrt{5}+1) \, e^{-\sqrt{5}t} + c\_2 \, e^{\sqrt{5}t} \, (\sqrt{5}-1) \end{bmatrix}$$

Section 4.7, pg 110

us=unstable; as=asymptotically stable; ns=neutrally stable

1a) us	1d) us	1g) as	3a) us	3d) us
1b) as	1e) as	1h) ns	3b) as	
1c) us	1f) us	1i) ns	3c) as	

Chapter 5
Section 5.1, pg 115

2a) $(u, v) = (1/2, 0), (1/3, 1/4)$ 2e) $(S, I) = (5, 0), (1, 2)$
2b) $(u, v) = (0, 0), (-1, 1)$ 2f) $(s, c) = (-1, 1)$
2c) $(u, v) = (1/4, 4)$ 2g) $(x, y) = (0, 0)$
2d) $(S, P) = (1, 1), (0, 0), (2, 0)$ 2h) $(x, y) = (0, 2), (0, -1), (2, 0)$

Section 5.2, pg 126
1a) $(u, v) = (1/2, 0)$ as; $(1/3, 1/4)$ as
1b) $(u, v) = (0, 0)$ us
1c) $(u, v) = (1, -1)$ us
1d) $(u, v) = (1/4, 4)$ as

1e) $(x, y) = (0, 0)$ as; $(x, y) = (2/3, 4/9)$ us
1f) $(x, y) = (0, 0)$ id
1g) $(x, y) = (0, 1)$ us
1h) $(x, y) = (0, 0)$ us; $(x, y) = (c/d, a/b)$ id
1i) $(S, P) = (0, 0)$ us; $(S, P) = (2, 0)$ us; $(S, P) = (1, 1)$ as
1j) $(S, I) = (1, 0)$ as; $(S, I) = (2, -1/2)$ us
1k) $(r, s) = (1, 1)$ us
1l) $(S, E) = (0, E_0)$ as

Section 5.3, pg 137
1a) $H = v^2 + 3e^{2u}/2 - 3u$
1b) $H = v^2/2 + \frac{1}{10}\ln(1 + 5u^2)$
1d) $H = 5v^2/2 + 7u^2/2 + \frac{3}{5}u^{10}$
1d) $H = v^2/2 + 1/3\left(u^2 + 1\right)^{3/2}\left(3u^2 - 2\right)$
4d) $\sqrt{3/2}$
4e) -1
4f) $2\sqrt{2}\int_{-1}^{1}[(3 + u^2)(1 - u^2)]^{-1/2}du$
5d) $\sqrt{2}(1 - e^{-1})$
5e) $-\ln(2 - e^{-1})$
5f) $\sqrt{2}\int_{-\ln(2-e^{-1})}^{1}[(1 - e^{-1})^2 - (1 - e^{-u})^2]^{-1/2}du$

Chapter 6
Section 6.1, pg 149

1a) $-(s - 5)^{-1}$
1b) $\frac{4+3s}{s^2}$
1c) $2s^{-2} + 4(1 + s)^{-1}$
1d) $-9\frac{1}{(s+2)(s-7)}$
1e) $8s^{-3}$
1f) $\frac{9s^2-6s+2}{s^3}$
1g) $(1 + s)^{-2}$
1h) $-2\frac{-3\cos(4)\pi-\sin(4)s}{9\pi^2+s^2}$
1i) $\frac{5s^2-8s+4}{(s-2)(s^2+4)}$
2a) $5\frac{e^{-2s}}{s}$
2b) $\frac{1-e^{-2s}}{s^2}$
2c) $-\frac{1-2e^{-s}+e^{-2s}}{s}$

2d) $\frac{e^{-1-s}}{1+s} + 3\frac{1-e^{-s}}{s}$
2e) $5s^{-1} - \frac{1-2e^{-3s}}{s^2}$
2f) $2\frac{e^{-12s}-e^{-15s}}{s}$
3a) $\frac{s}{s^2+9}$
3b) $28\left(s^2 + 49\right)^{-1}$
3c) $\frac{s+1}{(s+1)^2+\pi^2}$
3d) $2\frac{s^2+3}{(s^2+9)(s^2+1)}$
4a) $6\frac{s}{(s^2+9)^2}$
4b) $6\frac{s^2-49}{(s^2+49)^2}$
4c) $2\frac{s(s^2-3)}{(s^2+1)^3}$
4d) $10\frac{s+2}{((s+2)^2+25)^2}$

Section 6.2, pg 155

1a) $\frac{e^{-6s}}{s}$
1b) $\frac{e^{-s}}{s^2}$
1c) $\frac{e^{-2s}}{s}$
1d) $\frac{3e^{-2s}-4e^{-5s}}{s}$
1e) $4\frac{1-e^{-3s}}{s}$
1f) $\frac{3-e^{-s}}{6s}$
1g) $\frac{1-e^{-s}+3e^{-2s}-e^{-3s}}{s}$
1h) $\frac{e^{-2s}+e^{-4s}-e^{-8s}}{s}$

2a) $2/3\sin(3t)$
2b) $3te^{-4t}$
2c) $1/5e^t - 1/5e^{-4t}$
2d) $e^{-t}\cos(2t)$
2e) $1/4e^{2t} + 7/4e^{-2t}$
2f) $1/3e^{-t}(6\cos(3t) - 5\sin(3t))$
2g) $1/7\cos(3t) - 1/7\cos(4t)$
2h) $\cosh(\sqrt{2}t) - \cosh(t)$
2i) $\sin(2t) - \sin(3t)$

2j) $5t - 3\,\mathrm{e}^{2t}$

2k) $H(t-3)\,\mathrm{e}^{3-t}\cos(-9+3t)$

2l) $-1/2\,H(t-2)(t-2)(t-4)$

2m) $H(t-1) - H(t-2) + H(t-3)$

2n) $2 - t + 2t^2 - 7/6\,t^3$

2o) $H(t-5)\,t$

2p) $H(t-6)(5\cos(t-6) + \sin(t-6))$

4a) $\frac{1}{1-\mathrm{e}^{-2s}}\left(s^{-1} - \frac{\mathrm{e}^{-s}}{s}\right)$

4b) $-\frac{\mathrm{e}^{-s}s + \mathrm{e}^{-s} - 1}{(1-\mathrm{e}^{-s})s^2}$

4c) $\frac{1+\mathrm{e}^{-2s}-2\mathrm{e}^{-s}}{(1-\mathrm{e}^{-2s})s^2}$

4d) $\frac{1+\mathrm{e}^{-2s}-2\mathrm{e}^{-s}}{(1-\mathrm{e}^{-2s})s}$

5c) $\frac{1}{(\mathrm{e}^s-1)s}$

6a) $1 + H(t-1) + H(t-2) + H(t-3) + H(t-4) + \cdots$

6b) $1 - 1/2\,H(t-1) + 3/8\,H(t-2) - \frac{5\,H(t-3)}{16} + \frac{35\,H(t-4)}{128} + \cdots$

6c) $1 + t/2 - 1/16\,t^2 + \frac{t^3}{96} - \frac{5t^4}{3072} + + \cdots$

Section 6.3, pg 158

1a) $-1 + (s-4)Y$

1b) $4 + (2s+7)Y$

1c) $s^2 Y + 5Y + 2s + 1$

1d) $(s^2 + 3s - 2)Y - s$

1e) $(4s^2 + 2s)Y + 8s - 2$

2a) $1/2\,\mathrm{e}^t - 1/2\cos(t) - 1/2\sin(t)$

2b) $1/2\,t\sin(t)$

2c) $\cos t(\sin t - 2\cos t) + 1 + \mathrm{e}^{-t}$

2d) $-1/2\sin(t) + 1/2\sinh(t)$

2e) $1/2\,t^2 + \cos(t) - 1$

Section 6.4, pg 163

1a) $1 + \mathrm{e}^{-t/2}$

1b) $-1/2\,\mathrm{e}^{-t} + \mathrm{e}^{-t/3}$

1c) $1/3\,\mathrm{e}^{-2t} - 1/3\,\mathrm{e}^t$

1d) $2te^{3t}$

1e) $4 - 5\,\mathrm{e}^{t/5}$

1f) $-2\sin(t/2) - \cos(t/2)$

1g) $-\mathrm{e}^t\cos(t)$

1h) $-3\,\mathrm{e}^{-t}\sin(2t)$

2a) $4\,\mathrm{e}^t - \mathrm{e}^{-2t} - 6t - 3$

2b) $-1 + \cos(2t) + 2t^2$

2c) $\mathrm{e}^t - \sin(t) + \cos(t) - 2$

2d) $1/2\,t^2$

2e) $1 - 1/2\,\mathrm{e}^t\cos(2t) - 1/2\,\mathrm{e}^{-t}$

3a) $\int_0^t \ln(1+3\tau)\,\mathrm{e}^{-3t+3\tau}\,\mathrm{d}\tau$

3b) $\frac{1}{3}\int_0^t \sqrt{1+\tau}\sin(3t-3\tau)\,\mathrm{d}\tau$

3c) $-\frac{1}{5}\int_0^t \frac{\mathrm{e}^{-2t+2\tau}}{1+\tau}\,\mathrm{d}\tau + \frac{1}{5}\int_0^t \frac{\mathrm{e}^{t/2-\tau/2}}{1+\tau}\,\mathrm{d}\tau$

3d) $\frac{1}{2}\int_0^t \sin(1+\tau^2)\mathrm{e}^{-t+\tau}\sin(2t-2\tau)\,\mathrm{d}\tau$

4a) $\int_0^t \ln(1+3\tau)\,\mathrm{e}^{-3t+3\tau}\,\mathrm{d}\tau + \mathrm{e}^{-3t}$

4b) $\cos(3t) + \frac{1}{3}\int_0^t \sqrt{1+\tau}\sin(3t-3\tau)\,\mathrm{d}\tau$

4c) $8/5\,\mathrm{e}^{-2t} + 2/5\,\mathrm{e}^{t/2} - \frac{1}{5}\int_0^t \frac{\mathrm{e}^{-2t+2\tau}}{1+\tau}\,\mathrm{d}\tau + \frac{1}{5}\int_0^t \frac{\mathrm{e}^{t/2-\tau/2}}{1+\tau}\,\mathrm{d}\tau$

4d) $\mathrm{e}^{-t}\sin(2t) + \frac{1}{2}\int_0^t \sin(1+\tau^2)\mathrm{e}^{-t+\tau}\sin(2t-2\tau)\,\mathrm{d}\tau$

Section 6.5, pg 169

1a) $\mathrm{e}^{-4t} + 3/4\,H(t-1)(1-\mathrm{e}^{-4t+4})$

1b) $(-1+\mathrm{e}^{t/2-2})H(4-t) - \mathrm{e}^{t/2-2}$

1c) $2\,H(t-3)\,\mathrm{e}^{-t+3} - \mathrm{e}^{-t}$

1d) $-1/2\,H(t-2) + 1/2(1-H(2-t))\mathrm{e}^{4t-8} + \mathrm{e}^{4t-4}(H(1-t)-1)$

1e) $1/10\,H(t-5)(-5 + 3\,\mathrm{e}^{-2t+10} + 2\,\mathrm{e}^{3t-15})$

1f) $3/2\,H(t-4)(\sin(t-4))^2 - 3/2\,H(t-2)(\sin(t-2))^2$

1g) $3/4\,H(t-1)(-1+\mathrm{e}^{4t-4})$

1h) $-2\,H(t-2)\sin(t-2) + H(t-3)\sin(t-3)$

Section 6.6, pg 173

1a) $\begin{bmatrix} \frac{18\,\mathrm{e}^{-3t}}{5} + 2/5\,\mathrm{e}^{2t} \\[2mm] -6/5\,\mathrm{e}^{-3t} + 1/5\,\mathrm{e}^{2t} \end{bmatrix}$

1b) $\begin{bmatrix} 7/4\,\mathrm{e}^{t/2} + 9/4\,\mathrm{e}^{-t/2} \\[2mm] 7/2\,\mathrm{e}^{t/2} - 9/2\,\mathrm{e}^{-t/2} \end{bmatrix}$

1c) $\begin{bmatrix} 5/2\,\mathrm{e}^{2t} + 3/2\,\mathrm{e}^{4t} \\[2mm] -5/2\,\mathrm{e}^{2t} + 3/2\,\mathrm{e}^{4t} \end{bmatrix}$

1d) $\begin{bmatrix} \frac{13}{5} + 7/5\,\mathrm{e}^{5t} \\[2mm] -\frac{26}{5} + \frac{21\,\mathrm{e}^{5t}}{5} \end{bmatrix}$

1e) $\begin{bmatrix} 4\,e^{2\,t} \\ -e^{2\,t} - 4\,e^{2\,t}t \end{bmatrix}$

3b) $\frac{1}{s^2-1/4}\begin{bmatrix} s & 1/4 \\ 1 & s \end{bmatrix}$

1f) $\begin{bmatrix} -\frac{1}{2}\,e^t\sin\left(2\,t\right) + 4\,e^t\cos\left(2\,t\right) \\ -e^t\cos\left(2\,t\right) - 8\,e^t\sin\left(2\,t\right) \end{bmatrix}$

3c) $\frac{1}{(s-2)^2}\begin{bmatrix} s-2 & 0 \\ -1 & s-2 \end{bmatrix}$

3a) $\frac{1}{s^2+s-6}\begin{bmatrix} s & 6 \\ 1 & s+1 \end{bmatrix}$

3d) $\frac{1}{s^2-2\,s+5}\begin{bmatrix} s-1 & -4 \\ 1 & s-1 \end{bmatrix}$

Chapter 7
Section 7.2, pg 179

1a) $u\left(x\right) = -\frac{e^{2\,x}}{e^{-4}-e^4} + \frac{e^{-2\,x}}{e^{-4}-e^4}$

1b) $u\left(x\right) = -\frac{\sin(x)}{\sin(1)}$

1c) $u\left(x\right) = \frac{e^{-x/2}\sin\left(1/2\,\sqrt{3}x\right)}{e^{-1/2}\sin\left(1/2\,\sqrt{3}\right)}$

1d) $u\left(x\right) = -5\,\frac{e^{-x}\left(-1+e^2\right)}{e^{-2}-e^2} + 5\,\frac{e^x\left(-1+e^{-2}\right)}{e^{-2}-e^2} - 5$

1e) $u\left(x\right) = 1/2\,x^2 + 1/2\,\frac{e^{-x}}{e^{-1}-1} - x - 1/2\left(e^{-1}-1\right)^{-1}$

3a) $u_n = b_n\sin\left[\frac{\pi}{2}(2n-1)x\right]$, with $\lambda_n = -\left[\frac{\pi}{2}(2n-1)\right]^2$

3b) $u_0 = b_0$, with $\lambda_0 = 0$; and $u_n = b_n\cos\left(\frac{n\pi}{4}x\right)$, with $\lambda_n = -\left(\frac{n\pi}{4}\right)^2$

3c) $u = be^{-\lambda x/2}\sin(\pi x/4)$, with $\lambda = \pm\sqrt{4-(\pi/2)^2}$

3d) $u_n = b_ne^{-x/2}\sin(n\pi x)$, with $\lambda_n = -\frac{1}{4} - (n\pi)^2$

3e) $u_0 = b_0$, $\lambda_0 = 0$; $u_n = a_n\sin(2\pi nx) + b_n\cos(2\pi nx)$, with $\lambda_n = 4\pi^2n^2$

Section 7.3, pg 186

1a) $-4\,e^{-75\,\pi^2t}\sin\left(5\,\pi\,x\right)$

1b) $6\,e^{-363\,\pi^2t}\sin\left(11\,\pi\,x\right)$

1c) $e^{-3\,\pi^2t}\sin\left(\pi\,x\right) + 8\,e^{-48\,\pi^2t}\sin\left(4\,\pi\,x\right) - 10\,e^{-147\,\pi^2t}\sin\left(7\,\pi\,x\right)$

1d) $-e^{-27\,\pi^2t}\sin\left(3\,\pi\,x\right) + 7\,e^{-192\,\pi^2t}\sin\left(8\,\pi\,x\right) + 2\,e^{-675\,\pi^2t}\sin\left(15\,\pi\,x\right)$

1e) $2\,e^{-27\,\pi^2t}\sin\left(3\,\pi\,x\right) + 2\,e^{-3\,\pi^2t}\sin\left(\pi\,x\right)$

2a) $\sum_{n=1}^{\infty} -2\,\frac{(-1+(-1)^n)e^{-n^2\pi^2t}\sin(1/2\,n\,\pi\,x)}{n\,\pi}$

2b) $\sum_{n=1}^{\infty} -4\,\frac{(-1+2\,(-1)^n)e^{-n^2\pi^2t}\sin(1/2\,n\,\pi\,x)}{n\,\pi}$

2c) $-4/3\,\frac{e^{-\pi^2t}\sin(1/2\,\pi\,x)}{\pi} + \sum_{n=3}^{\infty} -2\,\frac{n\,(-1+(-1)^n)e^{-n^2\pi^2t}\sin(1/2\,n\,\pi\,x)}{\pi\,(n^2-4)}$

2d) $\sum_{n=1}^{\infty}\left(2\,\frac{\cos(1/2\,n\,\pi)}{n\,\pi} - 2\,\frac{1}{n\,\pi}\right)e^{-n^2\pi^2t}\sin\left(1/2\,n\,\pi\,x\right)$

2e) $\sum_{n=1}^{\infty}\left(\frac{-4\,(-1)^n+2\,\cos(1/6\,n\,\pi)}{n\,\pi} + 2\,\frac{1}{n\,\pi}\right)e^{-n^2\pi^2t}\sin\left(1/2\,n\,\pi\,x\right)$

3) $\sum_{n=1}^{\infty} 30\,\frac{(-1)^ne^{-n^2\pi^2t}\sin(1/3\,n\,\pi\,x)}{n\,\pi}$

4) $\sum_{n=1}^{\infty}\frac{(2\,\cos(1/4\,n\,\pi)-2\,\cos(3/4\,n\,\pi))e^{-5/2\,n^2\pi^2t}\sin(1/2\,n\,\pi\,x)}{n\,\pi}$

5a) $\sum_{n=1}^{\infty} b_ne^{-k_n^2t}\sin(k_nx)$, $k_n = \pi(2n-1)/2$

5b) $\sum_{n=1}^{\infty} b_ne^{-4k_n^2t}\cos(k_nx)$, $k_n = \pi(2n-1)/2$

5c) $\sum_{n=1}^{\infty} b_ne^{-k_n^2(t+t^2/2)}\sin(k_nx)$, $k_n = n\pi$

5d) $\sum_{n=1}^{\infty} b_ne^{-k_n^2t+e^{-t}}\sin(k_nx)$, $k_n = n\pi$

6d) $u = -24e^{(-k_3^2t+e^{-t}-1)}\sin(k_3x) - 12e^{(-k_{15}^2t+e^{-t}-1)}\sin(k_{15}x)$

Section 7.4, pg 198

4a) $\sum_{n=1}^{\infty} -4\,\frac{(-1)^n\sin(1/2\,n\,\pi\,x)}{n\,\pi}$

4b) $\sum_{n=1}^{\infty} -2\,\frac{n\,\pi\left((-1)^ne^2-1\right)\sin(1/2\,n\,\pi\,x)}{n^2\pi^2+4}$

4c) $\displaystyle\sum_{\substack{n=1\\ n \text{ odd}}}^{\infty} 4\,\frac{n \sin\left(1/2\,n\,\pi\,x\right)}{\pi\,\left(n^2-4\right)}$

4d) $\sum_{n=1}^{\infty} \left(\frac{6\,(-1)^n - 8\,\cos(1/4\,n\,\pi)}{n\,\pi} + 2\,\frac{1}{n\,\pi}\right) \sin\left(1/2\,n\,\pi\,x\right)$

4e) $\sum_{n=1}^{\infty} \left(\frac{-2\,n\,\pi\,\cos(1/2\,n\,\pi) - 4\,\sin(1/2\,n\,\pi)}{n^2\pi^2} + 4\,\frac{1}{n\,\pi}\right) \sin\left(1/2\,n\,\pi\,x\right)$

4h) $\sum_{n=1}^{\infty} \left(\frac{-6\,(-1)^n - 2\,\cos(1/6\,n\,\pi) + 6\,\cos(2/3\,n\,\pi)}{n\,\pi} + 2\,\frac{1}{n\,\pi}\right) \sin\left(1/2\,n\,\pi\,x\right)$

5a) $1 + \sum_{n=1}^{\infty} 4\,\frac{\left((-1)^n - 1\right)\cos(1/2\,n\,\pi\,x)}{n^2\pi^2}$

5b) $-1/2 + 1/2\,e^2 + \sum_{n=1}^{\infty} 4\,\frac{\left((-1)^n\,e^2 - 1\right)\cos(1/2\,n\,\pi\,x)}{n^2\pi^2+4}$

5c) $\cos(\pi x)$

5d) $-2 + \sum_{n=1}^{\infty} 8\,\frac{\sin(1/4\,n\,\pi)\cos(1/2\,n\,\pi\,x)}{n\,\pi}$

5e) $3/4 + \sum_{n=1}^{\infty} \left(\frac{2\,n\,\pi\,\sin(1/2\,n\,\pi) - 4\,\cos(1/2\,n\,\pi)}{n^2\pi^2} + 4\,\frac{1}{n^2\pi^2}\right) \cos\left(1/2\,n\,\pi\,x\right)$

5h) $7/6 + \sum_{n=1}^{\infty} \frac{\left(2\,\sin(1/6\,n\,\pi) - 6\,\sin(2/3\,n\,\pi)\right)\cos(1/2\,n\,\pi\,x)}{n\,\pi}$

8a) $1/3 + \sum_{n=1}^{\infty} 4\,\frac{(-1)^n\,\cos(n\,\pi\,x)}{n^2\pi^2}$

9a) $\sum_{n=1}^{\infty} -2\,\frac{(-1)^n\,\sin(n\,\pi\,x)}{n\,\pi}$

Section 7.5, pg 204

1a) $\cos(12\pi t)\sin(3\pi x)$

1b) $-\frac{1}{16\pi}\sin(32\pi t)\sin(8\pi x)$

1c) $-\cos\left(4\,\pi\,t\right)\sin\left(\pi\,x\right) + 4\cos\left(12\,\pi\,t\right)\sin\left(3\,\pi\,x\right) - \frac{3\,\sin(20\,\pi\,t)\sin(5\,\pi\,x)}{20\,\pi}$

1d) $5\cos\left(28\,\pi\,t\right)\sin\left(7\,\pi\,x\right) + \frac{\sin(32\,\pi\,t)\sin(8\,\pi\,x)}{16\pi} + \frac{\sin(48\,\pi\,t)\sin(12\,\pi\,x)}{16\pi}$

1e) $\cos\left(12\,\pi\,t\right)\sin\left(3\,\pi\,x\right) + \cos\left(4\,\pi\,t\right)\sin\left(\pi\,x\right) - \frac{\sin(32\,\pi\,t)\sin(8\,\pi\,x)}{16\pi}$

1f) $3\cos\left(8\,\pi\,t\right)\sin\left(2\,\pi\,x\right) - \frac{\sin(36\,\pi\,t)\sin(9\,\pi\,x)}{24\pi} + \frac{3\,\sin(20\,\pi\,t)\sin(5\,\pi\,x)}{40\,\pi}$

2a) $\sum_{n=1}^{\infty} \left(a_n\cos(k_n t) + b_n\sin(k_n t)\right)\sin(k_n x)$, $\;k_n = (2n-1)\pi/2$

2b) $\sum_{n=1}^{\infty} \left(a_n\cos(2k_n t) + b_n\sin(2k_n t)\right)\cos(k_n x)$, $\;k_n = (2n-1)\pi/2$

2c) $a + bt + \sum_{n=1}^{\infty} \left(a_n\cos(n\pi t) + b_n\sin(n\pi t)\right)\left(A_n\cos(2n\pi x) + B_n\sin(2n\pi x)\right)$

2d) $e^{-t/2}\sum_{n=1}^{\infty} \left(a_n\cos(\omega_n t) + b_n\sin(\omega_n t)\right)\sin(n\pi x)$, $\;\omega_n = \sqrt{4n^2\pi^2 - 1}/2$

3) $\sum_{n=1}^{\infty} -2\,\frac{(-1 + (-1)^n)\sin(2\,n\,\pi\,t)\sin(n\,\pi\,x)}{n^4\pi^4}$

Section 7.6, pg 207

1a) $1 - 2\,x + \sum_{n=1}^{\infty} -2\,\frac{(1+(-1)^n)e^{-4\,n^2\pi^2 t}\sin(n\,\pi\,x)}{n\,\pi}$

1b) $2 - 7\,x + \sum_{n=1}^{\infty} -14\,\frac{(-1)^n e^{-4\,n^2\pi^2 t}\sin(n\,\pi\,x)}{n\,\pi}$

1c) $-4 + 5\,x + \sum_{n=1}^{\infty} 8\,\frac{e^{-4\,n^2\pi^2 t}\sin(n\,\pi\,x)}{n\,\pi}$

2a) $1 - x$

2b) $-7 + 2x$

2c) $-1 + 3x$

2d) $Ae^x + Be^{-x}$, where $A = (2 - e^{-3})/(e^3 - e^{-3})$, $B = (e^3 - 2)/(e^3 - e^{-3})$

2e) $A + Be^x$, where $A = (1 + e^2)/(1 - e^2)$, $B = 2/(e^2 - 1)$

4) $-1 + 3\,x + \sum_{n=1}^{\infty} 2\,\frac{(1+2\,(-1)^n)e^{-n^2\pi^2\left(t + 1/2\,t^2\right)}\sin(n\,\pi\,x)}{n\,\pi}$

5) $1 - 2\,x - 7\cos\left(9\,\pi\,t\right)\sin\left(3\,\pi\,x\right)$

Section 7.7, pg 211

1a) $\dfrac{\left(4\,k_5\,\cos(t) + 4\,\sin(t) - 4\,k_5\,e^{-k_5\,t}\right)\sin(5\,\pi\,x)}{k_5{}^2 + 1}$, where $k_5 = 100\pi^2$

1b) $-\dfrac{e^{-k_3\,t}\left(-1 + e^{k_3\,t - 2\,t}\right)\sin(3\,\pi\,x)}{k_3 - 2}$, where $k_3 = 36\pi^2$

1c) $\sum_{n=1}^{\infty} -1/2\,\dfrac{(-1 + (-1)^n)\left(e^{-4\,n^2\pi^2 t} - 1\right)\sin(n\,\pi\,x)}{n^3\pi^3}$

3d) $\sum_{n=1}^{\infty} -4 \dfrac{(-1)^n e^{-\left(5+1/4\pi n^2\right)t} \sin(1/2 n \pi x)}{n \pi}$

Section 7.8, pg 220

1a) $5\sinh(2\pi y)\sin(2\pi x)/\sinh(4\pi)$

1b) $-3\sinh(12\pi y)\sin(12\pi x)/\sinh(24\pi)$

1c) $\sinh(\pi y)\sin(\pi x)/\sinh(2\pi) - 7\sinh(8\pi y)\sin(8\pi x)/\sinh(16\pi)$

1d) $-3\dfrac{\sinh(4\pi y)\sin(4\pi x)}{\sinh(8\pi)} - \dfrac{\sinh(7\pi y)\sin(7\pi x)}{\sinh(14\pi)} + 6\dfrac{\sinh(20\pi y)\sin(20\pi x)}{\sinh(40\pi)}$

2a) $\frac{1}{2}r^3\cos(3\theta)$

2b) $1 - 3(r/2)^{15}\sin(15\theta)$

2c) $(r/2)\sin(\theta) + 3(r/2)^5\cos(5\theta))$

2d) $4 - 2(r/2)^5\sin(5\theta) - 4(r/2)^9\sin(9\theta) + 8(r/2)^{14}\cos(14\theta)$

3d) $7\sinh(3\pi x)\sin(3\pi y)/\sinh(3\pi)$

3e) $-2\sinh(2\pi x)\sin(2\pi y)/\sinh(2\pi) + 8\sinh(7\pi x)\sin(7\pi y)/\sinh(7\pi)$

4b) $\sum_{n=1}^{\infty} c_n r^{2n}\sin(2n\theta)$

4c) $-3(r/2)^4\sin(4\theta)$

4d) $9(r/2)^2\sin(2\theta) - 5(r/2)^{14}\sin(14\theta)$

Bibliography

G. Bonani, S. Ivy, W. Wolfli, M. Broshi, I. Carmi, and J. Strugnell. Radiocarbon dating of fourteen Dead Sea scrolls. *Radiocarbon*, 34(3): 843–849, 1992. doi: 10.1017/S0033822200064158.

A. Coddington and R. Carlson. *Linear Ordinary Differential Equations.* Society for Industrial and Applied Mathematics, 1997. ISBN 978-0-898713-88-6.

A. M. Cohen. *Numerical Methods for Laplace Transform Inversion.* Numerical Methods and Algorithms. Springer, 2007. ISBN 978-0-387-28261-9.

B. Davies. *Integral Transforms and Their Applications.* Texts in Applied Mathematics. Springer-Verlag New York, 3d edition, 2002. ISBN 978-0-387-95314-4.

D. Eigler. Quantum Corral. Website, 2020. `http://www.nisenet.org/catalog/scientific-image-quantum-corral-top-view`.

R. Engbert and F. Drepper. Chance and chaos in population biology - models of recurrent epidemics and food chain dynamics. *Chaos, Solitons, and Fractals*, 4(7):1147–1169, 1994. doi: 10.1016/0960-0779(94)90028-0.

B. Friedland. *Control System Design: An Introduction to State-Space Methods.* Dover Publications, Inc., New York, NY, USA, 2005. ISBN 978-0486442785.

K. E. Gustafson. *Introduction to Partial Differential Equations and Hilbert Space Methods.* Dover Publications, 3d edition, 1999. ISBN 9780486140872.

M. H. Holmes. *Introduction to the Foundations of Applied Mathematics.* Texts in Applied Mathematics. Springer, 2nd edition, 2019. ISBN 978-0-387-87749-5.

R. F. Hoskins. *Delta Functions: Introduction to Generalised Functions.* Woodhead Publishing, 2nd edition, 2009. ISBN 978-1-904275-39-8.

A. J. Jerri. *The Gibbs Phenomenon in Fourier Analysis, Splines and Wavelet Approximations*. Mathematics and Its Applications. Springer, 1998. ISBN 978-0-7923-5109-2.

NASA. Drag of a sphere. Website, 2020. `https://www.grc.nasa.gov/WWW/K-12/airplane/dragsphere.html`.

F. Oberhettinger and L. Badii. *Tables of Laplace Transforms*. Springer-Verlag Berlin Heidelberg, 1973. ISBN 978-3-540-06350-6.

A. E. Parker. Who solved the Bernoulli differential equation and how did they do it? *College Mathematics Journal*, 44(2):89–97, 2013. doi: 10.4169/college.math.j.44.2.089.

L. Perko. *Differential Equations and Dynamical Systems*. Texts in Applied Mathematics. Springer, 2001. ISBN 978-0-387-95116-4.

F. W. Roos and W. W. Willmarth. Some experimental results on sphere and disk drag. *AIAA Journal*, 9(2):285–291, 1971. doi: 10.2514/3.6164.

I. Stakgold. *Boundary Value Problems of Mathematical Physics (Vol. 1)*. Society for Industrial and Applied Mathematics, Philadelphia, PA, USA, 2000. ISBN 978-0-89871-456-2.

W. A. Strauss. *Partial Differential Equations: An Introduction*. Wiley, 2nd edition, 2007. ISBN 978-0-470-05456-7.

A. M. Stuart and A. R. Humphries. *Dynamical Systems and Numerical Analysis*. Cambridge Monographs on Applied and Computational Mathematics. Cambridge University Press, 1998. ISBN 978-0-521-64563-8.

G. P. Tolstov and R. A. Silverman. *Fourier Series*. Dover Publications, 1976. ISBN 978-0486633176.

D. V. Widder. *Laplace Transform (PMS-6)*. Princeton University Press, 1941. ISBN 9780691627755.

Index